IN DANGER

CONTENTS

INTRODUCTION

Urban and 'modern' India has progressively grown alienated from nature. The rapidly increasing population and the spreading of 'modern' lifestyles and patterns of 'development' have created enormous pressures on Indian natural resources. 'Modern' society has become synonymous with the power of man to control, harness and submit nature to his own will, irrespective of the disruptions that accompany this process. Countless species of flora and fauna are thus disappearing faster than ever in human history.

Yet, in Indian cultures and religions man has always been linked to nature by relationships of respect and devotion. Though rituals that reveal such relationships still survive in some areas, nature's overall significance seems to have been lost, or is slowly fading away. Pressures of development, alienation of local communities, short-sighted policies, people's growing needs, changing religions, and loss of traditional cultural values combined with population pressure and its impact on the land and the environment are eventually taking their toll on India's wilderness areas.

This book reveals the threats to natural habitats and to wildlife through ten case studies among the most endangered species in the Indian subcontinent : the cheetah which is already extinct, the tiger, the elephant, the snow leopard, the lion–tailed macaque, the sea turtles, the great Indian bustard, the Asian lion, the dholes, the ibex. These species have been selected on the basis of them representing different ecosystems, as indicator species whose presence and survival directly concern the health of a particular ecosystem. The different species have also been described in the context and in relation to the traditional communities that have been sharing the same environment.

The selected species are obviously not the only ones under severe threat, yet by saving them many other equally endangered species will be protected, along with their own specific habitats. This in turn is an essential component for soil and water conservation, agricultural productivity, in short ... for the survival of man.

It is relatively easy to turn to the past and indulge in romantic visions of harmony between man and nature. Unfortunately the various pressures of today's world are sweeping away many traditional values and conservation practices that had survived from the past. We have reached a situation where the survival of many wild species can only be the outcome of a conscious choice. If the choice, with all its implications, is not made then the last wilderness areas and inhabitants will disappear.

While there is a growing awareness to protect and care for natural habitats and forests, it is much more difficult to find an equally positive response towards the animal species, especially the ones which are perceived either as threats to the safety of the human population or as direct competitors for space and habitats such as the tiger, the leopard and the elephant. Equally, there is a lot of emphasis on 'traditional knowledge' as far as flora is concerned, the same, however, cannot be said about fauna. We suspect that this has not happened because the 'economical' value of any traditional knowledge or practice concerning wild animals has not been found, except within the illegal wildlife trade!

The debate among environmental groups and national or international organisations about the issue of protecting wild animal species is getting increasingly heated. A few among environmental groups support and promote the idea that the concern for the survival of animal species within their natural habitat is 'elitist', or that it is reminiscent of colonial/Western concepts of conservation. An increased polarisation within 'the environmental camp' is taking place; on one side there are the 'people oriented' organisations which view as enemies the 'conservationists or species oriented' group, almost as if the two aspects — people and species — do not share a dialectic relationship.

A very dangerous situation for the survival of many wildlife species is therefore developing. Nobody openly states that wildlife species have to be eliminated, but by not addressing its specific constraints, one may end up doing just that.

The objective of this publication is to create awareness about the plight of wildlife and to encourage organisations and people to work for both the species and the habitats, since by doing that the benefits will be both for the local communities and for mankind. The efforts by different organisations that are actively involved with the saving of these endangered species and threatened habitats and that have developed their own approach to the linking of the problems of nature with the problems of the local communities living within the same area are also presented.

This publication contains contributions from leading conservationists and zoologists. The three dimensions of the equation — endangered species, people and threatened natural habitats — have been treated with as holistic an approach as possible, considering that each is strictly interdependent and interconnected to the others.

ELUSIVE LEOPARD OF THE MOUNTAINS

R S Chundawat

INTRODUCTION

The earliest depiction of snow leopard (*L'once*) was in 1761 by Georges Buffon but he mistook it for cheetah when he reported that it occurred in Persia and was used for hunting. In 1779, Peter Pallas first described the snow leopard in detail, identifying it as a species separate from the common leopard. However, until recently, little was known about this species, mainly due to the inaccessibility of the terrain it prefers to inhabit.

The snow leopard is a large carnivore found only in the rugged mountains of Central Asia and it is seldom seen in the wild. With its pale, whitish grey to light cream-coloured coat and very diffuse dark rosettes, the snow leopard is perfectly camouflaged to its surroundings. This gives it an uncanny ability to merge with its surrounding rocky habitat, even in open terrain with very little vegetation cover. Once, through radio telemetry, I knew that a snow leopard was present and moving across an apparently open mountain slope. Yet several of us scanned the slope with binoculars and telescope and failed to make out the animal. There were also several times when a snow leopard disappeared in front of my eyes and on one occasion I completely missed seeing it when only a few feet away. I was busy taking notes on a resting site that had been very recently used. It took me ten to 15 minutes to complete my notes and after taking a few pictures of the site, I loaded my backpack to follow its tracks. The moment I stood up, I saw some movement about 20 feet in front of me. A snow leopard was gazing at me! We stared at each other for a moment but a slight motion from me made it escape into a cliff below. It must have been lying there all the time watching me. While tracking snow leopards in the mountains, several times I knew that snow leopards were around me, but I saw them very rarely. Mountain people believe that this elusive cat has the ability to disappear; some call it the 'grey ghost of the mountains' or 'rock leopard'.

A little smaller than the common leopard, an adult snow leopard measures approximately 180 to 230 centimetres in length. At the shoulder it measures about 60 centimetres and on average it weighs 35 to 45 kilograms, ranging between 25 to 75 kilograms. The long, furry tail of the snow leopard is a prominent feature which immediately attracts the attention of an observer. The snow leopard uses it to help balance its body when negotiating the precipitous terrain. It also wraps the tail around itself to help keep the body warm. There are several stories in Ladakh concerning the snow leopard's tail. Some of these sound fantastic but they are based on the local people's experiences and their own interpretations. One story is that when a mother snow leopard finds her cubs are not able to climb over a rock or cliff, she helps them by hanging her tail down for her cubs to grab and use as a climbing aid! Another interesting story is that she uses her tail to make a loud noise by hitting it on the ground to scare people or command her cubs. I also had an opportunity to witness a snow leopard making this noise. According to the local people, when approached very close it makes this noise with its tail and the echo in a deep gorge amplifies its impact much more.

The snow leopard has adapted itself to the extreme environmental situation in which it lives. The head of a snow leopard is flatter and broader then other large cats, probably as an adaptation (broad nasal cavity) to the cold environment. The long tail and hind legs increase its agility in the rugged rocky terrain. Its massive paws and heavily built shoulders enable it to negotiate deep snow and to jump from one crag to another.

The snow leopard *Uncia uncia* is a member of the family Felidae (Order Carnivora) but its exact taxonomic position is still debated. There are two major schools of thought regarding its nomenclature and systematic position. One school prefers to include *Uncia* species within the genera *Panthera*, along with other large cats such as lion, tiger and leopard. Whereas, the other group believes, mainly on the basis of behavioural and morphological adaptations, that it has closer affinities with lesser cats and belongs to a separate genera *Uncia*. Recent research suggests that the snow leopard may have evolved from the golden cat. According to this hypothesis, during the course of evolution, the snow leopard radiated from the golden cat stock somewhere in China, before the evolution of mountain lions of North America. The only fossil evidence of its origin comes from Pleistocene remains of the Altai Caves in China suggesting its origin from China.

DISTRIBUTION

The snow leopard is widely but sparsely distributed throughout the mountain ranges of Central Asia. In the northern range

Snow leopard tracks on the snow

it occurs in the Altau, Altai, and Tien Shan mountain ranges of southern Siberia, Mongolia, Kazakhstan, Kyrgyzstan, Tajikistan and Uzbekistan. It has a wide distribution in the entire trans-Himalayan region, Kun-Lun, Tien Shan and Altau mountain ranges of the Tibet Autonomous region, Xinjiang, Qinghai, Gansu and Sichaun provinces in China. The mountain ranges of Pamirs, Hindu Kush and Karakoram in Afghanistan and Pakistan form the western limits. In the south it occurs throughout the Himalayan and trans-Himalayan regions of India, Nepal and Bhutan.

Throughout its distribution range, it inhabits alpine and sub-alpine regions and is usually found above the tree-line over 3,000 metres. It occupies a variety of habitats, ranging from the Gobi Desert of Mongolia, the rugged mountains of the trans-Himalaya, completely devoid of forest cover, to the forest habitat of the former republics of the USSR, where it has been reported as low as 600 metres. There are several species of wild sheep and goats and a host of small mammals that share the same habitat with snow leopard. This region has a rich diversity of wild sheep and goats, including blue sheep, ibex, great Tibetan sheep and Himalayan tahr. Blue sheep or *bharal*, occupy a large proportion of the snow leopard's range and is its major prey species in most areas. Indeed in several localities its very name connects the two: eg, in Garhwal it is known as *bharud bagh*, (*bharal* is *bharud* in the Garhwali dialect). The English common name, blue sheep, is a misnomer for this species; it is neither blue nor taxonomically classified as a sheep. Ibex, a true goat, is another major prey species of the snow leopard and like *bharal* generally prefers to live on steep slopes that are interspersed with cliffs. For these mountain dwelling herbivores such topographic features are important as they provide escape habitat from their predators. Whenever alerted by the presence of a predator, these animals take refuge in the cliffs where it is extremely difficult for the snow leopard or any other predator to make a kill. Snow leopards share their habitat with other predators — Tibetan wolf, lynx and wild dogs — and have evolved a complex system by which they are separated ecologically and use different niches in the same area. The snow leopard, being a cat, hunts by stalking its prey very close before launching an attack, whereas the wolf is a courser and likes to chase its prey. Wild dogs generally hunt in packs. Thus, the snow leopard requires cover for stalking whereas the wolf requires open areas where it can chase its prey over a long distance. Such specialised ecological requirements allow a diversity of large predators to survive in this ecosystem.

Sightings of snow leopard in the wild are extremely rare and its secretive behaviour coupled with difficult terrain make this a difficult animal for study. Very little work has been done on the ecology of this large endangered cat. Most of the information available on the species is either in the form of natural history observations or from status surveys conducted in the region. Many scientists have spent months in these rugged mountains in search of this elusive animal but often without luck. Much of the information gathered on the snow leopard's distribution and status is based on secondary information. Detailed study on the ecology and behaviour of snow leopard is only possible either by attaching a collar with a radio-transmitter and then radio-tracking its movement with the help of a very directional antenna or by monitoring indirect evidences, such as its spoor.

After a survey conducted in the northwestern Himalaya, a detailed study was initiated by the Wildlife Institute of India in the Zanskar Mountains of Ladakh, in the state of Jammu and Kashmir. The study site was part of Hemis National Park, named after the famous monastery, Hemis. The research was mainly based on indirect evidences. Snow leopard tracks, whenever encountered, were followed as far as possible and a detailed systematic record was maintained to gather information on the use of habitat and its movements. Initially I found it difficult to track their movement on the rocky terrain but as experience grew it became relatively easy to follow snow leopard tracks for long distances. On snow it was very easy, but movement on snow covered slopes is very energy sapping, especially at such altitudes (over 3,000 metres) where the atmospheric oxygen level is low. But I was able to follow the movements of snow leopard over several days at a time, covering ten to 15 kilometres regularly. Following snow leopard tracks in this mountainous terrain was not an easy job for other reasons also. On several occasions I found myself in places of no return. It was especially on these occasions that my local field assistants' help was invaluable, confirming the imperative that you should never venture out alone in the mountains. Despite its difficulties I found this method (from the indirect evidences) very reliable in gathering information on its ecology. Following snow leopard movements, was like reading a book on its natural history. You only have to document the happenings in a systematic numerical manner to apply statistics to find inferences.

During the study, radio-telemetry was also attempted and one snow leopard was radio-collared. In the mountains, it is inadvisable to tranquillize a free ranging animal because it may move to a precipitous slope before the drug takes its effect. It is therefore necessary to capture the snow leopard first in order to put on a radio-collar. It took many months before I could catch a snow leopard. That winter day, I reached camp earlier then usual and before it grew dark went to check the nearest cage. Looking through binoculars from some distance, I saw that the cage door was down. Several times before the door had been sprung but all we had found inside was a magpie! Since I was tired and had hoped not to have to climb any further, I cursed the bird. However, as I reached the site I found the cage unusually silent; typically, both the bird and tethered goat would be making a noise. I tried to discover what had caused the door to trip, but I could see nothing in the darkness of the cage. The silence kept me wondering — a snow leopard, I thought, would surely snarl or growl. Kneeling

The radio–collared snow leopard watches the author

on the ground I tried to open the door. I must have pushed it up by six inches, when I saw a movement. I stooped and bent further down to look inside. There were two shining eyes less than a foot from mine. It took me by surprise and I immediately pushed the door down and secured it with some heavy rocks.

I finally had one snow leopard trapped after months of effort. Since daylight was fading fast there was no time to tranquillize and collar it that day. Concerned for its well-being and over-excited by finally having a snow leopard 'in hand', we collected our sleeping bags and bedded down on the narrow ledge next to it, spending the night in the open although the temperature was around -17°C.

Both leopard and goat spent a peaceful night and appeared none the worse for their experience next morning! After weighing, measuring and radio-collaring the leopard, it was released and radio-tracked for several months. I soon learnt how difficult it is to radio-track an animal in mountainous terrain. Due to bounce from steep slopes, the signal comes from all possible directions so it is not easy to determine the direction of the signal. The best way was to climb to the top of a ridge, thus overcoming the bounce, every time we needed a location of the animal. This was physically impossible to achieve every day. Furthermore, if the animal had moved on to the other side of the ridge, we would not receive a signal unless we moved into that valley which could take several days, by which time the animal would be back! Through all the months of tracking, I saw the radio-collared snow leopard only once, on a kill! I would know where it was to within a 250 × 250 metre area but could never locate it — showing that 'chance' is more important than technology for seeing the 'grey ghost'!

Within the 100 square kilometre of the study area of relatively high prey density, I estimated that there were four to seven snow leopards, including three to five resident adults and two to three transients. Unlike other large cats, snow leopards were not territorial but they were separated by each other temporaily and spatially. During a detailed study carried out in the Nepal Himalaya, it was found that the average home range of a snow leopard was 20 square kilometres, varying between 12 to 39 square kilometres. Their home ranges overlapped considerably and this overlapping was most in areas with suitable habitat and where prey density was greatest. I found these overlapped areas more heavily marked by snow leopards. Snow leopards avoid intra-specific conflicts by intensively marking their travel routes by making a scrape on the ground, by spraying urine on the underside of any overhanging rocks and also by leaving scats. With the help of these markings, snow leopards communicate their presence to other individuals in the area and are thus able to share the common resources efficiently. It has been observed from the radio-telemetry studies that snow leopards, on average, keep an almost two kilometre distance from each other to avoid encounter. They also communicate through vocalisation. Unlike other large cats, snow leopards cannot roar, but a loud 'mew' is a call most frequently heard during the mating season from January to March. The snow leopard is generally a solitary animal although association of mates and mother with cubs are frequently observed. Cubs are born in the month of May or June in very broken terrain.

Generally the snow leopard is found in extremely rugged mountains, although it has also been found using relatively gentle terrain. My investigation, in the trans-Himalayan region of Ladakh, found that the snow leopard preferred very steep slopes interspersed with cliffs and that they usually avoided any open terrain. It rested most often on upper slopes, ridges and any other site which provided a good vantage point from where it could have a good look at the slopes opposite and below. Being a large stalking predator, the snow leopard needs cover and therefore prefers to move close to a terrain which provides concealment to its movements. In the open trans-Himalayan landscape, with little vegetation, any break in terrain, such as cliffs, river bluffs or ridges, provide cover to its movements.

It is generally believed that the snow leopard shows distinct seasonal movement by moving to lower altitudes during the winter months and back to higher slopes during summer, following the movements of its prey species. I did not find evidence of such seasonal altitudinal migration. Instead snow leopards patrolled the same area throughout the year. The only difference observed during the four year study was that it shifted its activity from lower slopes in winter to higher ones in summer. I also found that a large proportion (80 to 90 percent) of the prey population of snow leopard moves to higher slopes in search of lush pastures, reducing the availability of its major prey, *bharal,* from approximately five per square kilometre to 0.5 per square kilometre in the lower areas. Like other large carnivores, the snow leopard's distribution, movement and habitat use was related to its major prey. This it achieved by increasing its activity at higher altitudes, without shifting totally from its winter range.

The snow leopard is an opportunistic feeder and has a varied diet ranging from yaks, weighing 300 kilograms (ten times heavier than themselves) to animals as small as mouse-hares of 250 to 300 grams. It is also not adverse to scavenging if it comes across a carcass. *Bharal* is the major prey species in my study area although domestic sheep and goat and smaller mammals, such as marmots (a large bodied ground squirrel) and hares, contributed significantly to their diet. During the summer months, smaller mammals become the major prey for snow leopard. At this time *bharal* aggregate in larger herds in more open pastures and the openness of the terrain makes stalking difficult for snow leopard. However, availability of smaller mammals in summer increases as the marmots come out of their winter sleep (hibernation) and are relatively easy prey. I estimated that to sustain predation pressure of one snow leopard in such an environment, 45 *bharal* are required. I also calculated that in the area under study, the population of *bharal* in their present density is just enough to sustain this pressure. In this situation the presence of smaller mammals as alternate prey is crucial to reduce excess predation on the major prey. Therefore, they are also a very critical consideration in managing snow leopard populations.

The snow leopard is threatened mainly by excessive hunting, through poaching for fur and killing in retaliation for livestock predation. It is difficult to hunt snow leopard due to the precipitous terrain in which it is found; but it is killed opportunistically. The snow leopard usually stays with its kill and during that time, it is relatively easy to slaughter. This form of opportunistic killing is common in the higher pastures which are used by the migratory pastoralists. These pastoralists bring large numbers of sheep and goats and as a result, wild herbivores are either completely eliminated from the higher pastures or are pushed to poor quality ones. In addition to this, depletion of prey base due to excessive hunting is also a major threat and has resulted in complete elimination of wild herbivore populations from most of the snow leopard habitats in the southern side of the main Himalaya. This loss of prey base has resulted in increased predation on livestock, bringing the snow leopard in direct conflict with humans. The trans-Himalayan region is inhabited to a large extent by a Buddhist population who by religion are averse to hunting and also do not allow hunting by others. It is in this region that the snow leopard has its best chance for survival in the Indian Himalaya. However, even here the snow leopard comes into some conflict with the local people. This usually happens only in areas of heavy snowfall, where the villagers are forced to keep their livestock inside for most of the winter. Once a snow leopard manages to get inside the cattle pen, it inflicts heavy damage. It has been known to kill over 30 to 40 sheep and goats in one go, although most may die of trauma and shock. It is in these circumstances that the snow leopard is killed against the loss it had caused to the family. Otherwise in most situations they live in close harmony. In normal conditions, when a snow leopard makes a kill out in the open, it usually kills one or perhaps two animals. Such occasional small losses are accepted by the locals and in fact, in many cases it is actually welcomed! Being Buddhist, they prefer not to slaughter an animal even for meat, although it is their staple diet. At the end of winter when no fresh food is available and their meat stock is finished, the snow leopard acts as a butcher for them. They retrieve the dead animals from the snow leopard for meat for themselves.

I witnessed one such bizarre incidence during our survey in Ladakh. It was in the month of March and I was busy preparing for the camp around 2.30 pm, when I heard a young girl screaming loudly. Before I could reach the site, one of the goats which the snow leopard had just killed had already been retrieved by the girl and she was carrying it in her basket. She kept on shouting for help and trying to drive the goats away from the leopard. However, the goats and sheep, unbothered by what had happened to one of their kin, kept on grazing in the area and the snow leopard very soon killed

All male group of bharal or blue sheep, an important prey for the snow leopard

another animal and moved ahead. The girl immediately ran and threw it inside her basket, but before she could even get up, the snow leopard had already killed a third animal just 50 to 60 metres away. In her excitement the young girl started pulling the dead animal away without noticing that the snow leopard was still holding the other end of the goat. Only when it growled at her did she realise the threat and so backed away from the site. The snow leopard dragged the kill inside the bushes. Later we were told that such incidents are not very uncommon and during my stay in Ladakh, I saw the villagers bringing a kill home on several occasions. Amazingly, there has been no record of snow leopard attacking a human being. This is particularly extraordinary given such close encounters over food.

In fact, the snow leopard is not the major predator on livestock in the region. The Tibetan wolf, the other large carnivore, is a big menace and hated by local people. There are traditional ways by which wolf populations are controlled. At the start of a major valley or at the confluence of their major travel routes the villagers make traps for controlling the wolf menace in the region. They may be in the form of traditional leg hold traps or more commonly a large pit with overhanging walls of eight to ten feet. Much of the time they are not used, but when there is persistent predation pressure by wolves these traps are put into operation.

The lifestyles of the local human populations are based on the sustainable utilisation of natural resources. Such lifestyles and age old traditions have sustained these populations in these seemingly hostile and less productive ecosystems. Because of such traditions, vast areas with their natural attributes still exist and it is essential that such traditional practices be recognised by the managers and reflected in their administrative initiatives. In such areas, especially where the traditional lifestyle is in practice and local populations live in harmony with nature, it is argued that we do not require management. However, our experience from other parts of the world and the changing scenario in this region, means we can ill afford to sit and watch the changes occurring in this fragile mountainous region.

The riverine vegetation, home to several unique bird and animal communities, was converted by early settlers into cultivated land. Increasing human populations and developmental activities in the major valleys have put tremendous pressure on the limited resources of the neighbouring areas. As a result, riverine vegetation, once extensive, now exists only in a few remote valleys, as relict patches of the past. In addition, over-grazing has resulted in severe habitat degradation, especially in areas where migratory herders from outside bring livestock in huge numbers. The activities of these herders conflict with the locals', increasing the tension between these two communities and creating a matter of great concern for the administration in several localities.

Although the snow leopard is fully protected under India's Wildlife (Protection) Act, 1972 and is classified as an endangered species in IUCN's Red Data Book, the conservation status of the species and its habitat, throughout its range, is extremely poor. The status of the existing protected areas in the Himalayan region is also very depressing. This is one of the least protected regions of India; less then two percent of the habitat is covered under the protected area network, a great deal less than the target of ten percent for the conservation of wildlife in the Himalaya. More ecological surveys are required to assess the snow leopard's status, identify new sites and determine the possibilities for extending existing protected areas.

In planning a protected area network for this region, the size of the protected area is a very important consideration for conserving viable populations. In the high altitude desert ecosystem, animals occur in low density and therefore require larger areas to maintain a viable population. Being a large carnivore of this environment, the snow leopard is considered its 'flagship' species. I estimated that for the conservation of 50 snow leopards in the trans-Himalayan region, a minimum of 1,275 square kilometres containing a population of 2,200 *bharal* would be required. In reality most of the existing protected areas are not able to provide such a large area at one site. There are a few protected areas which are sufficiently large in size but which only cover a very small proportion of the snow leopard's preferred habitat — not enough to protect a viable population.

Seasonal migration is a natural phenomenon; it is therefore also necessary to provide year round habitat within the protected area. Most of the existing parks and sanctuaries in the Indian Himalaya are too small for migrating populations. They protect either the wintering grounds only or the pastures used for grazing in summer.

At present, the protected areas have continuous habitat available for wild animal populations to interact with those of other populations. But developmental activities, such as new roads and new settlements can break these once large and continuous populations into several small, isolated populations which will be more prone to extinction. It is, therefore, crucial that a network of protected areas be created to establish several metapopulations. A metapopulation is a group of several sub-populations interacting with each other. These sub-populations can be linked by continuous habitat or through corridors which provide viable links through a regular gene flow by dispersing individuals. Dispersal in a population not only helps to regulate the population but also makes it more stable. For the long–term conservation needs of a population we need to create several metapopulations. This also requires creation of new protected areas and also extension of existing areas, with consideration given to the ecological boundaries and requirements of a metapopulation.

Mouse-hare or pika

With new roads, more and more areas are now easily accessible by vehicle and poaching of wild animals has become relatively easy. Where before it would have taken several days of walking to reach a particular area, now that same area can be visited in one day. This adds to the difficulties of wildlife protection which is already tough due to the mountainous terrain which requires more vigilance, funds and infrastructure than elsewhere. Uncontrolled tourism in the region also presents a potentially major problem for management.

The increasing pressure of people and their livestock inevitably leads to some direct conflict with wild animals. Such conflict areas need to be identified with careful consideration and managed as multiple-use areas. These are the areas which need intensive management, whereas at present more attention is given to the core areas where very little conflict exists. Including core areas of little biological value (glacier and rocks) is of no use in the conservation of wildlife in the region. Moreover, the need for core areas

Wild dog of the trans-Himalaya

Camouflaged snow leopard in hippophae

in a mountain environment is a debated subject, because it is difficult to find suitable areas to relocate human habitations in an acceptable manner. Evaluation of the dependency of the human population on the natural resources, its values and impact on the habitat is urgently required. Solutions to the problem could be found in the techniques of use rather than in the actual utilisation. This may require, in some cases, recognition of appropriate methods and in others, modification of techniques to minimise the dependency by regulating and then gradually eliminating it through acceptable alternatives. In this dialogue management should not be seen to be only interested in the welfare of wild animals which may not be of any value to locals, but they must also act as a concerned agency for the well being of the society.

The flight from Leh to Delhi goes right over the Rumbak and the Markha valley. Looking back through the scanty cloud cover, at the vast expanse of Ladakh's mountain ranges, one gets lost in their beauty and forgets everything else! But not for long — the moment the flight passes over the lower Himalayan ranges, their degraded status always bring me back to reality. Just a thought of this happening in the trans-Himalayan region shakes me up completely and makes me wonder for how long it will remain as I had left last time! So far this region has conserved its natural attributes through a religion, culture and lifestyle harmonious to nature. But with every visit, I observe changes and they are happening at a very fast rate. As a conservationist, I am not against these developmental activities that are taking place in a region which had remained ignored by the planner for a long time. But what does concern me are the eco-**un**friendly activities which ignore the ill effects on the ecology of this fragile ecosystem. There are numerous examples from the Himalayan region, where unplanned developmental activities have completely altered the ecology of the region. The situation is not yet as bad in Ladakh as it is in other regions of the Himalaya, but we cannot sit with our eyes closed and hope that everything will be fine. There are still several possibilities to conserve areas in their natural pristine condition and also to plan future developmental activities in a sustainable and ecofriendly manner. Returning from the airport through the horribly polluted streets of Delhi, I am already missing the deep blue sky and cool fresh air of the mountains and wish I had not left.

17

ASIATIC IBEX, A GOAT OF THE DESOLATE COLD DESERT

Nima Manjrekar and Yash Veer Bhatnagar

Cold, dusty winds, heavy snowfall with temperatures going down to 30°C below zero, azure blue skies, avalanches, sparse spinescent vegetation, and brown to red barren mountain slopes with loose rocks, characterise the environment above 3,000 metres in the trans-Himalaya. Adapted to live in such hostile ecological conditions are a number of plants, birds and mammals, as well as local people.

To the summer visitor, Pin Valley leaves a memory of picturesque landscape and comfortable weather. But little is he aware of how different life is during the rest of the year. All activities, both of humans and of animals, revolve around the necessity of survival through winter, when resource availability and movement are highly restricted. Through the summer and autumn, people stock up food for themselves and their livestock, and store fuelwood to keep themselves warm in the winter. Those animals that depend on the ephemeral plant life have to build up stores within themselves to see them through the winter, when all is hidden under a thick blanket of snow.

The mammals in these environments include the Asiatic ibex *Capra ibex sibirica*, snow leopard *Uncia uncia*, red fox *Vulpes vulpes montana*, pika *Ochotona roylei*, Himalayan weasel *Mustela sibirica*, Beech marten *Martes foina* and a variety of rodents. The extremes in climate allow very limited seasonal plant growth, and are therefore responsible for low animal densities. Plant availability influences large herbivores like the ibex, the abundance of which, in turn, influences the presence of its major predator, the snow leopard.

Neither of us had a clear image of the kind of area that we were going to. We had absolutely no idea of the difficulties involved in having to be part of such a system for some time. We were going to follow the ibex for the next three years, in Pin Valley National Park, in the trans-Himalayan region of Himachal Pradesh, bordering Tibet.

Ibex are mountain goats, adapted to barren, extreme, dry conditions, and possessing an outstanding climbing ability. They inhabit mostly alpine areas, above the tree-line, in Eurasia and North Africa. Evolving from a stock of goral-like animals of South-East Asia, where they were better adapted to warm, moist forests, they moved towards the exposed mountains during the last deglaciation period, in the Pleistocene epoch. Eventually, geographical separation resulted as forests sprung up in the intervening areas during warmer climes, leading to the evolution of various subspecies, that are now sprinkled over all the larger mountainous areas of the Palaearctic region.

The Asiatic ibex is one of the six subspecies of *Capra ibex*, the others being the alpine ibex *Capra ibex ibex*, the Walia ibex *Capra ibex walie*, the Nubian ibex *Capra ibex nubiana*, the East Caucasian ibex or Dagestan Tur *Capra ibex cylindricornis*, and the West Caucasian ibex or Kuban Tur *Capra ibex severtzovi*.

The range of the Asiatic ibex stretches from the Hindu Kush mountains in Afghanistan to the Sayan mountains in Russia, with populations found in the Pamirs, Tien Shan, Kara Tau, Tarbagatay, and Altai mountains. It inhabits areas varying in altitude from 500 metres above sea level, as in Russia and Mongolia, to above 5,000 metres, as in the southern trans-Himalayan parts of its distribution.

The Upper Shyok River and the vicinity of Leh mark the eastern boundary of ibex distribution in India. To the south, along the Himalayan chain, their distribution extends eastward to the River Sutlej.

Unlike the alpine ibex, which has been extensively studied, the Asiatic ibex, despite its wide distribution, is a relatively poorly studied animal. Except for a few surveys in the Himalaya that have included the ibex, among other animals, no study had been conducted on the ecology of the Asiatic ibex. In India, the species is now considered endangered and is awarded protection under Schedule I of the Indian Wildlife (Protection) Act of 1972. Despite this, hardly any information on its biology was available, and it was thought important to study this animal and be able to suggest measures for its conservation.

Various estimates have been made of the Asiatic ibex population size in its vast distributional range of 41,000 square kilometres in the Indian trans-Himalaya. These figures suggest a total of 9,000 to 15,000 ibex, of which Pin Valley has 700 to 1,200 animals. We, therefore, chose Pin Valley National Park as our study site. The national park encompasses 675 square kilometres of the catchment of the Pin River, which joins the Spiti River downstream, in the northeastern part of Himachal

Asiatic ibex in its Himalayan habitat

19

Pradesh. This area lies in the trans-Himalayan cold desert, sandwiched between the Greater Himalaya and the Tibetan Plateau. The climate here is extreme, with very cold winters and cool summers. Most of the precipitation in the area is in the form of snow, with very little monsoonal rain reaching the area because the Great Himalayan Range to the south blocks its passage.

Being above the tree-line, the area has alpine vegetation, consisting mainly of herbs, and very little woody vegetation. Pin Valley remains green only for about four months every year, between May and August, during which time the entire process of producing leaves, flowers and fruits is completed. At the end of this, the area acquires its red to golden autumn hues, after which everything dries up, in preparation for the snow that is to come and conceal it all. The vegetation consists of a large proportion of dicotyledonous herbs like *Nepeta* of the catmint family, *Lindelofia*, a relative of borage, *Artemisia*, *Tanacetum*, *Tragopogon* and *Saussurea* from the daisy family, legumes such as *Cicer* and *Astragalus*, and *Epilobium*, a kind of willow herb. Grasses make up the rest, along with some shrubs like juniper *Juniperus*, honeysuckle *Lonicera*, rose *Rosa*, *Cotoneaster* and willow *Salix*; all these species are used as fuelwood. Most of the juniper and birch trees that existed in the smaller water courses or springs have been exterminated, despite the belief that disease will afflict those that remove these species.

The year begins with the shortest days. When you need the sun the most, it shows itself above the towering mountains only at ten o'clock in the morning, and disappears at three in the afternoon. Everything around is a dazzling white, with layer upon layer of snow being added for the next three months. Snow accumulates on the slopes, and continues to compact with every sunny day.

During the peak of winter, ibex stay mostly in the wind-blown cliffs, crests and ridges, which are relatively snow-free. Cliffs are also necessary for the animals as thermal cover from the cold winds and as escape cover, offering security from predators. They also prefer relatively snow-free areas as feeding sites during winter and feed on species like *Artemisia*, *Arnebia*, *Lindelofia* and *Tragopogon*, which are some of the few herbs whose above-ground parts survive the winter. But when the area is covered in snow, the ibex will dig in the snow with their forelegs, to get at the food plants below. From experience, they seem to have some kind of an indication of the presence of certain plant species, that are relatively more palatable during this time of year. The nutritional quality of food plants in winter also definitely plays a role in their choice of species. Fruits, which have a high fat and sugar content, form an important component of their winter diet, and ibex feed on the fruits of some of the more woody species like *Rosa* and *Cotoneaster*. These plants are usually tall enough to avoid being buried in the snow. The fruits are often left exposed which makes it easier for the animals to get them.

Movement in winter is not easy. There were times when we couldn't move farther than 25 metres from camp for ten days at a stretch, because of heavy snowfall. Following ibex during such times is out of the question.

In March, with yet more snowfall, the last straw is reached, and the entire piled-up mass of snow may come down as a thunderous avalanche. It is not uncommon to find dead ibex in the avalanche debris. Avalanches are a regular phenomenon when the climate becomes warmer, and avalanche paths — the snow-free areas formed by the passage of an avalanche — are a common sight. Ibex will quickly move to these avalanche cleared paths to take advantage of the snow-free ground. They may remain there for a long time as later, the season's first green vegetation sprouts in these areas.

As winter ends and temperatures begin to rise, the snow melts and plant growth begins, first on the slopes with a southern aspect, and finally on those with a northern aspect. Rock-falls accompany the snow-melt, making movement in the area dangerous. The water in the rivers gradually turns from a slow-flowing, clear blue-green, to strong currents of very muddy brown. By this time most of the snow has disappeared, and plant growth is at its peak. Beginning just a little above the valley bottom, at around 3,800 metres above sea level, ibex follow the receding snowline and the corresponding highly nutritious sprout, moving first from one aspect to another, and then altitudinally, until they reach the higher limit of vegetation growth, at around 4,800 metres. They have no need to venture above these heights where there is negligible plant growth, unless such areas happen to be en route between two parts of their range.

Agricultural fields are also sought-after places in the spring, and ibex often have to be driven away. In the early summer, the diet consists almost entirely of leaves. Flowers are also eaten later in the summer, and some fruits towards the end of summer and in winter. In the autumn, the temperatures fall and the vegetation dries up. During this season, the diet of ibex consists mainly of herbs, of which various parts are eaten. Forage quality at all altitudes is assumed to be similar by the end of the growing season, and the animals move to the lower areas again to avoid the low temperatures that occur with the strong wind speeds of the higher altitudes. With this, they start returning towards the valleys for the winter.

Ibex are attracted not only to green vegetation but also to another major ingredient of their diet: salt. This is especially so in summer, when their forage has a high moisture content. We took advantage of this craving to bait the animals with salt, and capture them with drop-nets for radio-collaring and ear-tagging, as part of the first long-term study on this subspecies. Earlier, tranquillization with dart guns was attempted, but without success. Thirteen animals were finally ear-tagged, and seven of these were also radio-collared. This was the first ever successful capture operation using drop-nets in such terrain. Radio-tracking of these animals gave us information on the seasonal movement and home ranges of individuals, and their social affinities — how and when they move between groups — information that would otherwise have been impossible to gather.

As in most wild caprids, there is marked sexual dimorphism in the Asiatic ibex, with the males being about one-and-a-half times the size of females, and possessing a thick, dark beard, and large, conspicuous horns that are characteristic of the species. An adult male weighs between 80 and 120 kilograms, while an adult female weighs between 40 and 60 kilograms. The size differences in turn dictate different food requirements. As availability of food varies with terrain, the sexes use different areas, and this reduces competition for food. This phenomenon — known as sexual segregation — is most pronounced after the kids are born, when the lactating females require food that is highly nutritious.

The adult males of the Asiatic ibex have the largest horns among all the *Capra ibex* subspecies. The horns are thick and curved backwards, growing throughout the life of the animal. Horns in males are products of sexual selection, functioning as organs of intrasexual contest and display. Males can easily be aged, by counting the divisions or annual rings that are well-defined along the sides of the horns. These rings are a result of the stark variation in the horns' seasonal growth, with almost no growth during the winter and a rapid spurt during spring. Asiatic ibex are known to live as long as 16 years, although the oldest male that was recorded during this study was 11.

Females have shorter, thinner and straighter horns without any knobs. It is more difficult to determine the age of a female, since there is very little annual horn growth and the rings are, therefore, not as clear as they are in the males. Female horn size is also likely to be minimally influenced by the forces of sexual selection that primarily impinge on male reproductive success. Compared to the alpine ibex, the horns of the male Asiatic ibex are more arched with distinct knobs on the front. An average of two knobs are formed between consecutive annual rings, between the second and tenth years of the animal's life. As the animal ages, growth decreases, and usually only one knob is formed every year, with the rings becoming less distinct.

The colour of the coat (pelage) varies seasonally. During the summer, animals of both sexes are a uniform, light, reddish brown, with a paler underside, blending well with the mountains. With the arrival of the harsh winter, the ibex acquires a coat of soft, dense underwool (*pashm*) to keep warm. The females and young males acquire a dark, greyish brown pelage, while the adult males are contrastingly dark brown, with a dull white saddle-back and neck patch. The acquisition of this coat coincides with the beginning of the rut or mating season. The oldest males have the most distinct saddle-backs, a sign of their sexual maturity. The winter coat is shed in spring, during which time the animals look extremely ragged, and constantly make use of any shrub or rough rock that comes their way to rub against and rid themselves of the unwelcome underwool. The shed underwool is collected by the people, whenever they come across some, for making into clothes that are considerably warmer than those made from sheep wool.

The differences in grouping behaviour of male and female ibex over the year present as stark a contrast as their physical differences. With the beginning of summer, large males separate from the mixed groups, leaving adult females and the young, both males and females, in separate groups. The adult males form all-male or buck groups until the end of summer, during which time the female-young groups move to areas in the vicinity of cliffs. The pregnant females move away from the rest of the group, into the cliffs for a few days, where they give birth. Twinning is fairly common in the Asiatic ibex, unlike in the alpine subspecies. Females are more selective about areas to use during the summer, since pregnant and lactating animals require more nutrition. The male groups usually consist of animals of similar age. During summer, dominance hierarchies are established within these groups, and mixed groups begin to form again, just before the peak rut, between early December and late January. By the time the rut sets in, the hierarchy is already established, usually with the older and bigger males being at the top.

During the rut, large mixed groups are formed, and courting begins. Throughout the rut, the bucks assume a characteristic posture, the low stretch, in which the tail is raised, and the body stretched out most of the time. The upper lip is pulled

Ibex in flight

up (an action called lip-curl) and the protruded tongue is waggled rapidly up and down. In the mixed groups, bucks follow the does around, occasionally swinging one of their forelegs forward (foreleg-kick or *Laufschlag*), towards the doe. The highest ranking buck gets to mate with most of the does in oestrous, and the remaining does are mated by the younger bucks.

One might wonder why the rut takes place in the peak of winter, when the most inhospitable conditions prevail. The reason for this is to time the births of the young to coincide with the period of abundant food availability. When the kids are born in June and July, after a gestation of 170 to 180 days, there is no lack of nutritious food for the lactating females, since it is the peak of the plant growing season. After parturition, the mother rejoins her group, and the kids constantly follow their mother for a few days, before beginning to participate in other social activities of the group, like the daring play that is often seen among kids on steep cliffs. An obvious decrease in play behaviour is seen in winter, apparently to conserve as much energy as possible, in these times of food shortage.

Predation probably has a major influence on the distribution of ibex in Pin Valley. The only wild predator of ibex here is the snow leopard although in the Spiti Valley, wolves *Canis lupus chanco* also hunt ibex. On one occasion in April, a nine-year-old male ibex escaped the clutches of a snow leopard and moved into an open area on the slope close to camp.

23

The animal sat alone in a strange posture for over four hours. Later in the evening, it moved even closer to camp, onto a steep slope, collapsed, slid some way down the slope, and died. Its neck had been punctured by the snow leopard, and it was a wonder that it managed to escape and survive for so long after that!

The snow leopard usually guards its kills closely, but very often, scavengers like foxes and vultures (Himalayan griffon and lammergeier) manage to steal it. The local people also steal snow leopard kills whenever they get an opportunity to do so, often using griffons as reliable indicators of a snow leopard kill nearby.

***

The future of ibex and Pin Valley is enmeshed with the lives of the people who have traditionally shared these pristine mountains with them. The local inhabitants of the area are of Tibetan origin, speak a Tibetan dialect called *Bhoti*, and follow similar traditions as those of people in Tibet. Traditionally, the social system is polyandrous. Some boys and young men are made *lamas* or monks, and many girls *chhomos* or nuns. This system is breaking down fast and monogamy is becoming the trend. This, along with medical facilities ensuring greater child survival, could potentially lead to an increase in population and correspondingly more pressure on resources.

Some areas in Pin Valley enjoy religious protection, and are considered the property of the local *gompa* or monastery. Collection of fuelwood is not allowed in these areas, a self-imposed restriction on resource use that testifies to their traditional conservation wisdom. One family is appointed to look after every such area, and they see to it that no illegal fodder and fuelwood extraction is made. This family, however, is allowed to collect the bare minimum fuel and fodder required for their stay there. Once every three years, the sanctity of the area is verified by the head monk of the *gompa*.

The traditional subsistence-based lifestyle and customs of the local people are now increasingly affected by external pressures and changes. Development of the area began, with the road network improving rapidly in the 1980s, followed by the rest of modernisation, which has now made them increasingly dependent on the outside world. Development activities in the area today include the construction of irrigation canals, walls to prevent soil erosion and trekking paths. Tourism is increasing rapidly, and ill-effects, like over-exploitation of resources and littering, will not take long to ruin the area. Increased human presence in the ibex areas will have direct adverse effects on the animals. Temptations to hunt the animals might also arise. However, in Pin Valley itself, ibex are quite fortunate, as they are relatively well protected from adverse human influences. The inaccessibility and ruggedness of their habitat, by itself, provides protection to the animals. Uncontrolled livestock grazing in these areas during the summer is, however, a threat to the conservation of ibex habitat, in that excess trampling and grazing by the livestock may accelerate soil erosion. Land-use methods should be modified in such a way that erosion can be minimised. Livestock in these areas might also be potential carriers of disease, and hence a threat to the wild animals. Expansion of agriculture, habitat destruction, and commercial harvesting of flora and fauna of the area, such as medicinal plants, should not be allowed. Wherever poaching is a threat, legal protection needs to be implemented.

The local people use the national park for grazing their livestock and cultivation of barley, peas, potatoes and mustard. They also collect from the park fuelwood, dung and fodder, for stall-feeding their livestock in winter. For these purposes, several summer settlements exist, up to ten kilometres from the village; these settlements now lie inside the national park area, and the village in the buffer zone. When the final notification for the creation of the national park is made, theoretically, these settlements will have to be moved out. There is already some resentment among the people in this regard, since no alternatives have been provided. The legal protection given to wild animals is another sore point among the people; snow leopards kill their livestock, and they are neither allowed to retaliate nor are given adequate compensation for the loss.

The summer settlements are inhabited between April and December, and the livestock that use the area include yaks, *dzos* (yak-cow hybrids), horses, donkeys, sheep and goats. Except for the horses, these animals are usually not accompanied by people in their grazing areas, and stay in groups varying in number from ten to 60. These relatively small groups of animals do not seem to interfere with ibex movement, as indicated by records of ibex and livestock feeding in close proximity to each other. Horses are the most valuable of the domestic animals in Pin Valley. The particular breed here, well-adapted to life in the mountains, is sold for large sums of money in either of two places, the annual fair at Rampur in Shimla district, or in the Changthang region of Ladakh. In the latter place, the barter system still exists, and goods like carpets, shoes, locks and crockery, apart from yaks and sheep, are brought back.

Some grazing areas are over 15 kilometres from the village. Here, the people stay in a small stone enclosure or *pulu*, and survive on almost only barley flour (*tsampa*) and salt tea. To reach these areas, they have to cross fast-flowing rivers, involving considerable effort. Thick, strong wires are stretched across the river, held on either side by stone supports. The device used to cross the river along this wire is locally called *garu-thakpa*, and consists of a small piece of male ibex horn, cut to shape (*garu*), and the rope (*thakpa*) to make the special knots and loops around the *garu*. You then sit in these loops, secure yourself with the remaining length of rope, and pull yourself across the wire. When the water is flowing too fast, the accompanying animals have to be literally pulled through using ropes, or taken across on similar devices.

In September, when it is time for the harvest, the horses are taken back to the village, where their help is required for threshing the crop. Eight groups of migratory graziers, from the adjoining districts of Kullu and Kinnaur, also use the park area between late June and mid-August every year, with a total of about 4,500 sheep and goats. Ibex have not been observed any-where in the vicinity of these groups; one possible explanation for this is the large group sizes, and the fact that they are accompanied by people and dogs. However, it is very likely that the ibex have already moved to higher altitudes in search of greener pastures.

Buddhism, the religion of the local people, does not allow them to hunt, and, therefore, ibex in the area do not face this threat, one of the major threats to wild animals the world over. However, ibex killed in avalanches are consumed. A few years before we went to Pin Valley, 27 ibex had been brought down in an avalanche, and there was great excitement among the villagers initially, until they realised they had trouble dealing with the excess meat! By the time the winter is over, and the meat stocks in the homes are exhausted, people are out looking for signs of ibex remains in avalanche debris. Digging in the snow by foxes is a positive sign. Activity begins again in spring, after a relatively dormant winter. Agriculture, and collection of fuelwood and fodder, occupy most of the people's time during the summer. They return to their villages from the summer settlements before the first significant snowfall.

Considering that it is quite rare to have all optimum conditions for the existence of ibex, and that humans are omnipresent, Pin Valley has a relatively undisturbed ibex population. Difficult access to and within the area accounts for this. Buddhism has also helped in the protection and preservation of ibex populations.

The colours of the male monal pheasant

The study that we undertook on the ibex in Pin Valley, provided data on most aspects of its ecology. Such information will be extremely useful in formulating management strategies in areas inhabited by ibex, considering the increasing threats to these fragile habitats, mainly due to developmental activities. Information obtained from these areas can also, in some cases, be extrapolated to similar areas elsewhere in the Himalaya. However, before any strategies are implemented, it is important to ensure that an area large enough to support viable ibex and snow leopard populations, is legally protected. Fortunately, areas between those that are protected today have a low human density, and correspondingly less pressure on the habitat. Therefore, the concept of a Biosphere Reserve, in which a large contiguous area which includes Protected Areas categorised as core areas, buffer zones and multiple-use areas is applicable to the entire ibex range. However, the wildlife values of the multiple-use areas should be carefully guarded.

As George Schaller writes in his book on the ungulates of the Himalaya: 'With many uplands already so seriously modified that the future of some plants and animals is in jeopardy, it is essential that a network of relatively unmodified areas be preserved as national parks and reserves. .... Large reserves are obviously needed to preserve mountain ungulates, especially those which require vertical migrations between their summer and winter ranges. ....But the great age of mammals in the Himalaya need not be over unless we permit it to be. For epochs to come the peaks will still pierce the lonely vistas, but when the last snow leopard has stalked among the crags and the last markhor

Long–tailed marmot

has stood on a promontory, his ruff waving in the breeze, a spark of life will have gone, turning the mountains into stones of silence'.

Let us hope that ibex will continue to rut in Pin Valley, and snow leopard stalk them, for many more centuries!

Two hundred million years ago, a part of Gondwanaland broke off and drifted for 130 million years before crashing into Eurasia. The surface of the earth crumpled under the impact pushing up the mountain range which later came to be known as the Himalaya. This houses a unique and threatened variety of flora and fauna

Top: *Musk deer, a unique species falling somewhere between deer and antelope, are extremely threatened by poaching for the musk pod of the male*

Left: *Unlike ibex, markhor lack warm underwool and therefore generally inhabit precipitious slopes below the snowline*

Top right: *Hangul or Kashmir stag is a species of red deer found only in the Dachigam National Park and surrounding areas*

Bottom right: *Himalayan black bear and cub feeding on a hangul carcass*

The Cheetah in India — Extinct

Divyabhanusinh

The subcontinent of India was blessed with a variety of fauna, the severely depleted remnants of which win the admiration of all who pause to marvel the diversity of nature. Among the family Felidae we have the lion, tiger, leopard and several smaller cats. The only animal that has become extinct in historical times in the plains of India belongs to this family and it is the cheetah *Acinonyx jubatus*.

The cheetah is quite unlike any other cat. Compared often with the greyhound, it is the only member of the family whose claws are semi-retractile and are prominently seen at all times. Not surprisingly it has a genus all to itself — *Acinonyx*. The Indian name, by which it is known the world over, is derived from the Sanskrit word *citraka*, the spotted one. To an uninterested eye it appears to be no different from the leopard. Yet, its black spots on a yellow background are quite distinct from the latter's rosettes and the cheetah's longer legs and tail, its leaner body and the black line, running from the anterior of each eye to the upper lip, will clearly distinguish it from a leopard on closer scrutiny. It also has a unique, monumental burst of speed which it attains for short distances. It is the fastest land animal and clocks one hundred kilometres per hour. According to a Muslim tradition, cheetahs flew when they hunted, whereas birds of prey walked! It is, therefore, not surprising that several *Baznamas* included a chapter on hunting with cheetahs.

In the Indian subcontinent variations in appearances of cheetahs have been recorded. The animals of the plains or deserts were said to be lighter in colour, bigger and faster and, therefore, better for coursing with, than the ones found in mountainous regions. Emperor Jahangir's autobiography contains the only recorded instance of a white cheetah. Actually, he was so astounded by it that he devotes an illuminating passage to it in his autobiography. He writes: 'On this day (in 1608) Raja Bir Singh Deo (of Orchha in Madhya Pradesh) brought a *yuz-i-safed* (white cheetah) to show me. Although other sorts of creatures, both birds and beasts, have white varieties, which they call *tuyghan* (Turkish for white), I had never seen a *yuz-i-safed*. Its spots which are (usually) black, were of a blue colour and the whiteness of the body was inclined to the same colour'.

Cheetahs of India and Asia are a little different from Africa, the most noticeable difference being that the tip of the tail of cheetahs from Asia is predominantly black in most cases, whereas it is white in most cases of animals from Africa. Several subspecies were recognised earlier, though now only two are generally accepted: *Acinonyx jubatus venaticus* of Asia, of which less than 200 survive, in Iran, and *A. j. jubatus*, the nominate race, from Africa. However, some scientists believe that the differences are too few to deserve subspecific status for the cheetahs from Asia and Africa; the matter is in flux. These apart, a very different looking cheetah has been reported from the Sahara. There the 'desert' cheetah population is believed to be less than 500, spread over the desert regions of Mali, Niger, Chad and Algeria. The sub-Saharan African population is now estimated at between nine and twelve thousand, a serious reduction from the 14,000 estimated during an IUCN survey by Norman Myers in 1974.

Along with the caracal *Felis caracal*, the cheetah was the only other member of the cat family which was tamed for hunting. In India, it appears to have been tamed 2,000 years ago and the earliest detailed description of its being used for coursing is from *Manasollasa* of the Chalukya king, Someshwara III, written in the 12th century. The earlier Muslim kings and potentates of India hunted vigorously, but under the Great Mughals the sport reached its zenith. The cheetah and the hunts were a vital sport at the Mughal court and these activities are recorded profusely in the literature and paintings of the time. It was a common practice at Emperor Akbar's court to give names to the favoured animals and some of them were adorned with jewel–studded collars. In 1572, one such, *Chitr Najan* by name, cleared a stream at Sanganer (where Jaipur airport is now located) to successfully bring down a blackbuck. Akbar was so impressed that he 'raised the rank of that *cita* and made him chief of the *citas*. He also ordered that as a special honour and as a pleasure to men, a drum should be beaten in front of that *cita*'. The tradition of hunting with cheetahs continued on a more modest scale in India until after

A Family of Cheetahs in a Rocky Landscape, attributed to Basawan, the great painter from Akbar's atelier, Mughal c. 1570. This is the oldest known picture of cheetahs in the wild in India. Sensitively painted, it depicts the family at peace in its surroundings. Mughal painters travelled with the emperor and had first hand knowledge of wild animals. Collection: Prince Sadruddin Aga Khan

the integration of Indian States in 1947 and their merger thereafter. It may, however, be noted that from the 1920s cheetahs were imported from Africa for the sport as they were no longer available locally.

The method of training cheetah in India was developed into a fine art, if not an exact science. Cheetahs were usually caught in snares from the wild. Though cubs could be trained, usually adults were used. J Lockwood Kipling (Rudyard Kipling's father), writing in 1886, gives the following account of the capture: 'There are certain trees where these great dog-cats (for they have some oddly canine characteristics) come to .....whet their claws. The hunters find such a tree, arrange deer-sinew nooses around it and await the event. The animal comes and is caught by a leg and it is at this point that the trouble begins. It is no small achievement for two or three naked, ill-fed men to secure so fierce a captive and carry him home on a cart'. Then his training commences where the combined effects of hunger, want of sleep and 'anti-soporific feminine scolding' soon subdue it. Later, it was taken for walks in the bazaars and gradually it became used to moving around in human company. Lockwood Kipling informs us of the 'curious intimacy' that existed between the cheetah and those who had charge of them. 'The cheetah's bedstead is like that of the keeper, and when the creature is tamed, animal and man are often curled under the same blanket. When his bedfellow is restless, the keeper lazily stretches out an arm from his end of the cot and dangles a tassel over the animal's head, which seems to soothe him. In the early morning I have seen a cheetah sitting up on his couch, a red blanket half-covering him, his tasselled hood pushed awry, looking exactly like an elderly gentleman...'

In the course of time it was made to chase disabled blackbuck in sub-optimal terrain, the cheetah being kept in check with a long rope. Once the prey was brought down, it was offered food in a long–handled ladle from which it was fed in captivity and with which it was familiar. It would thus give up the prey for ready food leaving the former to be tackled by the keeper. It was taught to go for a male blackbuck by only offering males during its training.

The entire process of training took anything from six to 12 months, although shorter periods were known. When a cheetah was fully trained, it was taken out to the hunting ground on a bullock-cart, horse-carriage or a car, and it was unhooded when the quarry was within the coursing distance of a couple of hundred yards. A well–trained cheetah usually made short work of it and it was promptly hooded thereafter. In a day, cheetah could course four to six times and it was fed only when it was to course no more that day.

The cheetah's range in the final phase of its existence extended throughout the grasslands of the Indian subcontinent from Sind and Punjab in the west, to Bihar in the east and to Mysore in the south. It is pertinent to note that the cheetah's range was more extensive than that of the lion which was not found south of the Narbada in the recent past. Its prey base consisted of the blackbuck *Antilope cervicapra*, chinkara *Gazella bennettii*, hare *Lepus nigricollis*, nilgai fawns *Boselaphus tragocamelus*, wild boar *Sus scrofa*, and often domestic livestock. The blackbuck was its most preferred prey, with chinkara following thereafter.

From British records the life of the cheetah in the wild can be pieced together. The animals hunted in daylight hours and though they were found to be solitary, often groups of about four animals — presumably subadults — lived and hunted together. Cubs were caught in grasslands but very little is known about their reproductive habits in the wild. In captivity it seems they could be difficult to breed. Emperor Jahangir recorded the birth of three cubs at his court in 1613 and wrote in his autobiography: 'It is an established fact that cheetahs in unaccustomed places do not pair off with a female, for my revered father once collected together 1,000 cheetahs. He was very desirous that they should pair but this in no way came off. He had many times coupled male and female cheetahs together in the gardens, but there too, it did not come off. At this time a male cheetah, having slipped its collar, went to a female and paired with it, and after two-and-a-half months three young ones were born and grew up. This has been recorded because it appeared strange'. However *Saidnamah-i-Nigarin*, the early 20th century treatise on cheetahs from Ajaigarh in Madhya Pradesh, details procedures for breeding them in captivity as a matter of course without any mention being made of any difficulty.

Many species have become extinct as a result of natural causes. More than any other species, this one's nemesis was human interference. In India, the cheetah had been caught for the sport of coursing antelope for hundreds of years. The tradition was already an established practice by the 12th century and it continued uninterrupted until our century. During Emperor Akbar's reign the sport attained its climax. At his court there were a 1,000 cheetahs at one time and during his reign of half a century, 9,000 cheetahs were caught for the purpose.

Both male and female cheetahs coursed efficiently. Thus there was not only a steady removal of large numbers of them from the wilds, but also the removal of females implied a significant decline in the survival rate of cubs. This certainly was an additional factor in depleting the animal's wild population in India. In Africa too, the cheetah has come under tremendous pressure from human intervention although there was not the same history of removal for sport. Cheetahs were only removed from the wilds in Africa in Ancient Egypt and later for the court of Emperor Haile Selassie of Ethiopia and for the requirements of princes in India.

In India, the cheetah in the wild must have faced predation from other carnivores such as lions, jackals *Canis aureus*, and hyenas *Hyaena hyaena*. However, British period literature does not record these interactions save in one solitary instance of a tiger killing a cheetah, which it had chanced upon, in an act of 'mere wantonness'.

The cheetah's hunting technique is highly specialised insofar as it runs down its quarry with lightening speed over short distances. This habit required the animal to hunt during the day which made it more visible and hence open to attack from humans. Further, such a method of hunting meant that the animals had to inhabit open grasslands and plains. It is precisely such areas that are the first to come under pressure and disappear as a result of increasing human population. Irfan Habib, in a study of human population growth, has estimated that the population was under 150 million in the Indian subcontinent in 1600 and it grew to 200 million by 1800, an increase by 33 percent in two centuries. But the following century-and-a-half saw an increase of 94 percent — by 1901 the population had increased to 283.9 million and by 1941 to 389 million. Vast areas of grasslands disappeared as a consequence and with it went the cheetah's most preferred habitat along with its most preferred prey, leading the cheetah towards extinction.

A recent study of the blackbuck concludes that the species eventually gained from clearance of forests and their substitution by agricultural fields. However, the cheetah could not course efficiently in ploughed or planted fields as indeed such fields reduced their habitat for cover and breeding.

There are many British period records of domestic livestock being lifted by cheetahs. This in turn brought them in direct conflict with farmers. Actually, one British observer went as far as to say that it is strange that the leopard was believed to be the bigger marauder when the cheetah did more damage.

The Mughal emperors, their entourage and the Indian princes, were interested in the cheetah to the extent of procuring them from the wilds for stocking their cheetah paddocks for coursing. They did not as a rule hunt them as they did other large cats. However, the British started spearing them from horseback as they did the wild boar for the sport of hog hunting. The cheetah itself became the object of shikar and in the final phase of its existence it came to be shot by British sportsmen and Indian princes for trophies.

An extensive though not an exhaustive analysis by the author has revealed that in the 150 years of British rule — from the 19th century to the first half of the 20th century — about 125 cheetahs only were encountered, painted, photographed, shot, speared and skins of dead animals reported. This is apart from general references to cheetahs. If we compare this figure with that of the 9,000 cheetahs that Emperor Akbar alone had collected in the 50 years of his reign in the second half of the 16th century, remembering also that his courtiers and potentates of the empire also kept cheetahs (although the figures are not known), the rate of rapid decline in the number of cheetahs in the subcontinent over 200 years between 1600 to 1800 becomes amply evident.

During the British period, the records show that the cheetah was living in less preferred habitat in the clearings in or on the edge of jungles. In fact, the last cheetahs were shot or encountered in Madhya Pradesh, Bihar and Orissa. They subsisted on domestic livestock and poultry apart from pickings of ungulates' young in the jungles. The last three cheetahs were shot in Korea, Madhya Pradesh, in 1947. Towards the end of that year the maharaja of the principality chanced upon them while driving at night. The three animals were shot with two bullets. All three were males and in all probability they belonged to the same litter.

Fears for the cheetah becoming extinct grew and the topic was debated by the Indian Board for Wildlife in 1952 and it called for 'assigning special priority for the protection of the cheetah in central India'. In 1955, its members talked of a 'bold experiment' to preserve the animal, but by that time it was too late.

The question of reintroduction of the cheetah has been discussed on and off in government and other circles. In the 1980s, Dr Asad Rahmani, a scientist from the Bombay Natural History Society, conducted a survey for identifying sites for its possible reintroduction. Though his report was not formally made available he informed the author that in his view no suitable site was available.

Dr MK Ranjitsinh prepared a preliminary project proposal and identified Khadir *bet* (island) in the Great Rann of Kutch as a possible site for reintroduction. It is 320 square kilometres in extent and is remote enough to have little interference from cattle, domestic livestock and humans as it is situated in an extensive vegetationless salt pan which gets waterlogged in the monsoon. The chinkara, nilgai, wild boar, wild ass *Equus hemionus*, hare and peacock *Pavo cristatus* exist. Blackbuck are not found on the island, but the habitat is suitable and they could be introduced. Of the predator species, caracal, desert cat *Felis lybica* and fox *Vulpes vulpes*, would compete with the cheetahs on a part of their prey base. To start with cheetahs could be released in a small enclosure of say 1,000 acres, Khadir could support eight to ten.

The fate of the cheetah has been debated since India's Independence. However, no serious steps have been taken, a clear result of a singular lack of political will to bring back this graceful animal that once sprinted in the open grasslands of India.

VENERATED ANTELOPE OF THE INDIAN GRASSLANDS

There is hardly a wild animal more representative of India than the blackbuck Antilope cervicapra.

Endemic to the subcontinent where it is the sole representative of the genus Antilope, this most handsome member of the Bovidae family was once the most ubiquitous of the larger wild mammals of this region. Its preference for the open country and its penchant for crop-raiding brought it in direct contact and conflict with man. No wild ungulate in the subcontinent has suffered so drastic a decline through hunting pressure.

Independence ushered in a period of severe wildlife destruction, particularly of those animals that caused greatest crop damage. Guns were issued freely to farmers by the government in a drive to protect crops and help mitigate food shortages. It was this that resulted in the virtual extermination of the blackbuck as a 'crop pest' although until then it was found in large numbers over much of the subcontinent. One estimate puts the figure at four million in 1947. The present estimate is that there are perhaps 30,000 to 40,000 blackbuck in India, making it one of the more isolated and threatened animals. It has become extinct in Bangladesh and Pakistan and has been reduced to a handful in Nepal.

Mentioned in the memoirs of Babar, the founder of the Mughal dynasty in India, blackbuck became both a favourite pet and an object of sport with the Mughal emperors. Akbar, an ardent hunter whose tally with his favourite gun 'sangram' alone exceeded a thousand head of game, collected during his reign about 9,000 cheetah Acinonyx jubatus venaticus for his menagerie, with as many as a thousand at one time. This vast number of captive cheetah bespeaks of the immense populations of blackbuck which could sustain such a large population of cheetah from which such extensive captures could be made. Blackbuck is an object of special veneration for the Bishnoi community of western Rajasthan and for the Kathi community, especially the Wala Kathi clan, and the Vala Rajputs of Saurashtra. These communities zealously protected blackbuck which are associated

with their past history, folklore and religious practices. They still continue to protect blackbuck herds in their areas of habitation, despite the damage that the blackbuck cause to their agricultural crops. It is on account of this primary reason that blackbuck have survived and even thrived in isolated areas and have been saved from the holocaust which overwhelmed the species outside protected areas elsewhere in the subcontinent.

THE GREAT INDIAN BUSTARD

Asad R Rahmani

We reached Rollapadu, a small, nondescript village 45 kilometres from Kurnool, quite late, so could not cover the whole of the nearby rolling grasslands. Even so, within no time we could count 25 bustards. It rained throughout the night so we took shelter in the verandah of a temple. The wet ground, the hot Andhra food generously given by villagers, and the anticipation of seeing more bustards, prevented proper sleep. Next morning, even before sunrise, we were in the field, in our rickety old jalopy. In the early morning light, with a soft wind and light drizzle, we found the largest flock of bustards seen in recent years. There were 35 bustards, foraging in small groups of three to five birds. They were everywhere. After three days, 40 great Indian bustards were counted. Just as every sighting of a tiger is a memorable experience, for me every sighting of a bustard, especially in a new area, is etched in my mind. It was my second visit to Rollapadu, the first being in 1983 with the Chief Wildlife Warden, Mr Pushp Kumar, when we had seen 12 bustards. I felt during this first visit that there should be more birds as it was one of the best bustard habitats that I had come across in the Deccan. I had decided to visit again during the monsoon when the bustards flock. The presence of so many bustards in a small area of six square kilometres brought Rollapadu into the limelight and soon the Andhra Pradesh Forest Department took measures to protect the area. Now Rollapadu is one of the most important bustard sanctuaries of India. Later we saw many more bustards in Rollapadu, but this first sighting of such a large number is unforgettable.

BACKGROUND

Among the 67 species of birds currently listed by BirdLife International as threatened or endangered in India, the great Indian bustard *Ardeotis nigriceps* is perhaps the most famous. This large bird of the short grass plains and arid areas of the Indian subcontinent was quite common about 100 years ago but the twin onslaught of indiscriminate shooting and habitat destruction reduced its population to dangerously low levels. Despite the fact that the bustard was one of the first birds to be protected in India under the Wild Animals and Birds Protection Act promulgated in 1953, its population kept on declining because enforcement of the law was practically non-existent, especially in non-forested areas where the bustard lives. Although comparative population figures are not available, the bustard population kept on declining in the 1950s and 1960s till 1972, when a more stringent Wildlife (Protection) Act was passed by the Indian government and killing of protected species such as the great Indian bustard and the tiger was made a penal offence, with a mandatory jail term.

The turning point in the conservation of the great Indian bustard came in December 1978 when certain Arab princes entered India from Pakistan ostensibly for houbara falconry. However, as the largest population of the great Indian bustard survives in the Thar Desert where the houbara bustard *Chlamydotis undulata* winters, there were fears the Arab guests would not leave the Indian bustard if they saw one. A popular public outcry in a large number of cities against this killing surprised even the conservationists and forced the Indian government to ask the Arab falconers to leave the country. Although the falconers left India without doing much harm to the bustards, their presence generated great interest in the plight of the bustard.

Another turning point was the organisation of an International Conference on Bustards in 1980 by the Tourism and Wildlife Society of India. Many Indian states in which the bustard was still found established sanctuaries to protect it. A stamp was released to mark this occasion which further highlighted the sad situation to which the bustard had come. In 1981, an Endangered Species Project, to study the ecology, behaviour and status of the great Indian bustard, was started by the Bombay Natural History Society, under the guidance of India's foremost ornithologist, Dr Salim Ali. The project was funded by the US Fish and Wildlife Service.

Until 1981, no detailed work was done on the great Indian bustard, although there were many brief accounts, notably by Dharmakumarsinhji, a former prince of Bhavnagar state in Gujarat, where the bustards were quite common during his youth in the 1930s and 1940s. Incidentally, Dharmakumarsinhji's brother — who was the king of Bhavnagar — was the first to protect bustards in his jurisdiction.

The great Indian bustard survives in six states of India — Rajasthan, Gujarat, Madhya Pradesh, Maharashtra, Andhra Pradesh

A female great Indian bustard zealously guards her chick

and Karnataka. It has disappeared from Punjab, Haryana, Uttar Pradesh, Orissa and Tamil Nadu. In the 1980s, my estimate, based on extensive surveys, was that between 1,500 to 2,000 bustards were left, and that half of these were in Rajasthan. My latest estimate (1994) is that not more than 1,000 may be left in total. This decline is mainly due to the drastic reduction in bustard numbers in the Thar Desert.

As the major aim of the Endangered Species Project was conservation of bustards, I had to spend considerable time in identifying grasslands, convincing the officials to protect the habitat, meeting villagers to seek their cooperation and writing letters and articles to generate interest in bustard conservation. In the beginning, it appeared that all these efforts were not in vain and the chances of bustard's survival had improved. There was a slight increase in the number of bustards in some of the protected areas and this resulted in complacency by the forest departments. But the destructive forces on the bustard habitat have increased during the last 15 years, and now the bustard is again in trouble. Presently, there are nine sanctuaries which were specially developed for the great Indian bustard and an equal number of multiple land-use conservation areas where the bustard population is either stable or increasing. For instance Nannaj, where at the start of our study in 1981 we saw eight to ten bustards; in September 1993, 45 were estimated. But such an increase is by no means reflected throughout the bustard protected areas.

BUSTARD FAMILY

Bustards belong to an ancient family of birds called Otididae. The oldest fossil record of the bustard is from the Eocene period, 40-50 million years ago and thus they evolved much before the appearance of modern man. There are 22 species of bustards in the world. Of these 16 species are found in Africa, the real home of bustards. From Africa, the centre of divergence of bustards, the family spread to Europe, Asia and Australia. In the Indian subcontinent, beside the great Indian bustard, three more members of the bustard family are found: the houbara bustard which is migratory and seen only in winter; the lesser florican *Sypheotides indica,* of the short grasslands of central and northwest India; and the Bengal florican *Houbaropsis bengalensis* found in the north Indian *terai* region and the Brahmaputra Valley.

ECOLOGY AND BEHAVIOUR

The great Indian bustard is a large cursorial bird, with great sexual size dimorphism: the adult males reach up to 122 centimetres in height; females are 15 to 20 centimetres smaller. Some old cocks become very heavy and may weigh up to 14.5 kilograms. Most of the year, males and females live in separate flocks, except in good feeding grounds where both can be seen together.

The great Indian bustard is catholic in its diet which ranges from insects, spiders, small lizards, snakes and eggs of ground-nesting birds, to cereals, leaves of horseradish, groundnut and Bengal gram. It also picks up small stones and pebbles to grind the food in its stomach. It is feared that while feeding in crop fields it may pick up pesticides and herbicides which are being increasingly used in India.

Earlier descriptions of the sociality of this species mentioned that the great Indian bustard lives in pairs or small groups but we never found it moving in pairs. Male and female bustards live in their own flocks. Mixed flocks are rare and temporary. Even in a mixed flock, different sexes form their own sub-groups. Most of the mixed flocks were seen in good feeding areas such as certain crop fields where the birds had congregated to forage.

As the breeding season approaches, the adult males of an area start separating from the male flock and return to their respective territories. Similarly, the female flocks also break into smaller groups of two to three birds and soon the adult females begin to separate for nesting. Solitary hens were more commonly seen during the breeding season than in the non-breeding season. Only the late nesters or the immature hens move together. In the males also, the immature birds live in flocks but the territorial cocks are solitary.

Male bustards appear to be more parochial and traditional in their habitat use than the females. If the males are not disturbed, they can be repeatedly seen in an area for many months, whereas the hens appear to move in a much larger area and with greater unpredictability.

The adult male bustard has a very large territory which may extend up to one square kilometre. The size of the territory depends on the terrain: the territory extends as far as the male can see or hear from its display arena. The territorial cock is very pugnacious and does not allow any other adult male in the area.

According to Dharmakumarsinhji, who did some pioneer studies on the bustard, fighting among two cock bustards is not heard of. Our studies reveal that in fact territorial fights among adult bustards are as common as in any other avian species.

The great Indian bustard territories are traditional and some have been occupied for the last 15 years of our study and monitoring periods. A colour-banded adult cock occupied the same territory for three consecutive years. After its disappearance, exactly the same spot was selected for display by another male. At Nannaj, in Solapur district, an adult bustard is seen displaying on the same ridge now as it was when our study began in 1981 and the same territory has been occupied throughout this period.

During the breeding season, the adult cock bustard selects a prominent place from which he can have a panoramic view

Adult male bustard displaying during courtship

of his territory. The cock spends most of his time in the arena where he struts with a semi-pendulous gular pouch. At the time of display he stands at his favourite spot and looks all around, holding his head as high as possible. Slowly he puffs and the chin feathers are erected. After more puffing and gulping of air, the gular pouch starts inflating. Slowly the pouch becomes more and more pendulous till it hangs like a balloon in front of its legs. The size of the pouch appears to depend on the age of the cock. The older cocks have bigger pouches. In some males we have seen the pouch touching the ground while in others it is not so large. The tail is cocked. Cocking of the tail coincides with inflation of the pouch. On an average, every 14 seconds it gulps air and utters a deep moaning resonant call which can be heard up to a distance of one kilometre or more, depending on the direction of wind. The bird calls only when it is at a peak display activity.

Thanks to his white gular pouch, the male becomes very conspicuous during the display and he can be seen from more than a kilometre. He also turns in all directions to advertise himself to the hens and to rival males. In the green grassland with dark monsoon clouds in the horizon, the white neck and white inflated pouch of the bustard become very conspicuous. The effect is further highlighted by his far-carrying, booming call.

Most of the displays are seen during the early morning and evening. Starting and termination of the display depend much upon the local weather conditions. Display is generally not seen during the hotter parts of the day and in strong sunlight but if hens are present, males will display in any weather condition. Once we found a male displaying at 12.15 pm near four hens. Strong winds and heavy rainfall hamper display. They sometimes display during moonlit nights.

The female moves from one territory to another and mates with a male of her choice. After mating the hen selects a secluded spot in the grassland and lays one egg. We found that nesting is the most crucial period in the life of a bustard. The greatest danger nowadays to a bustard egg is from the hordes of free-ranging domestic animals found in all the bustard areas which could easily trample an egg. Even if the egg is not destroyed, frequent disturbance to the hen during the incubation period decreases the chance of successful hatching.

The great Indian bustard is a determinate layer and the clutch consists of one egg and on rare occasions, two. Out of the 130 nests studied by us, only two were a two-egg clutch. Incubation and chick rearing is done solely by the hens, with the male taking no part whatsoever. The nesting season coincides with the increase in the insect populations, which is not unusual as most birds breed when the food resource is at a maximum. We found that the hatching success in protected grasslands was around 60 percent. Fledgling success could not be studied properly because it was extremely difficult to follow the hens with chicks due to their extreme wariness.

It was a similar wariness that added to the difficulties of attempting to photograph the male's dramatic display but the whole operation was a most memorable experience. Since 1981, we had been studying bustards in a grassland near Nannaj village in Solapur district. There was a large territorial male occupying a ridge in the middle of a protected grassland. We could see its elaborate courtship display through our telescope, but it never allowed us to approach closer than 500 metres. At this range it was not possible to get a good picture with my 300 mm lens. All my efforts to get closer by crawling on the ground and pretending to look like a stone could not fool the wary bustard. Twice I kept hides near the display spot, but the rutting blackbuck became too interested in them! In the treeless grassland, it provided some sticks against which to rub their horns. Every morning I would find the hide in a heap. I could not afford to put up a costly hide for the fear of having it stolen by inquisitive village boys. I needed a hide which was cheap, sturdy, easily movable and unattractive to boys and blackbuck. One day, I remembered seeing chickens being kept in a large dome-shaped basket called *taapa*. This *taapa* can be moved easily so it could be brought closer to the bustard progressively over four or five days. Moreover, it would not have sticks to attract rutting blackbuck. Properly furnished with old cheap gunny bags and a few branches here and there, it could look like a seasoned termite mound, overgrown by vegetation. I could fool a bustard after all.

Fortunately I found basket-makers in Solapur town who were rather amused by my unusual demand. As the bustard had become quite popular in the area, they thought I was going to keep some bustards in the *taapa*. When I told them that I was going to sit inside and wait for the bustard to come near me, they thought that long days in the open sun had played havoc with my mind. The sight of an old jeep with a large *taapa* precariously tied over it, gave another reason for people to laugh at our antics. One afternoon, when the male bustard, whom we used to call Alpha, was taking a rest away from its territory, our precious 'cargo' was unloaded from the jeep, and kept nearly 200 metres from the display spot. The covering of brown gunny sacks, branches and grasses succeeded in making it look like an abandoned termite castle. Fortunately it did not attract the attention of villagers but our Alpha male did not like such a big structure suddenly cropping up in its display arena. Luckily, however, three hens landed near the arena which encouraged the male to forget his uneasiness and soon he started attracting the hens for mating. After two days, we moved the hide closer. By now the Alpha male had become tolerant to the initially unwelcome hide. After ten days, the male was displaying only 20 metres away from the hide. So I finally decided to sit inside and try my luck.

I had to go into hiding before the male comes to display at its spot at around 3 pm. From inside, the hide was much smaller than I had thought. As soon as I took out my lens, the male became suspicious and left the arena. Something had to be done to camouflage the long lens or to make the bustard accept the lens as it had accepted the hide. The solution came in the form of an old Vim bottle; this I covered with black paper and placed a circular glass on one side so that it crudely resembled a zoom lens. It was left sticking out of the hide for five days. Within a few days the bustard was back again displaying close to the hide.

On the 16th day after putting the hide, I again sat for photography but soon after settling inside, it started to drizzle and then rain. As I did not want to alert the bustard by coming out in its presence, I sat inside the uncomfortable damp hide, camera bag in my lap, for the next two hours, while the bustard foraged close by, unmindful of my presence. Next day I again went inside the hide but the bustard decided to display at a different spot where the light was unsuitable because from my position the sun was in the background. The 18th day was 'my day'. Everything went perfectly. Within an hour of my going inside the hide, Alpha came, looked contemptuously at the hide and started displaying only ten metres from me. It could not differentiate between the Vim bottle and the real lens. I stopped photographing only when the film rolls were over. The pictures were shown to Dr Salim Ali in Bombay and he promptly sent me a note of appreciation. He made 'my day'. After that I took better pictures of bustards in Karera and in the Desert National Park, but the pictures of our Alpha male of Nannaj are still my favourite.

HABITAT PROTECTION

Habitat destruction and now poaching have played a major role in the rarity of the bustard. The great Indian bustard prefers short-grass plains — the habitat which has been more or less totally occupied by man and his livestock. It is estimated that in India there are 420 million head of livestock. To feed such a huge population, we need at least 100 million hectares of good pasture land. However, we have only 12.4 million hectares of permanent pastures, 43.8 million hectares of absolutely barren land and 33.3 million hectares of uncultivated land. Even in the sanctuaries developed for conservation of the bustard overgrazing is the major problem. For instance, in the Karera Bustard Sanctuary, the stock density is 1.79 per hectare.

One of the major aims of our project was to give recommendations for habitat improvement. Our studies on the habitat preference of the great Indian bustard showed that it lives in areas where the grasses and shrubs are below its eye level, so if the areas are over-protected and the vegetation becomes tall and dense, the bustards abandon that area. According to plant ecologists, grasslands in India are at the stage of preclimax and easily turn into scrub and finally into forests if they are not grazed or cut or burnt annually. This happened in some of the plots of 100 to 200 hectares developed for the bustards. For the first two or three years of protection, they were suitable for bustards as the vegetation was sparse and low (from 40 to 70 centimetres). But when grazing and grass cutting is stopped, to the considerable resentment of local people, these

Female bustard with chick in the Thar Desert

plots soon become unsuitable for the species for which they were developed. As the bustard is widely distributed in areas with different edaphic conditions and variable precipitation — from an annual average of 150 millimetres in certain parts of the Thar Desert to 900 millimetres in northwest India — the same yardstick of habitat management cannot be applied everywhere. Therefore, for every bustard sanctuary, we gave some specific recommendations for habitat improvement based on the local conditions of soil, vegetation and annual precipitation.

Most parts of India suffer from overgrazing and impoverishment of natural resources, resulting in soil erosion, depletion of sub–surface water and scarcity of fodder and fuel. To mitigate these conditions, the Indian government has started various projects for eco-development in which local people are involved to raise trees, reserve some parts of the common grazing lands for fodder production and construct percolation tanks to save run-off water during the three months of the monsoon. Most of these schemes, are undertaken in semi-arid, drought prone regions of India which are the areas where the bustard survives. As bustard conservation basically involves habitat improvement or rather maintenance of natural habitat, we have suggested to the Indian government to integrate bustard protection with some of these eco-development schemes.

Owing to the tremendous human pressure, it is now impossible to develop large sanctuaries of a few hundred square kilometres exclusively for the great Indian bustard and other fauna of the Indian grassland. We simply do not have that much land to exclude from human use. Even if we can establish one or two sanctuaries in some relatively remote parts of the Indian Thar Desert, a very small percentage of the total bustard population could live in such sanctuaries. Most of the bustards would be in marginally agricultural areas. Therefore, instead of establishing a few larger areas of 20 to 30 square kilometres, we suggested that many smaller areas of one to two square kilometres be developed. These should be dotted all over the bustard habitat to serve as breeding plots. These areas should be managed in such a way that local people use the natural resources on a sustainable basis. It is not difficult to get people's cooperation if we can show that habitat conservation for bustards improves grass productivity, stops soil erosion and increases sub-surface water. If we want to see this grand Indian bird survive the next century, I think eco-development of the arid areas of India, keeping in mind the requirements and aspirations of the local people, has to be the major strategy for conservation of this bird. We can secure the future of the great Indian bustard if its protection leads to betterment of the local people with whom the bustard has to share its habitat.

STATUS OF BUSTARDS IN DIFFERENT STATES

The bustard still survives in six states, but its number is precarious in Madhya Pradesh, Gujarat and Karnataka. Only Maharashtra

Following spread: *Great Indian bustards, Desert National Park, Rajasthan*

and Andhra Pradesh have taken effective conservation measures, resulting in increase in bustard numbers. Rajasthan, where more than half of India's bustards are living, has not taken effective measures. It is seen in many areas in the Thar Desert but conservation measures are inadequate to face the increasing pressure of livestock and human populations. Even the Desert National Park in Jaiselmer and Barmer districts of Rajasthan, is facing threats of habitat alteration by the construction of a tributary of the Indira Gandhi Canal, earlier known as the Rajasthan Canal. According to the census figures of the Forest Department in the mid–1980s, 200 to 400 bustards were found in this 3,162 square kilometre park. But my estimate in 1994 is that probably not more than 100 to 150 are left in the park. The tributary of the canal will bifurcate the park. Presently the human population is very low (less than ten/square kilometre) but once the tributary is completed, outsiders will settle in the area and a large part of the park will be colonised by man.

The following is a brief state-wise status of the great Indian bustard in 1994:

Madhya Pradesh: Ironically, the greatest decrease in bustard number is seen in Karera and Ghatigaon bustard sanctuaries which were specially established in 1980 for the protection of this species. In Madhya Pradesh there were four known bustard areas: Karera, Ghatigaon, Pohri and Panna. In the mid-1980s, the total bustard population in these four areas was estimated to be around 50, with Karera and Ghatigaon having 30 to 35 birds. However, since the late 1980s there has been a progressive decrease of bustards in these sanctuaries. In Karera, not even a single bustard is left. Even territorial males which were seen for many years, and as long as villagers remember, were not seen during the display period in 1993. Condition of Ghatigaon is almost as bad as Karera. The Forest Range Officer, in charge of bustards at Ghatigaon, in six months saw only two birds once. In May 1994, after much difficulty, I could locate only three bustards. A few bustards still survive in Pohri and Panna but I could not visit these areas in recent years.

Gujarat: In Gujarat, by the 1980s the bustard had become extremely rare and survived only in two districts ie, Bhatiya in Kalyanpur taluka of Jamnagar, and Abdasa and Mandvi talukas of Kutch. There was a stray record from Surendranagar district. In the whole of Gujarat, the total population was estimated to be between 20 and 30 bustards. During the last ten years, there appears to have been an almost 50 percent drop in bustard numbers. In 1990, a small bustard sanctuary of 200 hectares was established near Lala village where breeding was also noted. In 1994, nine bustards were seen.

In the Bhatiya area of Jamnagar district, the Gujarat government is planning a bustard sanctuary where four to five birds are still present. In 1983 we had seen five birds, including an immature male which shows successful breeding. During our visit in August 1993 we could not see any bustard but found evidence that less than five may still survive. It is doubtful if the population can recover from such a low number.

Maharashtra: Nannaj area in Solapur district of Maharashtra has shown the most satisfactory increase in bustard numbers, mainly because the forest department provided good measures to protect its grassland habitat. In 1981, the maximum number seen by us was only eight. Between 1981 and 1984, we did intensive studies, and later between 1985 and 1990 we regularly monitored the population. From 1991 studies were resumed under the Grassland Ecology Project. Every year we have seen successful breeding. In August 1993, we counted up to 37 bustards, and our estimate is that there are about 45 birds in Nannaj and surrounding areas. This increase is due to successful breeding and to the immigration of birds from surrounding areas.

Andhra Pradesh: Rollapadu Bustard Sanctuary in Kurnool district has also shown positive results, thanks to effective protection given to the bustard and its grassland habitat, especially during the initial stages of establishment of the sanctuary. Territorial males and successful breeding are seen every year. However, there appears to be some laxity in protection when the birds go out, hence the increase in the bustard number is not as projected. We have unconfirmed reports of bustard shooting by rich vehicle-borne poachers from Hyderabad. This could be one of the

Thar Desert — vegetation held sand dune

reasons why the bustard numbers have not further increased. During 1987-88, we estimated around 50 bustards in the Rollapadu grasslands. Our present estimate (in 1993) remains the same.

Karnataka: In Karnataka, bustards are chiefly seen around Rannibennur Blackbuck Sanctuary and Guttal plantation in Dharwad district. However, as the sanctuary itself is not very suitable for bustards due to excessive growth of eucalyptus, the birds are seen outside the sanctuary in grazing land which suffer from over-exploitation. Most probably, there are about ten bustards left in these areas.

Rajasthan: During our studies on bustards in the 1980s, we estimated that more than half of the bustards in India are present in Rajasthan, mainly in the Thar Desert. The bustard populations appeared to be secure, and a sort of complacency had developed. In my recent four surveys in 1993 and 1994, I found that all over the Thar Desert, the bustard population has drastically declined. My estimate in 1994 is that probably 500 bustards are left in the whole of Rajasthan.

Chinkara males

REASONS FOR DECLINE

Destruction of breeding areas: Destruction or alteration of grassland habitat is perhaps the most important reason for the decline of bustards in Madhya Pradesh, Gujarat and Karnataka. In Karera Bustard Sanctuary we had identified four important breeding areas and had strongly recommended that the State Forest Department should give special protection to such areas at least during the bustard's breeding season. However, not much was done to prevent unrestricted movement of people and livestock as a result of which bustards could not breed successfully.

Spiny-tailed lizard

The great Indian bustard is a long living, slow breeding bird. It is not unusual for adult birds to live in an area for 10 to 15 years. The survival of adult birds gives a sense of complacency that all is well. Unless these adult birds breed successfully and leave progeny, long term survival of bustard cannot be assured. If these birds do not breed then what will they leave once they die? Conservation success should not be measured only by giving protection to adult birds, but by giving protection to their breeding areas as well.

The tragedy of Karera, Ghatigaon and other bustard sanctuaries is that protection was given to adult birds only and not to the areas where these birds breed. When Karera Sanctuary was established in 1982, we found 14 adult bustards and there were still a few areas where adult males used to display and hens used to lay eggs. Between 1982 and 1986, there was a slight increase in bustard numbers mainly because nests were identified and given protection. Some of the increase was due to immigration from surrounding areas. Based on our five years of fieldwork, we had strongly recommended that at least four areas of Karera Bustard Sanctuary, consisting of less than ten square kilometres out of the 202 square kilometre sanctuary, should be taken over by the forest department and scientifically managed but our suggestions were not implemented. Even though by 1987 it was clear that bustards were not increasing satisfactorily, false reports of increase in bustard population were given every year. In the absence of successful breeding, as the adult birds died naturally the bustard population declined. In contrast, at Nannaj in Maharashtra, where the main emphasis was on protecting bustard habitat, the result was a four-fold increase in bustard numbers over ten years.

A great Indian bustard in front of a bullock cart reveals the link between this endangered species and its environment

Disturbances: There is no bustard area in India which is free from human disturbance. We do not have any large patch of grassland of 200 to 300 square kilometres where a few hundred bustards can live peacefully. All bustard areas suffer from severe overgrazing, spread of cultivation and increase in human population. Moreover, every bustard area/sanctuary has its own specific problems, such as construction of canals in Karera and Ghatigaon bustard sanctuaries, construction of gas pipeline in Pohri bustard area in Madhya Pradesh, the planning of a large spinning mill very close to the main bustard area in Nannaj in Solapur district, and plantation of *Prosopis juliflora* in the Lala Bustard Sanctuary in Gujarat.

Shooting: Fortunately, at Karera, Ghatigaon, and Nannaj, poaching of bustards is under control. However, shooting appears to be playing a major role in the decimation of bustards in the Thar Desert. During my surveys in 1993, in most of the areas, villagers told me about poaching by outsiders. These poachers generally come for houbara and sandgrouse but also shoot the great Indian bustard. We found many indirect evidences of shooting by observing the behaviour of wildlife. In all these areas, the chinkara *Gazella bennettii*, used to run away from 500 to 600 metres, clearly indicating poaching. In Bishnoi areas where wildlife is totally protected, chinkara can be approached to 20 metres. In parts of Bap area, where we had seen 11 bustards ten years ago, the chinkara were so terrified that they could not be approached to even one kilometre. In the adjoining Bishnoi area, chinkara were seen as close as 30 metres from the huts. Six bustards were seen by us during February 1993 among Bishnoi settlements in the Bap area, and none in the non–Bishnoi area.

PROJECT BUSTARD

Among the four species of bustards found in India, the great Indian bustard is comparatively well known. Not many people know that the two florican species are also gravely endangered, and the population of migratory houbara bustard is declining rapidly, due to excessive hunting in the Thar Desert and neighbouring Pakistan. The ecology, behaviour, status and conservation of Bengal and lesser floricans have been studied recently. All bustards are in Schedule I of the Wildlife (Protection) Act, 1972.

All the four species of bustards found in India have the highest legal protection and there is not much we can do in this direction except for implementing the law more stringently to eliminate poaching. The habitats of the bustards are, however, not so well protected and this constitutes the biggest threat to the survival of the bustard. Therefore, our major conservation efforts have to be addressed to habitat protection.

As the great Indian bustard and floricans are perhaps the best avian indicator species of grasslands, they can be used as flagship species to protect our grasslands. Here I propose that like Project Tiger and Project Elephant, the Government of India should start Project Bustard to preserve not only bustards and floricans but also all the associated species of Indian grasslands and deserts.

WHY PROJECT BUSTARD?

The grasslands which are the preferred habitat of all the three resident Indian bustards are under represented in the protected area network in our country. Similarly, the desert regime is also under represented. The Wildlife Institute of India and the Bombay Natural History Society have identified many potential areas which could be developed as new sanctuaries. Additionally, many existing sanctuaries need expansion, to make them more viable and/or need active habitat and human management. As these existing/potential sanctuaries occur in different states, the degree of management and protection varies from area to area depending upon the interest and inclination of the state governments. There are many reasons to have a nationally coordinated conservation project for the Indian bustards and their habitats:

Need for cooperation: Each state is taking its own course of action to conserve bustards and floricans without knowing what the other states are doing. There is no cooperation among the states even though the bustards and floricans move from one state to another. In some cases, officials of one state do not even know that the same species of bustard is found in other states as well!

Need for better management of sanctuaries: After the initial enthusiasm to protect bustards in the early 1980s, with most attention on the great Indian bustard, in many cases sanctuaries have been neglected as a result of which bustard populations have declined. The establishment and maintenance of some of the bustard and florican sanctuaries was mainly due to the active interest taken by some individuals such as Messrs Ranjitsinh, J J Dutta, P M Lad, Pushp Kumar and Kailash Sankhala (to mention a few names). Once such people retired or were shifted to other departments, the conservation of bustards and floricans received a set back [eg, Karera, Ghatigaon, Sailana (for lesser florican) and Sonkhaliya are now totally neglected].

Research and implementation of findings: Little work has been done on the ecology and behaviour of the bustards, except for the work done under the Endangered Species Project of the Bombay Natural History Society. Bustard and florican populations need constant monitoring. Moreover, changes in some of the sanctuaries are taking place so fast that by the time the results are published, the situation is completely different. Worse, there is no authority or mechanism presently in existence to supervise the follow-up action on the recommendations of scientific studies.

Long-term plan: There is no proper long-term planning to protect the habitats of the bustard (except perhaps in the Bengal florican areas but that is being done for other reasons). As the great Indian bustard lives in marginal agriculture areas and the lesser florican is seen in many private grasslands, a greater administrative and scientific input is required to keep the habitat suitable for both bustards and floricans.

Protection to associate species of bustards: By starting Project Bustard, grassland habitats and their associated species such as wolf, jackal, fox, chinkara, blackbuck, swamp deer, swamp francolin, raptors, coursers, etc, will greatly benefit.

RECOMMENDED OBJECTIVES FOR PROJECT BUSTARD:

1. To conserve all the four species of bustards in India;
2. To conserve the habitat types of the Indian bustards and their associate species;
3. To establish with the cooperation of the state governments more bustard sanctuaries;
4. To upgrade the existing closed areas into wildlife sanctuaries;
5. To supervise and coordinate management of bustard sanctuaries;
6. To coordinate long-term studies on bustards and their habitats in different areas;
7. To integrate grassland (bustard habitat) conservation with national grazing policy.

Author checks the ring on a great Indian bustard prior to release

THE LIONS OF GIR

Ravi Chellam

INTRODUCTION

December 31, 1989. The last official day of fieldwork for me in the Gir forest. It was the usual routine. Setting out in the jeep before sunrise in search of the radio-collared lions, identifying, ageing and sexing all lions seen and collecting lion and leopard scats. I was attempting to track down one of the collared male lions but even after two hours I wasn't having any luck. It was very cold in the open jeep and the rising sun was just beginning to warm up my day. I drove up a slope and reached the top of a hillock which afforded a panoramic view of the forest in the golden light of early morning. Hardly 20 metres ahead of me on the road was a pride of nine lions. All the lions were relaxed and resting on the road. My noisy appearance on the scene disturbed the lions and they slowly got up and walked away from the jeep. It was an incredible sight, 36 paws silently padding away on the dirt track and nine tail tassels swaying from side to side, as the lions made their way into the forest.

Fieldwork, which includes working with wild animals, is very much part of my profession. At the same time everyday is not filled with excitement. A lot of time was spent in travelling through the forest to reach my various study sites and also in search of my study animals. Given the task on hand and the interesting animals I was fortunate enough to work with, I never really felt the rigour of my efforts.

Large carnivores, more specifically large cats, tend to excite all of us. With the Asiatic lion, the public at large, has maintained an extremely ambivalent attitude. The Asiatic lion evokes varied responses which depend upon who is the respondent and when the response is recorded.

The people of Gujarat, especially those residing in the Saurashtra peninsula, take great pride in the fact that they are custodians of the sole free-ranging population of lions in Asia. At the same time, if the opinion is asked of a cattle grazer in one of the surrounding villages outside the Gir forest, who has just lost his only milk yielding buffalo to lion predation, it is bound to be negative. The response would be outright hostile if he has either been mauled by a lion or has recently lost one of his kith and kin to a lion attack.

To contrast with all of these opinions we have the Maldharis resident in the Gir forest who graze their livestock and make a living by selling *ghee* (clarified butter) and milk to the villagers outside the forest. Maldharis resident in the Gir forest are probably the one group of people who have to deal with lions on a daily basis and at extremely close quarters. They frequently lose their stock to lion predation but, more often than not, with a typical shrug of their shoulders, carry on with their lives not really blaming the lions for their loss. These people have an innate respect and appreciation of the fact that they are privileged to be living in the forest. They also realise that the Gir forest exists today largely because of the lions. I shall later narrate more about the Maldharis and their life amidst the wildlife of Gir.

December 1985. I was travelling by a Gujarat State Transport Corporation bus, filled to its capacity, to Sasan Gir from Junagadh. For much of the journey we passed through agricultural fields, villages and towns. About 13 kilometres from Sasan (the headquarters of Gir Wildlife Sanctuary and National Park), is a forest department checkpost at Vaniavav. The bus halted there and, looking out of the window I saw a fresh, partially eaten buffalo carcass lying by the road. Delighted to see some evidence of lion's existence so early in my trip, at the same time my heart sank as it also meant that lions were still preying on livestock.

I was then a Junior Research Fellow with the Wildlife Institute of India, working on a project which aimed to collect baseline information on the ecology of the endangered Asiatic lion. The ultimate objective of this project was to explore the feasibility of a translocation effort to establish a second free-ranging population of the lions. If the lions were still largely preying on livestock then the prospects for their translocation would be bleak. Large cats tend to be creatures of habit and once individuals get accustomed to killing livestock they are likely to persist with their predatory habits. People close to the translocation site are unlikely to tolerate livestock predation by lions and would only look at it as an additional problem. This continued to bother me as the bus lurched ahead when the Forest Guard opened the gates for us to proceed. The dry deciduous and thorn forests of Gir dominated the scenery all the way to the dust-filled village of Sasan Gir, the sanctuary headquarters.

A Gir lion feasts

I was on a short exploratory visit and was eager to see as much as possible of the forest and the wildlife, and to meet and discuss with the forest department officials regarding my research project. I spent three days walking in the forest to gain a feel for the place and also to try and catch sight of the animal which I was planning to study for my doctoral degree. I saw plenty of indirect evidence of the presence of lions. Tracks covered many portions of the dirt roads which crisscrossed the forest. I located a few scats and even the remains of a chital stag killed and eaten a few weeks ago. I spent one night in a rest house located inside the forest and was awakened around midnight by the reverberating roar of a lion but the animal itself proved to be elusive.

It was my last evening in Gir. I had spent most of the day trekking through the forest. I was being accompanied by a ten-year-old boy who was acting as my guide. It was dusk and we were walking back to Sasan and had a couple of kilometres to go. Suddenly we heard some growls and out of the dense bushes by the roadside emerged a lioness and she was soon followed by three more lionesses. This was the moment I had been waiting for, ever since I left Dehra Dun for Gujarat. Excitement, ecstasy and fear formed a heady mixture of emotions, as an overdose of adrenalin coursed through my blood vessels. The lioness emerged about 30 metres from where my boy-guide and I were standing. All four animals approached us as if we were normal features of their landscape. I had come prepared to record this encounter with my camera and a telephoto lens, but I was simply too awestruck to react. Looking back now, I remember that they were sub-adult females playfully swatting each other, uttering low growls and they completely ignored our presence. By the time I gathered my wits and focused my camera I could take only one picture, and that too a rear view of one of the lionesses retreating into the cover of bushes. This brief encounter was the first of many hundreds of similar and more hair-raising ones that dominated my life till early 1990, when I completed my fieldwork and shifted my base to our headquarters at Dehra Dun.

* * *

The Gir lions have an interesting conservation history. The Asiatic lion in the Gir forest in Gujarat state is an excellent example of a conservation success story of our times. At the same time, it is also an enigma. For long revered as part of the religious and cultural heritage of India, it had the honour of being the national animal till the tiger replaced it in the early 1970s with the launch of Project Tiger. The lion still forms an integral part of our national emblem.

The Asiatic lion is a subspecies and has evolved from the African lion, having separated from the base stock about 100,000 years ago. It once was found in a vast area stretching from Syria, through Iran, Iraq into most parts of northern and central India. Historical accounts of hunting expeditions and other descriptive accounts enable us to reconstruct the past distribution of this cat. Despite its vast range and, I assume, very high numbers, the Asiatic lion very rapidly became endangered. In fact, in the latter half of the 19th century, in barely three decades, the lion was restricted to the Gir forest in the Indian subcontinent. A few stragglers continued to survive outside India, especially in the Euphrates and Tigris valleys but by 1945, Gir became the sole custodian for all the free-ranging Asiatic lions.

Survival for the lions in Gir has been far from assured. A perusal of the records indicates that the lion population in Gir came perilously close to extinction during a 35 year period from 1880. Population estimates then ranged from less than 12 to a maximum of 31. This population has since made a sustained and rather dramatic recovery to the recently estimated population of 304 (Gujarat Forest Department's lion census conducted in May 1995).

The nawab of Junagadh played a crucial role in the survival of lions in Gir. Hunting of lions especially by royal dignitaries was a fairly routine affair. In the early 1900s with the lion numbers in Gir being very low, the then nawab decided to ban lion hunting and gave the lions complete protection. The local people were also instructed to strictly follow the nawab's orders in this regard. Given the very low numbers and the time taken by the lion population to recover, this strict protection was very crucial. But for this the lions would have definitely become extinct. The Gujarat Forest Department has since followed up on this lead provided by the nawab and provided good protection to the lions which has enabled them to flourish. The local people in and around Gir continue to be very tolerant and supportive of the lions.

In the late 1950s the forests were overgrazed by livestock and the process of degradation was very evident. Some experts were then predicting that in two decades nothing would be left of the Gir forest or the lions. In this context what has been accomplished in Gir is quite remarkable.

The lion population in Gir has experienced what is known as a genetic bottleneck. A genetic bottleneck occurs when the population drops to very low numbers (normally less than 500 adult interbreeding animals is referred to as a small population), as a result the population loses most of its genetic diversity. Loss of genetic diversity can have catastrophic consequences for the long-term survival of the population. In case of the Asiatic lion the problem is compounded by the fact that not only has the population lost its genetic diversity, it is also the only population thereby greatly increasing its risk of extinction. When an endangered species is restricted to a single population it is very much like having all your eggs in a single basket. Environmental catastrophes and diseases pose very potent threats to the survival of species restricted to a single population. The Wildlife Institute of India's Gir project was designed to provide information based on which management action to improve the conservation status of the Asiatic lions could be planned and implemented.

Lioness in Gir, the last refuge of the Asiatic lion

Evidently the two major problems facing the lions were the small numbers and its restricted distribution. The Gir forest is an isolated patch of natural vegetation in Saurashtra peninsula. Most areas of the peninsula are either agricultural fields, human settlements or industrial complexes. The Gir forest covered more than 3,000 square kilometres, as measured by the Great Trigonometrical Survey of 1877. Today, the remaining forest barely cover 1,500 square kilometres. Even though the lion population has been increasing in the last few decades the fact that their natural habitat is restricted and what remains of the Gir forest is hemmed in by human settlements on all sides is a major limiting factor to its potential for growth. Lions, like other large cats, are fiercely territorial and they need fairly large tracts of land with adequate large ungulate prey to survive. The obvious conservation action that would go a long way in enhancing the long-term prospects for survival for the lions was the establishment of a second free-ranging population. Translocation of large carnivores is a complicated task which needs good knowledge and understanding of the ecology and behaviour of the species concerned. The major objectives of my study were to get information on the diet and predatory habits of the lions, to estimate the availability of prey for the lions in Gir, and to gather information on the habitat use and ranging patterns of the lions. This study was planned to provide information on the lion's choice of prey species, conditions under which they succeeded in hunting, their habitat choice, and the size of their home range. All of which is crucial for the scientific planning of a translocation project.

**

The Gir forest and the Asiatic lions are unique in the Indian wildlife scenario in the sense that scientific research has been carried out by numerous wildlife biologists since the late 1960s. Apart from this, Gir and the lions have also attracted the attention of many naturalists. As a result there is a considerable amount of written record of various aspects of the natural history and ecology of Gir. This allows me to compare the results of my studies with those obtained earlier and to interpret the results more meaningfully.

In the late 1960s, studies by Paul Joslin, Stephen Berwick and others found that the habitat still retained its productivity and only protection was required. Inside fenced plots, grass production was comparable to any similar habitat and much greater than in unprotected plots. Both Berwick and Joslin conducted organised vehicle based transects for estimating wild ungulate population. They both estimated a total of a little over 6,000 wild ungulates, with chital being the most abundant. This was a very important finding as it meant that if the lions had to survive over the long-term the wild prey base would need to increase dramatically. Six thousand wild ungulates was an extremely limited and inadequate prey base. This was further proven by Joslin's data on the lion's diet which was largely based on the analysis of the lion scats. He found that more than 75 percent of the lion scats contained remains of domestic livestock.

The habitat was being overgrazed by livestock and this depressed vegetation productivity. The wild ungulate population was very limited and not enough to support a population of lions. As a result the lions were largely dependent on livestock for their food. These findings did not augur well for the future. The obvious conflicts that existed between people and wildlife could not go on for long without negative impacts on the lions.

In the early 1980s, S P Sinha's research on the ecology of the lions in Gir indicated that the lions were gradually shifting their choice of prey from livestock to wild ungulates. Based on scat analysis he found that 52 percent of the lion scats had remains of wild ungulates which is a tremendous shift from the early 1970s when less that 25 percent of the scats had wild prey remains.

**

It was with this background information that my research began in Gir in early 1986. In early 1987 I was joined by my colleague, Jamal Khan. I concentrated on the ecology of the lion while Jamal focused on ungulates and their relationship

A lioness relaxing with her cubs

with the habitat. The Wildlife Institute of India has since had follow up studies on the lion-human conflicts and the impacts of management on wildlife habitat.

The major management recommendation of Berwick and Joslin was a reduction in the level of livestock grazing. This was implemented by the Gujarat Forest Department in two ways. Livestock from outside of the forest was completely banned from entering the forest and some of the Maldhari families were resettled outside the forest. A central area of the forest was cleared of all human settlements to create a national park. So when I began my studies these fairly significant changes had already taken place in the local ecology.

Jamal and I obtained data on ungulate populations by conducting vehicle based transects. The total population of wild ungulates was calculated to be around 55,000, with the chital population exceeding 52,000. Compared with the total of a little over 6,000 wild ungulates in the early 1970s it was a remarkable increase in wild ungulate population, especially for chital. Sambar was the next most abundant wild ungulate.

I obtained data on the diet and predation ecology of the lion by analysing their scats and investigating the remains of their kills. Scats are the droppings of carnivores. Large cats subsist largely by preying upon large ungulates. When they feed on the kills they have made, they not only consume the meat and the organs but also ingest the skin with the hair and crunch the bones. The hair of the prey species pass unchanged through the digestive tract of the cat and form part of the scat. It is these hair which enable the identification of the prey consumed by the cat. These hair have unique species specific patterns which can be discerned through a microscope. Collection and analysis of scats is a messy job but the valuable results thus obtained more than justify the efforts put in. Moreover, scat data is the most unbiased data that can be obtained on the diet of carnivores. The size of the prey animal and where the kill was made does not influence scat data to a great extent. The limitation of scat data is that only the prey species can be identified but no information on the age and sex of the animal killed or the site and micro-environmental conditions under which the kill was made can be gleaned. Such data are essential to understand the predation ecology of a large cat.

To obtain kill data, I had to search the forest for the remains of prey animals killed and fed upon by the lions. This is easier said than done. My field assistants and I had to put to use our senses of smell, vision and hearing to locate the kills. The cawing of crows scavenging on the kill remains was the best clue to their locations. Often there were drag marks on the ground, indicating that the carcass has been moved by the lions. Once we had located the kill remains, we had to establish whether the animal was killed by lion, leopard or any other predator or whether it had died due to other reasons and was scavenged upon by the predators. Data on numerous parameters relating both to the prey animal (species, age, sex, its physical condition), and to the habitat (vegetation type, terrain, proximity to water etc.) was collected. The entire exercise was very similar to that of a detective investigating a crime scene looking for the various clues to unravel the details of the crime.

When the opportunity presented itself I followed a lion over many days to determine the kills made in succession. I was not always fortunate enough to witness the hunt. The dense vegetation of Gir and the fact that most of the kills are made at night, means that the chances for seeing a hunt are greatly reduced. I was lucky to have observed a few. A lone lioness with two young cubs was located frequently by us during the early summer. She operated largely along the riverine tract at Pilipat, near Sasan. Following her on foot and getting information on the kills she had made was dicey because a lioness with cubs can be very aggressive. One evening I decided to observe a water hole from the cover of vegetation up a steep cliff. The opposite bank was sandy and covered with *Carissa* bushes. The water hole itself was on a boulder strewn stream bed. Around 18.30 hrs I saw the lactating lioness

The author's shadow as he studies the Gir lions

emerge from the vegetation and crouch to drink water. After slaking her thirst she disappeared into the vegetation. Soon after, a sambar doe came to drink water, followed by a herd of five chital. The deer approached the water very cautiously, intently gazing into the vegetation, sniffing the air and moving very slowly. Eventually the deer reached the water edge and began to drink. As the deer put their heads down, the lioness in full alert crept to the edge of the vegetation stalking potential prey. All muscles taut and with complete concentration on the deer drinking about 25 metres away, the lioness crept forward ever so slowly towards the deer. Suddenly she charged, scattering sand and water in the wake of her powerful surge. The deer were taken completely by surprise. They called out in alarm and fled up the slope on the opposite bank. I lost sight of the action at this stage but could hear the sounds of a struggle between a predator and its prey. Sounds of hooves thrashing, low growls and groans indicated that the lioness had been successful in her hunt. Only next morning was I able to determine that it was the sambar which had been brought down and that she was pregnant. It is possible that the lioness chose to go for the sambar as it meant a lot more meat to feed upon and it is equally likely that pregnancy had slowed down the deer. Even though lions are social cats they often hunt alone and the rest of the pride then joins in to feed on the carcass. In fact, in the forests of Gir, group hunting might not necessarily be the best strategy for the lions to adopt as the dense vegetation prevents visual contact and mitigates against group action.

Our scat data indicated that about 75 percent of the scats contained remains of wild prey and the remaining had the remains of livestock. This is a complete reversal of the patterns observed by Joslin. Chital was by far the most frequently killed prey followed by sambar. Buffalo and cattle were the most often killed species of livestock but they ranked below chital and sambar in the frequency of occurrence in the lion scats. This was good news. It meant that the lions were tracking the increasing availability of wild prey and shifting their predation from livestock to wild animals. They continued to prey on livestock largely because of the large number of livestock available to them. Male lions were seen more often on livestock kills than lionesses. This was probably because predation of livestock involved an element of risk. Livestock in Gir are herded by the Maldharis who would make all attempts to defend their herd against predation by lions. On sighting lions they make lots of noise, throw stones and herd their livestock into a tight group; all in an attempt to disturb the lions and to protect their herd. Lionesses are normally accompanied by cubs or sub-adults and they are wary of any disturbance which may pose a risk to the survival of their young.

During Joslin's study lions frequently jumped the thorn fence surrounding the Maldhari settlements, to kill livestock. This was essentially an unproductive exercise as the lion seldom got the opportunity to feed on the carcass. The rest of the herd would stampede and the Maldharis themselves would attempt to drive the lion away. The lions were desperate to make kills as wild ungulates were limited in numbers. During my study I investigated only two reports of lions jumping the thorn fence. This is yet another change in the predation ecology of the lions and probably another indication of the increased availability of wild prey.

Water plays an important role in the predation ecology of the lions especially in the drier part of the year (December to May). Since Gir is an semi-arid habitat, water gets restricted to the perennial streams and water holes around December. All the animals are forced to congregate around these water sources. Since the vegetation tends to be dense around water sources it offers ample ambush cover to the lions and also the increased density of prey animals close to water increases their chances of a successful hunt. The lions also exhibited active selection of stags in their kills. Stags are larger in body size and hence more meat would be available for the lions to feed and also they tend to be much less alert than the does.

I tranquillized lions to radio-collar them. This was essentially to study their ranging patterns and habitat use. I calculated seasonal home range size based on the radio tracking data. Female home range was 85 square kilometres in the dry season and 67 square kilometres in the wet season. Males did not exhibit much seasonal variation in their home range size. Both males and females exhibited seasonal shifts in their ranging pattern; in that they did not use the same areas in both the seasons. Annual home ranges were really huge, it was 120 square kilometres for females and 200 square kilometres for males. These values are based on the ranging patterns of individual collared lions but they really reflect the home range size of groups of animals as lions are social cats. Males did not exhibit any obvious choice in their habitat use but females definitely preferred to use riverine habitats during the dry season. This establishes the crucial importance of riverine habitats for the lions. Riverine habitats are threatened habitats in Gir. They are restricted to the banks of the perennial rivers (which are not many in Gir), and they only extend to a maximum of 30 metres from the water on either side. Since most Maldhari settlements are close to rivers, these riverine habitat gets degraded either due to cutting or due to constant trampling by livestock.

The social organisation of the lions in Gir is significantly different to lions from the savannas of East and South Africa. In Africa when lions are sighted, invariably adult animals of both sexes are found together. The converse is true for the lions in Gir. On the majority of the occasions when bisexual groups of lions are seen in Gir, it is either because they are mating or because they are sharing a large sized kill like a domestic buffalo or a sambar stag. I hypothesise that this difference in the social organisation is largely a reflection of the distinct environmental conditions under which they live in Gir. To begin with, they live in a forest which affords denser ambush cover, not available in open grasslands. Males, with their conspicuous manes, would be very easily detected by the prey animals in the savannas and would have a very low success rate in their hunts. Moreover, male lions also prey a great deal on livestock in Gir which is much easier to hunt than wild animals. Having attained nutritional independence from the lionesses the males in Gir, unlike their cousins in Africa, tend to range independently. Additionally since chital is the most frequently preyed upon species it would not be beneficial to the pride to have the male sharing the kill. It is a small sized prey compared to those on which the lions prey in Africa and the lionesses and young would get very little food if they had to compete with the males.

Life for the lions is very often long periods of rest and sleep, with short periods of intense activity. In fact, the social status of the cat plays a very large role in its daily life. Adult territorial males, which form groups known as coalitions, have to range over their territory, roaring and scent marking, to assert their ownership to other competing males. Following these males is very exciting. They often cover very large distances (eight to 25 kilometres), roar regularly and scent mark on every suitable tree trunk and rock. Life for the pride females and young is more to do with obtaining food and ensuring that the young survive and grow up to the age of about three when they have to leave the pride and disperse. Life is most difficult for the lions which have dispersed but have still to settle down in a territory. These are the nomads. They have no fixed territory. Young males have to form coalitions and then challenge ageing resident males to gain a territory; some females settle down with their mothers but others have to seek entry into new prides. Males which have been ousted from their territory also end up as nomads, with very little hope of ever regaining the status of a resident male. Males do get killed when the 'battle royale' is on for a territory. A territory ensures a relatively safe and settled life with access to females for breeding.

***

The Maldharis have a very close association with the lions in Gir. Currently the Maldharis living within the forest realise that the very existence of the Gir forest is largely due to the lions. They have witnessed the rapid and complete destruction of the natural vegetation in Saurashtra and consider themselves lucky to have the luxury of a forested habitat which meets many of the needs of their pastoral existence. These simple people live in a thorn fence enclosed settlement called *ness*. Their houses are constructed out of locally available wood, grass and clay. Each house has an open courtyard in which the herd is penned in for the night. There is little to protect the livestock from the lions and leopards that live in Gir. In fact, I have spent many nights in a *ness* and heard lions roar at very close quarters. It is an adventure that can only be experienced. Previous resettlement programmes to create the national park have not benefitted the Maldharis. In fact, the resettled Maldharis have become poverty stricken as many of the commitments given in the mid 1970s are still to materialise.

Apart from the Maldharis, the other group of people of interest are the Siddhis. Siddhis are of African origin and the story goes that they hail from Somalia and Ethiopia. They were brought to India by the nawab of Junagadh to help him with the management of lions in Gir. Shirvan village is the home for the Siddhis. These people look African and retain many of their ancestral songs and dances and at the same time have integrated into life in Gujarat. They speak Gujarati and many of them have moved into the nearby towns and villages in search of work. Most of the Siddhis living in Shirvan village are presently agriculturalists.

The lions have endured many a crisis in their battle for survival in Gir. These lions are unique in that they live in a forest, prey on deer and interact very closely with man on a regular basis. I have outlined some of the risks faced by the Gir lions. We have reached a stage when we cannot afford to sit back and continue to ride our luck and hope that the lions will continue to flourish for another century. The action required to ensure their long-term survival includes increased and continued protection to the lion population and habitat in Gir and implementation, without any further delay, of the translocation project to establish a second free-ranging population of lions.

A Maldhari boy models clay animals in Gir

GIANTS OF THE FOREST — ELEPHANTS

Peter Jackson

For many a visitor to India their first sight of an elephant may be of a tame one among the bustling traffic in Delhi or Bombay, perhaps ridden by saffron-robed Hindu holy men. It is an appropriate introduction to the Indian elephant, for in India, elephants and people have lived together for thousands of years. Seals depicting elephants with riders have been recovered from the ruins of the Harappa civilisation, which flourished 5,000 years ago in the valley of the Indus. Ancient Hindu writings in the Vedas mention tame elephants in 2000-1500 BC. Alexander the Great faced an elephant phalanx when he fought King Porus on the Indus River in 331 BC. He had with him his own elephant corps, established after his victory over the Persian king, Darius. That was his first encounter with these live war machines. Although he died before his return to Greece, his followers introduced elephants to Mediterranean wars.

In Alexander's time, Asian elephants were found as far west as the Euphrates and Tigris valleys in Mesopotamia. They put to flight African elephants when the Seleucid king, Antiochus II, defeated Ptolemy IV at the battle of Raphia in 217 BC. Those African elephants were probably from the now extinct North African subspecies, which was smaller than Asian elephants, unlike the well-known bush elephant of sub-Saharan Africa.

Both Asian and African elephants are members of the same family, the Elephantidae, but they have been placed in separate genera. The Asian elephant is *Loxodonta africana,* while the Asian elephant is *Elephas maximus.* An African bull bush elephant can be as tall as 13 feet (four metres) at the shoulder and weigh over 10,000 pounds (4,500 kilograms), compared with 11.5 feet (3.5 metres) and 8,800 pounds (4,000 kilograms) in the Asian elephant. The African elephant's big ears clearly distinguish it from the Asian elephant, but there are several other differences. Asian elephants have rounded or flat backs, but African elephants have saddle backs. African elephants have 'fingers' at the top and bottom of the tip of their trunks, but Asian elephants have only one at the top. Female African elephants have tusks like the males, but Asian females have only small tushes which seldom show below the upper lip. Many Asian males are tuskless, but they are no less powerful than tuskers.

Strictly speaking, animals in different genera cannot breed. But, in 1978, at Chester Zoo in England, a hybrid Afro-Asian elephant was born. It had distinctive features of both species, such as the twin mounds on the forehead like its Asian mother and a single central mound like its African father. It died after 11 days of a common intestinal disease, for which its mixed parentage is not thought to have been at all responsible.

The bearing of tusks has a curious pattern in the Indian region. While 90 percent of male elephants in southern India have tusks, only five percent have tusks across the narrow strait in Sri Lanka. In northeast India, only 50 percent of males have tusks. Although tusklessness may be a natural genetic feature of Asian elephants, it is possible that selective killing and capture of young tuskers may have resulted in the regional differences.

The elephant's trunk is its most intriguing organ. Primarily a nose for breathing, the trunk is also a pneumatic hose capable of sucking and blowing liquids when drinking and showering, and to collect dust to blow over the body. It serves as a trumpet and a sounding board. It picks up scent. As a highly flexible working tool it is almost as versatile as the human hand. Elephants can tear up grass, bang the dirt off the roots, and convey it to their mouths. They can select fruits, or break off branches. With equal facility they can hoist huge logs or pick up a small coin, placing both with delicate accuracy. Trunks are used to greet and caress fellow elephants. They can also function as flailing weapons, but in a serious charge an elephant will coil its trunk out of the way — it is too valuable to risk it being injured.

Rudyard Kipling's Just-So story of the epic battle between an elephant and a crocodile which resulted in the elephant's nose being stretched into a trunk was probably based on the Hindu legend of just such a battle, which ended when the god Krishna killed the crocodile. In fact, the trunk probably evolved so that the short-necked elephant could reach the ground to feed.

At what date people began taming and using Asian elephants is lost in the mists of time. Perhaps orphan baby elephants were found and cared for in ancient Mesopotamia, the source of most of our domestic animals. They quickly became tame and lived like family pets. It is easy to imagine that people found they could ride on them and teach them to obey orders. Even adult elephants can be quickly trained. Although tame elephants are often referred to as 'domesticated', almost all have

A tusker dwarfed by the forests of Corbett National Park

Decorating an elephant at the traditional elephant fair at Sonepur in Bihar

been taken from the wild and they are still truly wild animals, unlike the cow, the horse, the sheep and the pig.

Elephants have a prominent place in ceremonial in India. Maharajahs emphasised their lofty role as they rode in state in lavish howdahs mounted on the backs of big tuskers, moving with dignity among their cheering people, and followed by their family, courtiers and retainers on dozens more elephants. Perhaps the greatest such spectacle was the annual Dussehra procession in Mysore. The procession is still a major attraction, although it is not quite so splendid in present-day India. Maharajahs have been abolished, and an image of the local goddess is mounted on the star elephant. During Republic Day parades throughout India on 26 January each year the brightly caparisoned elephants get a special cheer.

In the southern state of Kerala, elephants can be seen in many places. Hindu temples often keep elephants, which take part in ceremonial and parades. At the inauguration of industrial plants, decorated elephants are lined up with riders standing on their backs holding aloft great parasols. In timber yards, elephants drag and manipulate huge logs.

The commander of the British Army in Burma in World War Two, Field Marshal Lord Slim, lauded their ability, declaring: 'It was the elephant's dignity and intelligence that gained our respect. To watch an elephant building a bridge; to see the skill with which the great beast lifted the huge logs and the accuracy with which they were placed in position, was to realise that the trained elephant was no mere transport animal, but indeed a skilled sapper'.

Nothing compares to exploring the jungle on an elephant, observing other wild animals from close quarters. Guided mainly by the feet of the mahout, the great animal wades through rivers so deep you have to lift your feet to stay dry. The elephant raises its trunk above the surface to breathe, like the snorkel of a submarine. It pushes through grass towering above the riders' heads, and a threatening branch in the forest is easily broken off on a brief command from the mahout. When well trained, an elephant will face up to a tiger or a rhino, despite its inbuilt nervousness. Elephants can climb and descend steep banks, although their natural inclination is to make trails following easy gradients, which engineers often find ideal tracks for making roads.

Keeping domestic elephants is no longer common because roads have been built in formerly wild country where they were the only means of transport. But some people still keep them for old time's sake or as a status symbol. They may lend them or hire them out for a bridegroom to ride in the marriage procession to his bride's home.

North Bihar, between the Ganges River and Nepal, was an area where domestic elephants were common. Demand led to several great elephant fairs, of which one survives at Sonepur, near Patna. At the full moon in the Hindu month of Kartika (October-November), when hundreds of thousands of devout Hindus visit Sonepur for a ritual bathe in the river, more than a 1,000 elephants used to be on show. There were still about 300 when I visited the fair in the mid-1980s. I joined the throng of pilgrims: holy men in saffron robes, smeared with ashes and carrying tridents; women draped in colourful saris; and men with the sacred threads of a caste Hindu hung across their bare chests, as they moved admiringly through the elephant lines. Some elephants were painted and caparisoned for show only. One great bull was said to have killed 16 of his mahouts, but remained the pride of his owner. Just like horse dealers, elephant traders examined the mouths and feet of elephants on the market. Top dealers sat in tents, their hands hidden under a cloth as they secretly negotiated, using their fingers to indicate and fix prices.

At dawn I walked with the parade of elephants to the river to watch them bathe and drink en masse as the sun rose. On the orders of their mahouts they lay down in the water as their hides were scrubbed and their nails trimmed. Then the long lines climbed the river banks and marched back to the fair.

Because of declining numbers, capture of wild elephants has been banned in India. In the past, the most spectacular method was the *khedda*. The last in southern India took place on the Kabini River, near Mysore. I watched tame elephants called '*koonkies*' gently pushing a wild herd to a point close to a strong stockade hidden in the forest. Then came a powerful drive, with the tame elephants trumpeting and roaring, and their riders shouting and banging drums to drive the herd through a camouflaged entrance into the stockade.

At one time it was customary to leave the herd without food and water to weaken it before an attempt was made to secure the elephants with ropes. But a British forester, A J Milroy, demonstrated that it was possible to ride a tame elephant among the wild ones and slip ropes around necks and legs. This was done at the *khedda* I saw in Mysore. A few wild elephants were pushed into a small arena where *koonkies* ridden by the catchers awaited them. Surprisingly, the wild elephants made no effort to attack the riders, which they could easily have done with their trunks. Thick ropes were slipped round their legs and necks and when they were secure they were led away by teams of *koonkies*. Tied between trees, some settled quietly, while *koonkies* stood on either side to calm them and encourage them to feed. One young bull struggled against the ropes, tore off a branch with his trunk and flung it at me as I stood there watching.

At a *khedda* in north Bengal, the catchers performed a little religious ceremony at the gate of the stockade during which they released some chicks, symbolising giving life while taking life from the forest.

Rather like cowboys roping steers, elephant catchers also lasso elephants in an operation known as '*mela shikar*'. I watched a young wild elephant separated from its herd and manoeuvred by *koonkies* so that a heavy rope noose could be pulled over its head. The other *koonkies* kept its angry mother at bay. Some elephants are also trapped in concealed pits dug on their accustomed trails.

Koonkies play a large part in calming captured animals by feeding, drinking and bathing with them. The wild elephants have to be accustomed to people and may be held tightly in a narrow stockade, while being stroked and sung to for hours. Within a matter of days training starts. In one method, a trainer stands in front with a sharp rod against the elephant's forehead, while another holds its tail. A mahout on its back gives commands to go forward and back, and to turn. Tame elephants, roped on each flank, carry out the orders, pulling the trainee with them. Within a month or so, a captured elephant learns a dozen commands, and ultimately more than 40.

Domestic elephants have a close relationship with their mahouts, and often with their families too. A mahout's wife may well leave her baby safely in the care of the family elephant while she carries out some chores. Nevertheless, the relationship is ultimately based on the elephant's fear of physical punishment by its mahout. In a timber yard I saw a big tusker standing unattended while feeding. A long cane leant behind his ear. He knew that if he moved and it fell, he would be beaten by his mahout. Mahouts often deliberately rub sores on their elephant's heads. If the elephant misbehaves, a light touch with a stick or the traditional iron '*ankh*' on this tender place is sufficient to bring it to order.

Using the elephant to help destroy its habitat

Following spread: *An elephant herd at a salt lick in Nagarhole, Karnataka*

Two tuskers wrestle in the grasslands of Corbett National Park

That such powerful animals should accept such treatment is remarkable. But there are times when they rebel. Mahouts may be killed if they go too far, especially when a bull elephant is in the disturbed condition called *musth*. This normally occurs annually and lasts several weeks, during which a gland between the elephant's eye and ear can be seen secreting a dark liquid. At such times bulls become very aggressive among their own kind and seek out females for mating.

Early one morning in Kerala, I accompanied an elephant veterinarian on an emergency call to control an elephant which had killed its mahout. When we arrived, the elephant was thrashing around among the dense coconut trees. In a clearing, lay the body of the mahout, legs and arms torn off by the infuriated animal. Local people told us that the mahout had left the elephant without food or water for three days, and when he returned it immediately killed him. The veterinarian managed to creep close and dart the raging animal with a tranquillizer. Within ten minutes, it stood unmoving, head slumped, as chains were passed round its legs and it was secured to strong trees. The vet said its rage was largely because it was coming into *musth*.

Another day we were called to get an elephant out of a pond where it had been taken to bathe and wash. For some reason, it disobeyed its mahout's orders and remained in the water. When we arrived the pond was surrounded by several hundred people, some throwing stones at the bewildered elephant. It was not surprising that it refused to leave the pond. Wildlife officers managed to calm the crowd and mahouts tried to tempt the elephant out with succulent fruits. It came close to them and stretched out its trunk, but stayed in the water.

As it was known to dislike domestic buffaloes, a small herd was sent into the water. The buffalo keepers swam alongside their beasts, trying to guide them towards the furious elephant, which lashed the water with its trunk and roared. The buffalo fled. As there seemed to be no way the elephant could be persuaded to leave the pond while so many people were there, we left. Late that night we heard that in the quiet of the darkness, the elephant had walked out and returned to its stable.

The relationship tame elephants have with people is rooted in their natural character. Like dogs, elephants are highly social creatures. In the wild, herds consist of related females of various ages and their young led by the matriarch, who can usually be picked out as the tallest because elephants grow throughout their lives. There is close bodily contact during which trunks explore bodies, slip into mouths, and sniff glands and genitals. A female is attended during a birth by another female, popularly called the 'Auntie'. Usually there is only one baby, but twins occasionally occur. All the herd get excited by the new arrival and feel its hairy little body with their trunks. They protect the baby if danger is apprehended by clustering round it, helping it to keep up with the herd, and disciplining it if its playfulness gets out of hand.

Young elephants become sexually mature at about ten years old, but development can be delayed for several years, depending on their diet. Males leave the herd and join male groups, which are not closely related nor permanent like female herds.

Elephant herds have faced serious problems on their migratory routes due to fragmentation of habitats

They engage in wrestling matches, trunks entwined, thrusting to test each other's power and establish their ranking.

Females are in breeding condition for about 48 hours at a time. Bulls mix with the female herds to seek mates by sniffing their genitals. They carry the scent in their trunks to their mouths, where there is a sensitive organ which analyses the female hormones and indicates readiness to mate. There may be a short chase before mounting occurs, when the bull lays its trunk and forelegs along the back of the female. His penis, which is hidden within the body for most of the time, making it difficult to determine the sex, erects into an S-shape and is inserted into the female's vagina. Copulation lasts less than a minute.

Gestation takes about 22 months, but it is seldom possible to make out if the female is pregnant because of her natural bulk. Elephant owners have been taken by surprise by births.

Female timber elephants are often allowed to wander alone in the forest to feed. Then they may be mated by wild bulls. Elephant owners tend not to welcome pregnant working elephants because it means that the female may be off work for some time, while the baby is a liability until about ten years old.

Elephants spend most of their day feeding. They tear up grass by the roots and bang it against a foot to knock off the soil before conveying it to their mouths. Browsing on trees, they tear down branches and take fruits, which they will also pick up from the ground. Sometimes the fruits are fermenting, making the elephants tipsy. They seem to enjoy this. Wild elephants will enter villages and thrust their trunks into houses seeking liquor.

Elephants need a great amount of food to support their huge bodies. They eat 200 pound (100 kilograms) or more of green matter a day, and so they can be expensive to keep in captivity. There is an Indian saying that one should make a gift of an elephant to an enemy — it will ruin him.

Apart from food, water is the other great necessity and a great love. Once or twice a day, elephants go to rivers and waterholes, where they clearly take great pleasure in drinking and bathing. In Periyar National Park, in south India, herds can be seen swimming across the central lake. Babies love to play in the water, immersing themselves completely. Even mature bulls do the same, plunging and creating tidal waves in their enjoyment.

Tame elephants are taken daily to water, where they lie down while the keepers scrub their skin, remove ticks and inspect their feet for thorns or abrasions. At a word from the keeper the elephant turns over to offer its other side for attention. While this is going on babies romp over their supine mothers. Afterwards a dust bath is frequently in order. This helps to protect the skin, quite tender despite its thickness, from insect pests.

Elephants sleep for a few hours during the night and during the heat of the day. When standing their heads sink and their trunks rest on the ground. They sometimes lie on their sides. And they snore.

Trumpeting is the best-known elephant sound. It usually indicates excitement or other stress. But elephants also produce deep rumbles, bark, cry and snort. An important recent discovery is that they communicate subsonically. Apparently coordinated movements among elephants not within sight of each other and at considerable distances had long been a puzzle. In 1984, an American scientist, Dr Katherine Payne, who had worked on whale communication, felt throbbing in the air, like that produced by an organ, while watching Asian elephants in Portland Zoo, Oregon. Recordings showed that the elephants were reacting to events, such as the arrival and departure of keepers. Tests in the wild in Africa, with recorded calls, proved that communication was taking place. Males responded from as much as four kilometres to female mating calls, and females were found to be 'talking' to their babies and other members of a herd.

In former times, forests were continuous from India through South–East Asia to China and several million elephants probably inhabited them. Laos even had the name of the 'Land of Two Million Elephants'. Elephants were concentrated in the river basins, where food and water were plentiful. For the same reasons, people settled in these areas, converting forests into agricultural land and driving the elephants away as settlement expanded. Today, Asian elephants are confined almost wholly to the hills. Only 30,000 to 50,000 wild elephants survive. Half of them are in India, where there are two large elephant population zones. In the northeast there are between 9,000 and 12,000 elephants, while in the south there are 5,500 to 7,000. A small population of only about 500 is found at the foot of the Himalayas to the west of Nepal, while the 1,600 to 2,300 elephants in east-central India live in small groups in fragmented forest patches. Their future is doubtful.

Many elephants live in reserves, but these are seldom large enough to contain the huge ranges elephants need. Their life consists of migrations to seasonal feeding areas and they may move through hundreds of square miles. These routes are traditional and have been passed down through generations of elephants. The matriarch is the fount of wisdom who learned from her elders where to take the herd for food at each season. Within the lifetime of today's matriarchs the land has been transformed. In the Nilgiri Hills in south India, rivers have been dammed for irrigation and power production. Slopes are intersected now by great water pipes, cutting across traditional elephant migration routes. Forests and trails elephants have followed since time immemorial have been taken over for agriculture. Crops have been sown, especially sugarcane, rice and cereals, which are very attractive to elephants. They do enormous damage during nightly intrusions. Farmers fight to protect their crops, sometimes just by banging tin cans and shouting to drive the elephants away. But, all too often, the intruding elephants are pelted with stones and even petrol bombs, and fired at with crude guns. Many elephants today bear the scars of such conflicts and some are killed by poisons, or blown to pieces by bombs, hidden in attractive foods. Inevitably elephants have become vicious. They kill more than 200 people every year in India.

In the little village of Nagrakata, in north Bengal, I saw the villagers carrying their belongings to spend the night on the safety of a nearby hill because a herd of 60 elephants was rampaging through their fields and village after dark. Several of the flimsy houses had been flattened by the elephants, and one tusker had even punched a great hole in the wall of a brick house in order to insert his trunk and look for grain or liquor. A banana plantation was completely wrecked and great footprints marched across vegetable patches.

With some villagers I walked across the fields towards the forest where the elephants remained during the day. Usually they appeared at twilight, ready to move to the crops in the cover of darkness. This time we did not see them, but, as we made our way back we came across fresh footprints, and I felt a shiver of apprehension, knowing that we might be attacked at any moment. Back at the village, young men had bonfires blazing to scare any marauding elephants as they mounted guard. After a few days the herd moved away. Village life returned to normal. But everyone knew that the elephants would return once again during the next crop season.

Because only male elephants have tusks in India, and not all of them, the species does not face the same threat of extinction from ivory poachers as the African elephant. However, in southern India, where about 90 percent of male elephants have tusks, it is now rare to see a big tusker, for most of them have been poached in recent years. It was a deeply saddening experience for me to stand over the remains of any poached elephant, but especially so when it was all that was left of a tusker I knew well.

For many years, the Indian government permitted imports of African tusks for its traditionally expert carvers. But this supply provided a cover for use of poached Indian ivory. Import has now been stopped and trade in African ivory, including carved items, has been banned. The number of ivory carvers has declined sharply.

To conserve elephants, the Indian Government has undertaken Project Elephant. A Task Force of specialists has identified key populations, migration routes and habitats for conservation. While reserves are an important part of the project, allowance has had to be made for the fact that, unlike tigers and many other wild animals, elephant herds use large areas during their seasonal movements, including those occupied by human settlements and activities. Forest corridors need to be maintained, and some areas managed primarily for elephants. In these areas, human activities compatible with the presence of elephants, such as controlled logging and collection of forest fruits, flowers, bamboos, oils, gums and other non-timber products, are allowed.

A tusker in musth

A VISION FROM THE PAST

Less than 100 years ago, India held all three species of Asian rhino, animals which feature amongst the rarest on earth. The Sumatran (or Asian two-horned) rhino and the Javan rhino, once found in eastern India, are now almost certainly extinct in the subcontinent. The third species, the great one-horned rhinoceros, Rhinoceros unicornis almost went the same way.

In spite of once having existed across the entire northern part of the Indian subcontinent, inhabiting most of the Indo–Gangetic and Brahmaputra riverine tracts and neighbouring foothills, in the first decade of this century there were only a 'handful' of animals left, mainly in Kaziranga, Assam and Chitwan in Nepal. Fortunately their endangered status was recognised at the eleventh hour and protection measures initiated.

The world population is now estimated to be around 2,000, approximately 1,500 in India, mostly in Assam with perhaps 50 in West Bengal and a dozen in Dudhwa National Park in UP; these latter were reintroduced into the region from Assam and later Nepal, in 1984.

The original cause for the severe decline and local extinctions at the end of the 19th century was the widescale development of their riverine habitat for human settlement and agricultural use, combined with hunting both for sport and for the horn and other parts which have long been used for medicinal purposes.

While the remaining small pockets of habitat are now protected, poaching for the horn continues to be a serious problem. In spite of strong protection measures, well over 700 rhinos are known to have been shot, electrocuted or captured in pits and slaughtered over the last 15 years. Recent budgetry restrictions and political disturbances have added fuel to the fire and are a major cause for concern regarding the rhino's future.

The great one-horned rhinoceros is a solitary animal of open and marshy habitats. Its heavy build (over 1,800 kilograms), folded, armour-plated like skin and horned snout give it a distinctly prehistoric appearance. Indeed the rhinoceros has changed little over the last million years.

It features in many myths and legends and at one time was regarded as the fabled unicorn, a popular creature of European mythology. Until the late 18th century its horn was thus regarded as a potent drug and imported into Europe. In Asia it was also believed to have magical

64

properties. Cups were made from rhino horn in the belief that it would react to any poison poured into it either by splitting or by causing the liquid to froth and thus warn the drinker. In India and Nepal every part of the rhino has some medicinal or charmed use attached to it. Sadly it is such superstitions that have helped cause the rhino's decline and indeed still threaten its existence.

Though apparently so huge and menacing, rhinos are said to tame quite easily and old rhinos around Kaziranga National Park live peacefully near villages even allowing children to ride them and in one instance a dhobi to use it to carry his laundry.

SEA TURTLES — WILL THEY SURVIVE?

B C Choudhury and Bivash Pandav

On that humid morning of August 1975, squatting along the Madras beach in India, I was looking at a wriggling mass of baby sea turtles in a plastic tub. These tiny turtles, weighing 60 to 70 grams each, had hatched out of ping-pong ball sized eggs, barely 12 hours ago. These eggs had been kept buried in a makeshift simulated hatchery on the seashore, a little over eight weeks after being collected from the beach, by an optimistic group of reptile-crazy young people from Madras city, led by Romulus and his wife Zai Whitaker. This group of youngsters had walked along the 50-kilometre seashore from Madras to Mahabalipuram every night, for almost the previous five months, looking for adult female sea turtles emerging out of the sea onto the land to lay eggs. Their modus-operandi was simple. As an emerging turtle completed the egg-laying, covered the nest and returned back to the sea, the group would open the nest, collect the eggs and move them to a chickenwire-mesh fenced and covered makeshift hatchery. The eggs were reburied in pits in rows. The temperature and moisture of each pit was monitored for up to ten weeks. The wriggling mass of baby turtles I was watching were the results of the last batch of such eggs hatching out of the pits and the baby turtles were being taken to the shore to be released back to the sea. Little did I know at that point of time that for the next 20 years sea turtles would become an integral part of my professional career.

I was wondering why one should take so much trouble to move turtle eggs from the shore, protect them and after two months of laborious watch, monitoring and care, return the resulting hatchlings back to the sea. I kept these questions to myself, as one tub full of baby turtles was given to me to spread out along the edge of a receding sea wave. The baby turtles started walking towards the sea, the moment they were kept on the sand. An incoming wave swept them back to the shore and took them to the sea while receding. We released over 1,000 baby turtles that night and by the time the sun was up, they had all returned to the sea. My quizzical looks got back some simple answers: that the baby turtles were the olive Ridley sea turtles and the whole exercise was to prevent the naturally laid eggs from being robbed by people or predated by feral dogs, jackals and mongooses. Rom Whitaker also told me that it was a strategy, the Madras Snake Park Trust (MSPT) had adopted to make people aware of the plight of sea turtles along the Indian coast line.

In February 1976, I too joined the MSPT reptile-crazy volunteers in their nocturnal walks along the seashore. We would pick up some early dinner and start walking along the beach in the darkness, straining our eyes to detect movements in the shallow waters along the seashore. Many times we mistook floating logs, plastic sheets, garbage bags and other flotsam for sea turtles. The first sea turtle I witnessed emerging out of the water was after about ten to 12 such nights. It was an oval-shaped creature with a convex back, laboriously making its way up the beach, using its flippers and hind limbs. It was more of a dragging movement than a walk. We made ourselves inconspicuous by crouching down on the sand. What we witnessed that night, was my first, unforgettable view of the nesting behaviour of an olive Ridley marine turtle.

I had learnt by now that sea turtles are completely aquatic, except for the most vital function of egg-laying on land by the females. Male sea turtles almost never come on land. Even the female does not nest every year. Nesting intervals depend on the forage availability at sea. Looking at the female clumsily emerging out of the water to climb a not too steep sandy beach, I wondered at the remarkable urge of the process of reproduction that makes a totally aquatic animal come out onto the land where she is totally vulnerable. Perhaps, this vulnerability made the sea turtles adapt themselves to nest mostly at night.

My first observation of the nesting behaviour of the female olive Ridley was repeated many many times in later years on other nesting beaches of India and all were more or less similar. The adult females measuring about 75 to 80 centimetres and weighing around 60 to 70 kilograms, drag themselves almost 25 metres from the surf zone, out of the reach of the highest tideline. They use their flippers to make first a body-pit, into which a female almost fits, only a slight rise of her convex carapace (dorsal back) being visible above the beach. During my first observation in the Madras beach, we dared not approach the turtle, but in later years I could observe the female turtles using their hind flippers to dig the egg chamber. This period of making a body–pit and egg-chamber is most crucial. Any disturbance at this time, particularly by human beings, makes the turtles return to the sea without laying their eggs. However, once the process of egg-laying has begun, she has to complete the laying of up to 100 to 150 eggs, even though she is most vulnerable to predators then.

A washed up mangrove stump and turtle skull on Gahirmatha Beach

After laying, an olive Ridley turtle flattens the sand to disguise her nest site

After completing the egg-laying process, the female covers the egg-chamber by throwing sand into the pit using her flippers and then raises and thumps her massive body to pack sand over the nest. She throws dry sand over the nest for camouflage and begins the journey back to the sea. The eggs, buried almost 30 to 45 centimetres deep are now left to fend for themselves for the next eight to ten weeks. If the soft-shelled eggs survive the natural and subsidised (feral dogs) predators during this period, they absorb moisture and temperature from the beach sand and hatch. Thus begins the life of a sea turtle on the beach as a tiny hatchling. Soon after hatching, they dash for the sea-surf subjecting themselves to swooping birds, crabs and marine predators.

On my first day of watching and releasing sea turtles in to the sea, I also learnt that a baby turtle on entering the sea, enters into a mysterious world, known only to itself. Virtually nothing is known to scientific world of what it does or where it lives until it reaches adulthood. Scientists believe that the hatchlings drift on the high seas, eating pelagic crustaceans, jellyfish, algae, sea-grass and insects. As juveniles, each species appears to adapt itself to its own niche in the marine environment. As an adult, the female turtle most likely returns to the beach where she was born at an age of approximately ten to 12 years although some scientists believe that they may not reach sexual maturity until 20 to 25 years of age.

In her lifespan of 65 to 70 years, a female turtle probably lays 30 to 40 clutches which means that in her lifetime she will have laid a total of 3,000 to 4,000 eggs although only around one percent of these (ie, 30 to 40) may reach adulthood. An adult male sea turtle never really gets onto the land but courts and mates with 'ready to nest' females in the shallow off-shore waters.

Folklore and local inhabitants held the belief that turtles return to nest on the beach where they hatched. Genetic research and other evidence now suggests that this is true. Both the parents contribute DNA to the cell nucleus of an offspring, but the DNA in the cell mitochondria — the bodies within the cells which produce their energy — is passed directly from the female to offspring. Female turtles returning to their natal beaches to nest have similar and distinctive mitochondrial DNA. Scientists are now using DNA to match the turtles with their native beaches and learn their migratory patterns. Scientists believe that sea turtles are guided for this migration by a biological compass and an inborn sense of magnetic direction. This internal compass and sense of wave directions seems to help sea turtles across the oceans. Nesting sea turtles reportedly return to the same nesting site over the years after migrating several thousand kilometres across the sea.

Arribada

In most parts of their distributional range, sea turtles nest sporadically. However, in certain selected nesting sites, the nesting

Hatchlings from a previous arribada head for the sea with a female returning after laying her eggs

strategy differs. Sea turtles congregate in very large numbers in favourable coastal waters and synchronised nesting involving hundreds of thousands of individuals takes place on suitable nesting beaches. The exact nature of the coastal waters and suitability of nesting beaches for ideal mass-nesting is difficult to define clearly. The phenomenon of mass-nesting itself has so far been only partly understood by scientists. However, the event itself is well–known. Most authors attribute a survival value to this behaviour. Mass-nesting by sea turtles may also be a strategy that bewilders the local predator population by the sudden huge abundance of potential prey (the adult turtles, their eggs or two months later the hatchlings). Although, predators may consume all they can, the main feast is over so rapidly that many of the turtles will still survive, and excessive predator population levels will be inhibited, simply because they cannot be sustained by one or two big meals a year.

Among the sea turtles, only the members of the genus *Lepidochelys*; the olive Ridley (*L. olivacea*) and the Kemp's Ridley (*L. kempii*) form reproductive aggregations popularly known as *arribada* (a Spanish word meaning arrival). There are now only four significant *arribada* (mass-nesting) beaches of olive Ridleys known in the world: two on the Pacific Coast of Costa Rica, one on the coast of Mexico and one at Gahirmatha Beach in the Bay of Bengal along the Orissa coast in India. The Indian site stands alone as the one where more sea turtles nest than at any other spot in the world. Over half a million olive Ridleys nest there every year between January to May.

Over the next several years, I had opportunities to observe large-scale congregations of olive Ridley sea turtles, both male and female in the off-shore shallow waters of the Orissa coast in the Bay of Bengal, swimming with much agility before emerging onto the land, at Gahirmatha Beach.

So clumsy on land, sea turtles swim with grace and agility in the waters of every continent except Antarctica. Modern day sea turtles, represented by eight species, are clumped into two families, Dermochelyidae and Chelonidae. The family Dermochelyidae is represented by only one species, *Dermochelys coriacea,* the leatherback sea turtle which happens to be the largest among all the members, growing up to a length of six feet or more. The remaining seven species, belonging to five genera, are clumped under the family Chelonidae.

While the leatherback is adapted to both temperate and tropical waters — undertaking the longest seasonal migration of any sea turtle, the green sea turtle *Chelonia mydas* grazes sea–grasses in the tropics. The East Pacific black sea turtle *Chelonia agassazi* (many also believe it is a subspecies of green sea turtle *C. mydas agassazi*) ranges from the Baja California to the Galapagos Islands. The olive Ridleys *Lepidochelys olivacea* ply the high seas in the tropics of the Pacific, Atlantic and Indian oceans. The Kemp's Ridley *Lepidochelys kempi* inhabits the shallows of the Gulf of Mexico and North Atlantic. The loggerhead *Caretta caretta* populates the world's subtropics and the coral reefs attract the hawksbill sea turtle

69

Overcrowding on the nesting beach

Ertemochelys imbricata. The Australian flatback sea turtle *Natator depressa* is not found in the Western hemisphere and is restricted to the coastal waters of Australia.

Five species of sea turtles — leatherback, green, loggerhead, hawksbill and olive Ridley — occur in the Indian coastal waters. Except for the loggerhead the other four species nest along the Indian coast and bay islands. While the olive Ridley is the commonest species nesting all along the Indian coast, all the four species nest in the Andaman and Nicobar Islands. In fact, the Andaman and Nicobar Islands harbour some of India's best leatherback, green and hawksbill nesting beaches. Sporadic nesting of olive Ridley and green turtle have been recorded on the west coast in the states of Gujarat, Maharashtra, Karnataka, Goa and Kerala.

Sea Turtle Research In India

A year later on a chilly winter night of 1977, I was participating in a backbreaking exercise of counting turtles at Gahirmatha on the Orissa coast, the world's largest olive Ridley nesting rookery. After it came to the knowledge of the scientific world in 1975, the 35-kilometre stretch of the Gahirmatha Beach has been brought under the Protected Area status forming the eastern boundary of the Bhitarkanika Wildlife Sanctuary. One of the first tasks of the sanctuary officials was to protect and document the number of nesting turtles every nesting season.

In a promptly developed method of counting turtles, a small group of people were allotted a stretch of the beach. Each individual with a hurricane lamp and a small paint-box, would space themselves 50 to 100 metres apart and wait for the emergence of turtle from the sea. This began an hour or two after sunset and within minutes, hundreds of female turtles were walking out of the sea. We had to wait until they settled themselves in the body-pit and completed digging the nest chamber. We would then walk close to an egg-laying turtle, put a small 'X' mark on her dorsal back using the paint (so as not to repeat counting the same individual again). Walking the length of the 100 metre long and almost 50 to 80 metre wide beach for almost eight to ten hours, bending to put an 'X' mark on the carapace of thousands of turtles on a single night was tiring. Nonetheless, my first involvement in counting turtles in an *arribada* was an experience I wanted to repeat again and again. The whole beach as far as the eye could see was full of sea turtles, all in a frenzy of activity. Most of the time, it was difficult not to step on to a turtle. By the end of my first night, my group had counted 18,000 turtles in a two-kilometre stretch of beach. This method of counting has since been refined, using both total and sample counts. Wildlife biologist Dr C S Kar has collected volumes of information on nesting olive Ridleys in Gahirmatha from 1978 to this date and has documented them in a book, *The Turtle Paradise — Gahirmatha*.

Over half a million turtles nest on Gahirmatha Beach every year

Satish Bhaskar of the Madras Snake Park and Crocodile Bank Trust has walked the shores of every single island of the Andaman and Nicobar group to document sea turtle nesting. This new awareness and concern for sea turtles have also made the Central Marine Fisheries Research Institute scientists, wildlife officials of coastal states and several universities take up conservation management and research on sea turtles, on topics ranging from population dynamics, food and feeding, reproductive ecology to temperature dependent sex-determination in sea turtles.

But for occasional trips to the Bhitarkanika Sanctuary and other sporadic nesting sites in Tamil Nadu and Andhra Pradesh my involvement with sea turtles remained negligible until 1994, when we decided to investigate the Orissa coast and began a study on the status and ecology of sea turtle nesting beaches there.

Field researcher, Bivash Pandav, from the Wildlife Institute of India, walked the 480-kilometre length of the Orissa coast, several times, prior, during and after the mass-nesting of olive Ridleys. While the resultant discovery of another *arribada* site, 200 kilometres south of Gahirmatha, at the mouth of the Rushikulya River was an exciting and positive event for sea turtles, the problems faced by the olive Ridley in Orissa and other sea turtles in India causes concern for their continued survival. The scenario in India is more or less the same as it is for sea turtles elsewhere in the world. However, the demographic pressures and the irrational use of coastal habitat and its resources in India, directly infringes on the life of the five species of marine turtles that occur here.

PROBLEMS OF SEA TURTLES IN THE INDIAN COAST

The most bizzare scene, I witnessed involving marine turtles in India, was at the Tuticorin Beach in Tamil Nadu sometime in August 1975. Half an hour before dawn, there was a long line of people on the beach, with steel tumblers in their hands. Someone dragged a marine turtle (which I came to know later was a green sea turtle) upside down. Using sharp axes and knives, he opened the plastron (ventral plate) of the turtle. The turtle still alive was groaning and beating its flippers in agony. One after another the long queue of people dipped their steel tumblers into the open body of the turtle, took out a glass full of turtle blood, paid two rupees each, and drank it straight. The local people's belief that sea turtle blood taken before sunrise will cure them of asthma — a respiratory disease — led to this ritual.

Later in the day, interviewing several fishermen on this and other beliefs involving marine turtles, I came to know that but for medicinal beliefs, fishermen in the south do not really go for turtle killing. It is only the green turtle and the olive Ridley which are eaten; that too only during the winter months Occasionally, poisonous toxic substances in the body of the marine turtles have made fishermen sick and thus this reluctance. Marine turtle shells, livers and other organs are also used for medicinal purpose by the coastal fishermen. Shells are also used for storage of grains and other household goods.

All over the Indian coast, however, local fishermen consider the marine turtle as one of the incarnations of Lord Vishnu, the creator, and revere turtles. Most temples on the west coast and the southern Indian coastline keep sculptured turtles in front of the temple deities.

The organised marine turtle trade for meat and other useful products in Tamil Nadu, West Bengal, Orissa and Andhra coast is no longer prevalent. Sustainable, subsistence off-take by fishermen along the east coast of India is, however, fairly common.

During the nesting season, fishermen and some villagers along the sea coast dig out the sea turtle eggs and consume them. In fact, until the early 1970s the Orissa government used to collect a royalty of one paise per egg collected and transported to Calcutta market. With millions of eggs on the beach at the *arribada* site, such sustainable off-take does not really add any pressure to the sea turtle population.

However, the destruction process of sea turtles in the Indian coastal waters has been increased by the mechanised and trawler fishing activities and other coastal fishing related developments such as fishing harbours and jetties. Annually, as many as 10,000 nesting sea turtles die entangled in trawler fishing nets on the east coast of India. New fishing harbours and jetties, will mean more trawler fishing boats and increased dead turtles on the beach.

With the advent of mechanised marine fishing using trawlers, the deaths and threats to sea turtles have increased many fold. Turtles trapped in the sock-shaped nets of trawlers are unable to surface for air and so drown. Until recently, as many as 55,000 sea turtles were reported to be killed in shrimp trawlers each year in the US. In 1947, there were about 5,000 shrimping trawlers operating in the Gulf of Mexico but by 1989, the number had increased to an estimated 55,000 trawlers.

In 1994, during a survey of the Orissa coast along the Bay of Bengal, the authors recorded over 5,282 dead olive Ridley sea turtles on the beach, washed ashore after being removed and thrown from trawler nets. With the number of trawlers on the increase every year along the east coast of India, the death of sea turtles are expected to go up every year. In the 1970s, the Orissa coast had only about 900 mechanised fishing vessels. This increased to 3,000 by 1994. In addition to these, mechanised fishing vessels and trawlers from neighbouring states also operate along the Orissa coast endangering sea turtles.

There are ways and means to stop this unwanton mortality. Many countries have made it mandatory by legislation, to fit trawler nets with Turtles Excluder Devices (TEDs). A TED is a small additional net or metal grid inside the net that allows fish and prawn to pass to the back while rejecting turtles.

While the concept of enforcing legislation to use TED in trawler nets is not even in sight, coastal states in India are busy constructing additional fishing jetties and fish landing centres which will only increase the number and operation of destructive trawlers to the peril of sea turtles.

The rapid alteration and changes in the ecological profile of the nesting beaches, probably pose the greatest threat to the survival of marine turtles in the Indian coast. Constructions and infrastructural developments including hotels and beach resorts on the coast, almost touching the hightide line, have left very little nesting beach for turtles. Even on major nesting beaches, the coastal afforestation and shelter-belt programme of cashew and casurina plantations have taken up considerable width of the coastal beach and sand-dune formations, the most favoured nesting grounds.

When a baby turtle breaks through the sand after 50 to 70 days — how does it know where to go? It is generally believed that it is the brighter water surface that attracts baby turtles towards the sea. They also tend to crawl away from the land's higher horizon. Thus street lights and lights from buildings also disorient newly emerging hatchlings. Instead of going back to the sea, they run towards the light and perish. There are many instances in southeastern United States, where swarms

Turtle eggs spread across the sand due to erosion of the nesting beach

of baby turtles have walked onto illuminated beach basket- and volley-ball courts. Coastal states in the US have enforced legislation that prohibits unshaded beachlights and beach buildings from having lights which are focused towards the beach.

Marine pollution — particularly the crude-oil spills from oil terminals and harbours — pose a problem for marine turtles. Crude-oil in their eyes also disorient turtles from going back into the sea and they fall prey to mammalian predators on land.

The sea turtles have been on this earth for over 150 million years, spending most of their lifetime in the sea. Only for a very short period of time; that too only the females, come to lay their eggs on select beaches not exceeding 2 to 300 metres wide and leave behind the eggs buried under half-a-metre of sand with the hope that nature and perhaps man, the most advanced creature on earth will take care of the eggs and safeguard the future generation of both turtles and mankind. How concerned is the human race to this responsibility?

THE TIGER: POWER AND FRAGILITY

K. Ullas Karanth

On a cool October dawn in 1994, I drove along a forest road through my study area in Nagarahole, wearing earphones which blocked out all the delightful bird calls which filled the sun-dappled jungles around me. Concentrating intensely on radio signals coming through a receiver slung over my shoulders, I swung my hand-held antenna to capture these tinny beeps which sounded exactly like the green barbet's calls, which I was filtering out. The signals emanated from a tiny radio transmitter around the neck of a tigress named Sundari, whom I had collared five years earlier. Having 'fixed' her location, I now knew she lay concealed in a thicket of *lantana* about 30 metres to my left. I had positioned my green Gypsy between the tigress and a herd of gaur cropping the lush green *themeda* grass on the roadside clearing ahead of me on the right. I knew Sundari was hungry, having left her last kill about a week ago. I could imagine her inside the *lantana* thickets, her muscular form wound up like a coiled spring, waiting for the moment to strike. The gaur grazed placidly, the massive, deep brown forms of the adults, a striking contrast to the rich chestnut coat of a very young calf. They were a portrait of bovine serenity, except for an old cow who looked up from time to time. Suddenly, the radio pulses varied in volume, as the tigress manoeuvred stealthily inside the thickets, positioning herself for the deadly ambush. As I looked around taking off my earphones, the tigress broke cover and bounded across the road, within a couple of metres of my Gypsy. As the 150 kilogram lethal projectile hurtled towards them, the gaur scattered into the heavy shrubbery which lay on their side of the clearing. But she had managed to gain that crucial, split second element of surprise, before she was upon them. Barely breaking her stride, the tigress darted into an opening in the dense cover. She was trying to intercept her victim, before the gaur herd rolled away like distant thunder. A moment later, I knew she had succeeded in securing her victim, when I heard the pitiful braying of the calf in its death throes blend with her fearsome growls. The thick shrubbery shook violently for a few seconds, and then became still. The rest of the herd milled around at a distance, their low, throaty growls of fear filling the air.

Tiger is the most feared predator in its jungle domain. When we, the human species colonised Asia, tigers were already prowling in these forests, preying on deer, pigs, wild cattle and an ape as big as us — the orang utan. Like all these prey species, primitive men too probably feared the tiger. However, over the next few thousand years, humans culturally graduated from being primitive hunter-gatherers to master agriculture and animal husbandry. By cutting or burning down the forests in which tigers lived, humans gradually turned much of the landscape inhospitable for tigers. Primitive hunters even developed an ingenious array of techniques such as snares, pits, nets, spears and dead-fall traps to kill tigers. With the advent of the industrial revolution, human weaponry against the tiger expanded to include explosives, fire-arms and chemical poisons. The tiger's naturally endowed weapons — strength, speed, stealth, nocturnal vision, teeth and claws — were no match for the lethal inventions of the clever apes invading its habitats. Today, man's technological mastery over the tiger's fate is so complete, and yet his passion to tame the jungle so strong that many fear the tiger's roar may soon be silenced forever in the Asian forests. Because, for all its aura of invincible power, the tiger is a fragile species. Paradoxically, the tiger's ecological fragility is ordained by nature through the very same traits we fear — large body size and a carnivorous diet.

EVOLUTION AND RADIATION

Big cats like the tiger do not evolve out of thin air, overight. Throughout earth's geological history (4.5 billion years), large scale forces of nature such as global climate change, movements of continents, and geological variations induced by sun, rains and the winds, gave rise to a variety of life forms including a diversity of plant communities. An even more diverse array of herbivorous animals, ranging from tiny grasshoppers to giant elephants evolved to crop this vegetation. This complement of herbivores included several large mammals ancestral to the present day deer, pigs, wild cattle, tapirs, rhinos and elephants. Such a community of ungulates is not a mere collection of individual species, but an intricate ecological web in which large species feed on coarser plants, providing paths and access for smaller ones, and each ungulate specialises to feed on different plant species, plant parts or different stages of plant growth. In parallel, complex communities of large carnivorous mammals evolved from a civet-sized Miacid ancestor, about 40 million years ago, to exploit this diverse prey base.

A tigress with her cubs

All large predators (killers of prey much bigger than themselves) have evolved two basic hunting strategies: cursorial or stalk and ambush. Cursorial predators are built to chase prey over long distances and bring it down through exhaustion. The ambushers, on the other hand, are designed for stealth to get close to the prey, and for the short surprise rush. Barring the cheetah, all the other big cats — the tiger, jaguar, leopard, snow leopard, cougar, and, even the savanna dwelling lion — are essentially stalk and ambush hunters.

Evolutionary descent of the present day tigers has been reconstructed traditionally by comparing anatomical and skeletal features, as well as through more recent methods using molecular genetics. Geneticist Stephen O'Brien and colleagues who used 'molecular clocks', estimate that the genus *Panthera* (the big cats excluding the cougar) branched off from their ancestors four to six million years ago, and the tiger *Panthera tigris* separated from the Pantherine lineage less than a million years ago. Based on the relatively primitive skeletal features of the tiger subspecies *P.t. amoyensis* now surviving in southern China, taxonomists argue that tigers originated in that part of the world. This idea is supported by the fact that this forested region also harboured a variety of large-sized prey such as wild cattle and *Cervus* deer species.

Ecologist John Seidensticker has elegantly explained the subsequent radiation of tigers into different subspecies as the evolution of 'ecotypes' adapted to different prey bases. Siberian tigers (*P.t. altaica*) which evolved to fit the coldest climates and kill large prey such as moose and elk, are big, furry and pale. Indian and Indochinese tiger subspecies (*tigris* and *corbetti*, respectively) which adapted to hot weather and preyed on abundant large ungulates in forest-grassland mosaics, are medium-sized, short-coated and darker. The extreme adaptation to humid rain forests, where most prey are small and scarce (such as muntjac and pigs), is seen in the richly coloured island subspecies of tigers from Sumatra (*sumatrae*), Java (*sondaica*) and Bali (*balica*), which are barely larger than jaguars.

BORN TO KILL: PHYSICAL ADAPTATIONS

The tiger must be big enough to knock down, subdue, and quickly kill a prey much larger than itself. Another advantage of large body size is the ability to drag away, hide and defend large kills against other predators. Siberian tigers can weigh more than 300 kilograms. The Indian tigers are smaller with average males weighing around 200 to 250 kilograms and females a 100 kilos less. Indian tigers are about 155 to 225 centimetres long including head and body, with an additional tail length of 75 to 100 centimetres, if measured correctly along the body curves. However, many old shikar accounts report a nose to tail-tip distance, measured straight between wooden pegs (and, as a wag suspected, sometimes between pegs of whisky) making it difficult to get accurate size estimates from them.

The tiger's body structure (morphology) and internal chemistry (physiology) are, above all, evolutionary adaptations for predation. The tiger has to derive its energy needs for maintenance, growth and reproduction from the chemical energy stored in the body tissues and blood of its prey. Obviously, energy gain from the kill must exceed the energy expended in prey capture. Because catching small, scattered prey (rats, frogs or fish) involves energy loss higher than the energy which can be squeezed out of such prey, the tiger must meet most of its needs from large packets of energy — ungulates. However, large ungulates are always scarcer than rats or frogs, and can only be killed infrequently. Therefore, the entire physiology of the tiger is adapted to a regimen of enormous meals, at intervals of four to five days or even longer. A tigress I radio-tracked once went without making any substantial kill for two weeks. Tigers also save energy by lazing for over 15 to 16 hours a day, even when hungry. After making a kill, the tiger is virtually inactive for the next three or four days.

However, before the tiger can feed, it has to find the prey animal and kill it. This is not easy since most ungulates are extremely wary, and have acute hearing and a good sense of smell. To get within the striking range of ten to 30 metres without being detected, it takes all the skills a tiger possesses. The tiger's colourful contrasting coat of ochre and white, topped with black stripes, appear striking in a zoo enclosure. However, when it walks in the dappled shadows and brownish cover of the forest, the same contrasting patterns break the tiger's outline and blend it with the surrounding brush. Because tiger's ungulate prey cannot discriminate colours well, a still tiger is virtually invisible to them.

Other major predatory adaptations include padded feet, digitigrade ('on the toes') stance and a sinuous body, which permit noiseless stalking. Although tigers communicate among themselves using scent marks sprayed on tree trunks, and thus appear to have a good sense of smell, they seem to depend on vision and hearing to locate prey. The structure of the tiger's eyes and nerves connected to them suggest that, although they probably see the world in 'monochrome', their light-gathering ability (night vision) is extraordinary. Supplemented by long whiskers (vibrissae) to 'feel' their way around in dense cover, tigers can silently search for prey in a pitch dark forest. Tiger's acute hearing (with specially modified internal ear chambers and moving external pinnae), can detect and home in on the faintest sounds from an invisible prey.

A tiger's muscles can surge up the power needed to capture prey, but they get tired quickly in comparison with ungulate muscles. Bonded around the cat's strong bones and flexible joints, these muscles are only capable of a short rush, with lots of twisting, turning and flexing. A remarkable series of photos by Valmik Thapar show the amazing contortions of a tiger's body as it wrestles down a sambar. Even with our recent mastery of robotics, it is hard to imagine any machine attaining such capabilities.

A tigeress locked in combat with a sambar stag

When a tiger takes down powerful beasts like gaur or sambar three to five times its own size, it must avoid getting injured by their flailing hooves or horns. To do so, the tiger manipulates prey, using its forelimbs with their sharp, sheathed, retractile claws. Even its hind paws can inflict serious damage in close combat. However, the cat's chief weapons of execution are its four dagger-like canine teeth. Strong jaw muscles anchored to the skull, stab the canines into the throat, neck, or the brain case of the prey, immobilising and killing it swiftly.

DISTRIBUTION AND BIOGEOGRAPHY

The Asian continent and the Sundaic Islands off it, are the home of the tiger. In the past, tigers were distributed widely, if somewhat sporadically, in an arc north of the Himalaya extending from China to Siberia and through some Central Asian republics into Iran. Another arc went southeast into Indochina, later branching into Myanmar and across India, before being halted by the Rajasthan deserts, Himalayan ranges and the Indian Ocean. A second branch of the same arc expanded into the Malay Peninsula and the Indonesian islands of Sumatra, Java and Bali. John Seidensticker has explained tiger distribution patterns in relation to changes in sea levels and land-bridge connections during the Pleistocene epoch.

Over its vast distributional range, tiger once occupied a truly diverse range of habitat types. These included both coniferous and broad leaved temperate forests in Siberia, subtropical woodlands in China, reed beds in the Caspian region, and the dense tropical wet-evergreen forests in Thailand, Indochina, Malaysia, India and Indonesia. Optimal tiger habitats included the tropical deciduous forests (both dry and moist) in the Indian subcontinent and South-East Asia. Tigers also colonised mangrove swamps (in India, Bangladesh and Java), and peat swamps (in Sumatra). Although they could not adapt to open arid regions (unlike lions and leopards), given some cover and water, tigers are quite catholic in their choice of habitat.

However, one key requirement must be met before an area can support tigers: an adequate prey base. An incomplete list of tiger's ungulate prey would include wild cattle (gaur, banteng, kouprey and water buffalo), other bovids (nilgai, chousingha, chinkara, takin, vu quong ox), wild goats and goat-antelopes (tahr, goral, serow), several species of deer (moose, elk, sika, sambar, barasingha, thamin, chital, hog deer, Tiomorese deer and muntjacs), tapir, wild pig and occasionally rhino and elephant calves. Although tigers do kill smaller prey, ranging from prawns to peafowls, energetically, they cannot survive and reproduce if a habitat does not support ungulates at adequate densities.

ECOLOGY OF PREDATION: TIGER AND PREY NUMBERS

Scientific studies by George Schaller in Kanha (1964-65), Melvin Sunquist in Chitwan (1973-75) and my studies in Nagarahole

The author with a tranquillized tiger

(1986-95) have provided quantitative data on tiger predation. These show that a male tiger may require about 2,200 to 2,500 kilograms of meat and a female or a sub–adult about 1,850 to 2,300 kilograms of meat over a year. Considering wastage and inedible parts of the prey, this works out an annual requirement of about 3,000 to 3,200 kilograms of live prey for an average tiger. To meet this nutritional need a tiger has to kill 40 to 50 prey animals/year, and a female raising three juvenile cubs may have to kill as many as 60 to 70 prey. Research on tigers (and other big cats) suggests that they can only crop about eight to ten percent of the numbers of prey available in any habitat. This ratio of predator to prey numbers is related to the rates at which ungulate prey replace themselves, other mortality factors, and to the fact that tigers have to survive off the incremental growth. Biologist Louise Emmons, who compared big cat and small cat predation in South America, showed that the latter can annually crop even 40 percent of their prey (such as rats) which reproduce much faster than the ungulate prey of big cats. This 'ten percent' thumb rule for big cat predation shows that to support a single tiger, a prey base of about 400 ungulates may be needed.

Hunting Behaviour and Feeding Ecology

On an average, a tiger kills once in seven to eight days, although a tigress with cubs is compelled to kill more often to feed her family. Soon after the hunt, the tiger drags the carcass into nearby cover and hides it from vultures and other scavengers. Tigers usually start feeding at the rump, and avoid mixing up the rumen contents and intestines with the fleshy parts consumed. If undisturbed, a tiger stays with the kill for three to four days, eating 50 to 80 kilograms of meat. Although tigers in Nagarahole consumed about 65 percent weight from most kills, the proportion eaten was much less with large gaur kills.

Radio–tracking studies in Chitwan and Nagarahole showed that although tigers can hunt through the day, they are least active during the midday hours, and are most active from dusk to dawn. Tigers noiselessly pad on animal paths and trails, trying to locate prey. In Nagarahole, tigers make winding sweeps through dense patches of cover and search the edges of clearings, trying to flush and catch resting or feeding prey. The final rush for capture is usually short (ten to 30 metres). However, in open habitats around the lakes of Ranthambhore, Fateh Singh Rathore and Valmik Thapar documented tigers coursing after sambar over much longer distances, hunting like lions do in African savannas. Having observed more tiger hunts than most others, they estimated that only one in every ten attempts was successful even under optimal conditions.

The initial impact of a tiger's charge knocks the prey down in most cases, to be followed by a swift bite to the throat, nape or the brain case. With large prey such as gaur or sambar, a throat bite is more commonly used, whereas, with smaller prey, particularly pigs, a nape bite is often used. Death results from strangulation, severing of arteries, breakage of the spinal cord or even from shock. My studies in Nagarahole showed that tigers do not randomly kill prey which they encounter. Although chital were far more abundant, Nagarahole tigers appeared to select disproportionately more gaur and sambar. However, at other sites like Chitwan and Kanha, where large prey are relatively scarcer, chital appear to form a high proportion of tigers' diet. In Huai Kha Khaeng in Thailand, ecologist Alan Rabinowitz noticed that, because local hunters had reduced the densities of banteng, sambar and hog deer, tigers barely eked out an existence, subsisting on muntjacs and smaller mammals.

If livestock are found in tiger habitats, they are readily killed. Rare but persistent man-eating behaviour of individual tigers has still not been explained fully, although Charles McDougal has carefully documented the phenomenon. Normally, a human being standing tall and erect, is not a part of a tiger's mental image of its prey, and does not evoke the attack response. However, once particular individual tigers discover human vulnerability accidentally, cats being quick learners, they may kill again. The fact that man-eating tends to be endemic in certain tracts suggests that such behaviour may even be learnt by the cubs from their mother. However, reason for the historical rarity of man-eaters over large regions, such as in south India, still needs to be understood.

Behaviour: Spatial and Social Needs

Like all other animals, tigers have to find each other to mate, share food, or even to compete over resources. Sometimes, they have to escape to avoid encounters. Although they are solitary animals, tigers are a part of a society of their own, maintaining contact with each other through a remarkable chemical communication system involving spraying of scent and urine to mark their passage. Additionally, tigers use roars and other vocalisations to attract or avoid encounters. Contact is also maintained by scraping the ground and depositing scats (faeces) at prominent places.

A population of wild tigers comprises of animals belonging to different sex and age classes. The breeding females (also called resident or territorial) form the keystone of this tiger social structure. These tigresses hold on to fixed ranges of habitat containing high prey densities, monopolising the breeding within them. They mate with the large breeding males whose range may cover two to three female ranges. Then there are transient tigers, both males and females, who do not breed. After having dispersed away from its mother at the age of one and a half to two years, a transient tiger wanders back and forth through its natal range and surrounding areas, trying to establish a home range for itself. As transients grow older and bigger, they compete aggressively with the breeders, and, sometimes, manage to kill breeders and appropriate their ranges. However, many transients also perish in this process.

Tiger cubs are born (two to four per litter) in a helpless condition after a short 105 day gestation. They depend on mother's milk for the first eight weeks or so, after which the female takes them to her kills. They gradually acquire hunting skills over the next one and a half years, often learning from their mother's ways, so as to fend for themselves after dispersal.

Our present understanding of tiger social organisation comes from long-term scientific studies employing radio–telemetry conducted in Nepal's Chitwan Park by biologists Melvin Sunquist and David Smith during the 1970s. Their data have been later supplemented by telemetry studies in Nagarahole and Siberia. These new data suggest that the basic social patterns observed in Chitwan may vary, depending on factors such as prey density and vegetation type.

However, there is evidence that more breeding and transient tigers can 'pack' into a given area at higher prey densities. For example, in prime tiger habitats in Nagarahole, where ungulates occur at high density of 50 to 75 animals/square kilometres, I found that home ranges of breeding tigresses are small (ten to 15 square kilometres), and adult tiger densities can exceed 15 tigers/100 square kilometres. At the other extreme, in prey-scarce Siberian forests, female ranges may be larger than 200 square kilometres, and tiger densities correspondingly lower.

MORTALITY, SURVIVAL AND POPULATION DYNAMICS

A commonly asked question is how long do tigers live in the wild? Not very long in the case of most tigers. Based on limited studies in Chitwan and Nagarahole, supplemented by anecdotal observations in Kanha by H S Panwar, the following simplified picture can be drawn. A tigress produces, on an average, a litter of three cubs once every two and a half years. Disease, starvation, fires, floods, other predators (including man), and infanticide (killing of cubs of a previous male tiger by a new male who has taken over his range), all take a heavy toll of cubs. As a result, only about 50 percent of them make it

The territorial behaviour of a tigress as she sniffs a tree in Ranthambhore

Top left: *Gaur, a favourite prey species of the Nagarahole tiger*

Bottom left: *A marsh crocodile attacks a sambar fawn*

Above: *A leopard in Nagarahole*

Right: *A rutting swamp deer in Kanha*

81

through the first year. Of those surviving juvenile tigers, most make it to the dispersal age. After dispersal, transients compete hard among themselves and with the breeders over kills, space and mates. Some of them disperse into farmlands and get killed. Probably 20 to 30 percent of transient tigers die every year. Only those transients who are strong or lucky enough, survive to breed. Male tigers are about five to six years old and females three to four years old when they start breeding. The average breeding tenure of females may be around seven to eight years, and about half that for males. Although some resident tigers can live to be 12 to 15 years old, the life expectancy at birth, for the average tiger may thus be only about three to five years.

Despite such high mortality rates, with an adequate prey base, tiger populations produce surpluses every year because of their basic biological traits: early breeding, short gestation, large litters and year-round, short (three to four weeks) oestrus cycles. In a prey-rich habitat, a breeding tigress probably replaces herself several times during her lifespan.

MAN AND TIGER: THE BRUTAL ENCOUNTER

As long as human population densities remained low, and the technological capability to extirpate prey species or hunt tigers were primitive, tigers were safe over much of their range. Their ecological adaptability and high reproductive potential ensured their survival. No doubt, even centuries ago, landscape modifications had rendered many productive tracts such as the Gangetic and Deccan plains of India, the rice belts of Thailand, Vietnam and Java, unsuitable for tigers. Yet, there remained extensive forests where unsuitable climate, topography, soil and diseases kept out agriculture and high human population densities.

The picture began to change with the colonial penetration of Asia in 18th and 19th centuries, when fire-arms teamed up with the traditional hunting skills, enabling the colonials, kings and commoners to launch a war of attrition on tigers. At the same time, political stability and improved drugs against epidemic diseases increased human population densities, opening up hitherto inhospitable areas to intensive agriculture, often with new crops like sugarcane, coffee or tea. Probably the only positive factor favouring tigers in this era was the banning of shifting cultivation and protection of extensive wooded tracts as government owned 'Reserved Forests' which could not be cleared and farmed by the expanding human population. Therefore, despite considerable unsustainable logging by forestry departments, by the middle of this century, most remaining tiger habitats in India and Burma survived only in Reserved Forests. During the same period, in the absence of any protection to her forests against agricultural invasion, China lost most of its tiger habitats, while relatively lower population pressures alone saved tiger habitats in parts of Thailand, Indochina, Malaya and Sumatra.

By the middle of the 20th century, the Bali tiger subspecies was driven to extinction. When India gained independence in 1947, tigers were in full retreat. There were official bounties for killing tigers, enticing villagers and tribals to shoot, poison or otherwise slaughter tigers at every opportunity. The 'Grow More Food' campaign encouraged the honey-combing of remaining blocks of tiger habitats with agricultural enclaves, setting the stage for endless man-tiger confrontations. A liberal issue of gun licenses under this campaign added to the decimation of ungulates already caused by the more 'traditional' techniques. The advent of jeeps and dry cell torchlight in the post war era provided new tools to aid the poachers of tigers' prey. Simultaneously, licensed 'sportsmen', both foreign and Indian, contributed their own unsavoury bit to the massacre. A well-known taxidermist, estimates that during the 1940s he annually processed over 600 tiger skins for 'sportsmen'. A flavour of this era can be got from the fact that even less exalted bounty hunters, like my old friend nicknamed 'Naribodi' (tiger shooter) Chengappa, killed 27 tigers in the vicinity of a single village close to Nagarahole between 1947-64.

In the early 1960s, as a schoolboy helplessly witnessing the terminal period of this war on wildlife, I was certain that tigers would be extirpated during the next decade. What made the situation seem so utterly hopeless was the fact that, other

Comfortable in water, a tiger surfaces in the middle of a lake

than a few 'élitist' conservation pioneers, like E P Gee, Salim Ali, Billy Arjan Singh, Zafar Futehally and M. Krishnan, nobody seemed to realise or care about what was happening to India's wildlife. In 1967, George Schaller from Wildlife Conservation Society, New York, completed the first ever scientific study of tigers. Besides elucidating key facets of tiger's ecology, Schaller forcefully drew attention to the tenuous status of the animal, through his classical study 'The Deer and the Tiger'.

THE FIRST TIGER RESCUE: 1970-1990

In response to concerns of the international conservation community about the imminent extinction of the tigers, several Asian governments duly passed laws protecting them in the early 1970s. However, effective on-ground protection materialised only in a few reserves in India and Nepal. In India, a fortuitous combination of three factors — the committed political leadership of Prime Minister Indira Gandhi, the campaign by a small but informed wildlife lobby and the presence of a disciplined protective force in state forest departments, led to the actual implementation of the new wildlife laws in several reserves. At least in these refugia tigers, their prey and habitats were protected. With the partial exception of Nepal and USSR, other tiger range countries lacked the necessary ingredients for effective tiger protection. Consequently, over most parts of Asia, the tiger's decline continued. The Javan and Caspian tigers blinked out in the 1970s, even as international campaigns to save the tiger were launched.

To learn the right lessons for the future from this conservation history, it is important to analyse the factors anchoring the Indian tiger rescue effort. The most effective component of this effort was the practical, protectionist orientation given to the whole enterprise by Indian foresters who had to implement the new wildlife laws. Pioneers like J J Dutta, Saroj Raj Choudhury, Kailash Sankhala, Sanjay Deb Roy, H S Panwar, Fateh Singh Rathore and others charged with the task of protecting tigers did the most obvious, common-sense things. Controlling the hunting of tigers and their prey by employing sufficient, well-equipped guards in tiger reserves was one step. Reducing biomass exploitative pressures on tiger habitats by curbing cattle grazing, forest fires, removal of timber, firewood and non-timber forest products (MFP) was another.

At least in the designated Project Tiger Reserves, their directors even succeeded in stopping official logging by their forester colleagues. Another farsighted measure was the attempt to reduce human population densities within tiger reserves, by relocating human populations away from prime tiger habitats. Although this protectionist thrust of early tiger conservation efforts was sometimes inimical to the short-term interests of local people, the fact that tigers and the entire wildlife communities around them benefitted immensely from this thrust is a certainty.

Dramatic recovery of habitats, followed by a strong rebound of prey and tiger populations, was witnessed in the first decade of protection (1974-84) in many tiger habitats both inside the Project Tiger network (Kanha, Ranthambhore, Corbett, Manas, Kaziranga) and outside it (Nagarahole, Anamalai, Dudwa, Bandhavgarh). In protected areas exposed to tourism, like Kanha and Ranthambhore in India, or Chitwan in Nepal, visitors could even crowd around and watch tigers from atop jeeps or elephants. The flavour of those heady days is beautifully captured in the superb photographs and movies shot by Belinda Wright, Fateh Singh Rathore, Valmik Thapar and others. By the early 1980s this situation gave rise to a sense of complacency, with the Director of Project Tiger rhetorically asking 'what do you do after you have succeeded?' International conservation bodies, eager for a 'success story' rushed around claiming that they had 'saved' the big cat. Nobody realised that these few hot spots of high tiger density represented only a minuscule fraction of total tiger habitat. Over the rest of its range, the tiger's decline continued.

IGNORANCE: THE MOTHER OF COMPLACENCY

Although the hierarchical, authoritarian mind-set which characterised the Indian forestry departments was a major factor underlying the effective implementation of tiger protection in Indian reserves, the same insular mind-set also filtered out any possible infusion of wildlife science into tiger conservation measures from the very outset. For decades, Western ecologists had known that objective monitoring of animal populations is essential for evaluating the success or failure of any wildlife management programme. Realising early that it is impossible to count all individual

A tiger clasps the branch of a tree and rakes his claws on it

animals over large areas, ecologists developed several standardised sampling techniques to objectively estimate animal population densities, or, at least, to measure population trends.

Ignoring such objective, sampling-based techniques right from the beginning, Indian park managers set about the impossible task of counting every single individual of an elusive, low density species like the tiger on a countrywide basis. For this enterprise they even invented a simplistic, completely invalidated method called 'pugmark census'. Essentially the method assumes that track impressions of all tigers in India can be collected simultaneously, and from that collection each individual tiger can be distinguished and counted. There is, of course, anecdotal evidence that some individual tigers can be identified from peculiarities of track shape, by experienced field men, if all four tracks can be seen imprinted on fine dust on hard substrate. The problem, however, is with the assumption that **every** tiger can be identified this way, a premise which has never been validated even on zoo tigers. In fact, in limited validation tests carried out by me, this assumption failed.

A tiger shelters in a thick jamun grove

Compounding this basic false premise are ground realities such as a 15 to 20 percent annual turnover of individuals in a tiger population, variations in track shape caused by differences in soil, speed of the animal, collection of multiple prints of the same paw, and absence of suitable tracking substrate in most areas. Consequently, the tiger 'numbers' which were touted to 'prove' the success of conservation efforts, bore no logical relationship to real tiger numbers. Worse still, these seemingly exact numbers which were derived so easily, made the more complicated task of applying good science to tiger conservation seem totally unnecessary.

How does one apply good science to tiger conservation? To estimate densities of prey animals in the forest, I got several three kilometre long straight trails (called transects) cut through forests of Nagarahole. At dawn, I walked at full alert along these transects, scanning the forest for animals. Every time a gaur, sambar or other prey animal was seen, I recorded the species, number and the distance from the animals to the transect line, using an instrument called a range finder. After about 460 kilometre distance had been covered on the transects (with six assistants, over two weeks), these data were used to estimate the area covered in sampling, and the population densities of herbivores. Karnataka's forest rangers who worked with me were able to calculate densities of different ungulates quite accurately using this 'line transect sampling'.

By walking along forest roads which tigers patrolled regularly, my field assistants and I collected tiger scats (droppings), which, although they smelled like hell, were a mine of information on tigers. Since more tigers in an area meant there were more scats to find, a simple index of number of tiger scats seen for every 100 kilometre walked could be derived. This simple index could not tell how many tigers were in the area, but by accurately reflecting increasing or decreasing trends, it provided all the information which a park manager really needs to monitor his tiger populations objectively.

To identify individual tigers without any confusion, the best way is to use camera-traps, which are fixed on forest paths to be electronically triggered by the tigers themselves. Their dramatic self portraits show stripe patterns which are unique to individual tigers. Such identifications can then be used to estimate tiger populations in an area accurately, particularly if used in combination with 'capture/recapture' computer models which can analyse the frequency with which tigers repeatedly appear.

To know basic facts such as sizes of home ranges of tigers, hunting frequency, use of corridors, dispersal routes, long-term survival rates, and to observe their behaviour closely, radio–telemetry is an invaluable tool. Equipped with a receiver slung around my shoulder and a hand–held antenna, I covered Nagarahole forests driving on elephant back or on foot every day, radio-tracking my four collared tigers. With this technique I was able to enter the secret world of tigers, an impossibility otherwise in the dense forests of Nagarahole.

Findings from Chitwan's tiger research project, and later from the work in Nagarahole, showed up inconsistencies in the results of Indian tiger censuses. However, a decade ago, tiger policy makers and managers chose to ignore all criticism. They were equally apathetic to exploring alternative techniques: simple trend indices of tiger sign, prey density estimation or direct estimation of tiger densities using camera traps.

THE SECOND TIGER CRISIS

By early 1990s, several adverse socio-economic factors combined to seriously undermine tigers. The three pillars of the earlier limited success were collapsing. Political support for wildlife conservation weakened under successive prime ministers. The tough, no-nonsense field mangers at the bottom gave way to the smooth-talking officers more at home in the new political cultures which emerged. The pro-wildlife lobby of the 1970s was subsumed by a larger and more vociferous 'environmentalist' lobby which, despite paying lip sympathy to the cause of 'biodiversity', fought to promote market-driven forest biomass exploitation by local people.

Internationally, major conservation groups and funding agencies, prodded to be politically correct by social activists who knew little and cared less about wildlife issues, began advocating 'sustainable use' of even the three percent land earmarked to be the last refuge of tigers. An international symposium to mark the 20th anniversary of Project Tiger in Delhi turned into a forum to debate 'people's needs', while the tiger's own minimum ecological needs receded from the minds of the participants. An official documentary crowed that 'all was well with the tiger'. To say the least, this complacency was misplaced. In fact, in addition to the traditional pressures on tigers, a new threat was raising it's ugly head: the burgeoning demand for tiger bones to supply the medicine men of the Far-East.

The initial disquiet of a handful of tiger conservationists, based on scattered evidence like illogical census results and poaching of known tigers in Ranthambhore, gave way to serious alarm by mid-1993, following the relentless efforts of Delhi based tiger conservationist Ashok Kumar and his undercover agents at uncovering hard evidence of large scale tiger poaching in India. Although the Director of Project Tiger, initially maintained that the tiger was not a 'dying patient' and 'continued to be perfectly safe', mounting evidence from wider investigations showed otherwise. The true extent of this poaching or its impact are still unquantified in the absence of reliable estimates of tiger numbers and the numbers poached. However, it is clear that there is certainly no room for such complacency any longer. As the Indian Minister of Environment finally admitted, 'there is a serious problem'. The question is, are we doing anything about it?

REVERSING THE TIGER'S DECLINE

There are those who argue that loss of genetic variability caused by habitat fragmentation may become a long-term threat to some tiger populations. Others believe that only 'people friendly' conservation policies can save the tiger in the long run. But as Lord Keynes said, in the long run we will all be dead anyway, and we must not ignore the immediate crisis on hand. By over-emphasising long-term threats to the survival of tigers and thereby diverting scarce resources towards those, we may in fact be dooming the species to extinction in the next couple of decades.

My research on tigers in Nagarahole, in conjunction with those of biologists Melvin Sunquist, George Schaller and Alan Rabinowitz show that the low numbers of tigers over much of Asia is caused by the loss of their prey base due to hunting by people. Superimposed on this decline, poaching of tigers for the 'traditional medicines' (bone trade) may now be driving the final 'coup de grace' to the big cat.

As we now know, tiger home range sizes, densities and survival rates are all strongly linked to the maintenance of high prey densities. There is evidence that at higher densities, big cat populations can even withstand some degree of hunting pressure, because of the presence of 'surplus' transients. With lowered prey densities this 'buffer' of transients is lost, home ranges become larger, numbers of breeders decline, recruitment drops, and the tiger population becomes increasingly vulnerable. Ultimately, although a few individuals may linger on for a decade or so, extinction is dramatic and final, as the exit of the Javan tiger showed us two decades ago.

It is obvious that the tiger cannot change its natural traits, large size and carnivorous diet, to accommodate our changing policies. Either we accommodate the tiger's biological needs into our world view, or the big cat will go extinct. Therefore, the strategy to prevent tiger's extinction has to be built around this vulnerable species' ecological needs rather than around social attitudes which we perceive to be politically correct. This inevitably means making several tough, unpopular decisions.

Firstly, we have to recognise that tigers cannot coexist with high density human settlements living off market-driven economic activities like agriculture and forest biomass exploitation. Therefore, human and livestock population densities need to be reduced inside prime tiger habitats through sensible and fair relocation policies, to allow wild ungulate prey to recover from habitat pressures, poaching and competition with livestock. It is even worth sacrificing some non-priority forest areas to accommodate such relocation, if critical tiger habitats can be physically isolated from poaching and habitat pressures.

Secondly, recognising that market-driven biomass exploitation is the leading cause of habitat deterioration, all extractive linkages between tiger reserves and local or distant markets for forest biomass derivatives such as fuel, timber, fodder, dung

A dawn patrol of tigress and cubs in Nagarahole

and other 'minor' forest products should be snapped. Moreover, this forest-market linkage must be broken, regardless of whether the agencies extracting such products are governments, NGOs or local people.

Thirdly, we need to appreciate that, despite our best social engineering efforts, there will always be criminals in any society, who can only be stopped through effective use of force. Therefore, our effort to promote eco-development around tiger habitats has to be balanced by adequate investments in manpower and material resources for policing the tiger habitats. Threat from poachers operating inside tiger habitats, and, the threat from distant wildlife traffickers should both be ruthlessly countered.

Fourthly, we have to critically and continuously evaluate how our tiger conservation efforts are faring, by employing universally accepted methods of science. For this, our policy makers have to shed their intellectual apathy, and weave the science of wildlife biology into the fabric of conservation strategies.

Finally, without a committed political leadership and public awareness, it is impossible to usher in any such major changes. The only force which can perhaps induce the necessary attitude changes among the politicians, officials, media, social activists and the public, is an articulate, passionate 'tiger lobby' which clearly understands the ecological fragility of the feared predator.

When I see a tiger pad silently through the forest brush, literally melting into it, a deep sense of admiration and awe steeps through me, which no captive tiger can arouse. I cannot but help feel that it is this elemental passion we all feel for its wildness, one way or the other, which can either save the tiger — or destroy it forever.

WHY SAVE THE TIGER?

There are several sensible arguments which can be marshalled to justify why we should save the tiger. For instance, the productivity and welfare of our predominantly rural, agricultural society is critically dependent on the regulation of run-off and soil erosion, on recharge of ground water, and mitigation of local climatic fluctuations. Forests, which clothe the watersheds of most of our important river systems, play a dominant role in performing these functions, besides harbouring the tiger. If wisely managed, some of the forested landscapes can also provide our rural and urban populations the fuel, timber, bamboo, rattan and a host of non-timber products, needed for their sustenance.

More importantly, as the earth's mineral resources are getting exhausted rapidly, the needs of food, fibres, shelter, fuels and life-saving chemicals needed by an expanding population seeking better lifestyles will increasingly depend on biotechnology. However, so far, scientists have explored only a tiny fraction of the rich forest biota, which is literally a treasure house of potential life supporting products. Tiger is a key species of these forests which harbour millions of plant and animal life forms. Moreover, the tiger is at the end of a complex chain of ecological relationships; this also includes plants which directly produce energy from the sun, and the herbivorous animals upon which the tiger preys. These relationships are so complex

that it is virtually impossible to isolate and preserve only those life forms which may become useful to humans. One of the most effective ways of being sure of saving complex life form linkages and ecological processes is to ensure that top-predators, such as the tiger, are thriving in an intact assembly of predators, prey and plant communities. Surely, sacrificing the remaining three percent land on which tigers live now, to solve some problem or the other which society has not been able to solve despite full access to the remaining 97 percent over centuries, does not make sense.

There are other arguments one can advance: the last refugia of tigers are also wonderful natural laboratories to observe and from which we can learn. The tiger forests are our last links to a natural world from which we came, a rich source of education. They are an irreplaceable library of nature for generations to come, and advocating their destruction in the name of progress or temporary local benefits, is akin to burning down an ancient library.

However, for all their impeccable logic, the above arguments for saving the tiger are basically utilitarian and rather selfishly human-centred. In addition, I believe there are strong ethical compulsions for trying to save the tiger. Tiger (and other wildlife species) are products of millions of years of evolution. Global climate change, movements of continents, advance and retreat of glaciers, volcanic eruptions and other mighty natural forces led to the evolution and radiation of life on earth. During these upheavals, life forms evolved and died out, only to be replaced by new ones. However, humans have now so drastically modified the earth's landscape that the wonderful process of evolution has been virtually negated, for all but the smallest creatures.

The amazing process of natural selection (jokingly but appropriately attributed to a 'blind watchmaker' by evolutionary biologist Richard Dawkins) gave rise to a species like the tiger. Do humans who evolved during the last few 'seconds' of the history of life on earth, have a fundamentally superior moral right to wipe other species off the face of the earth? Or do we have a moral duty to protect some of these creatures on at least a tiny fraction of the earth's landscape? If the latter is the case, at least in its last refugia, the tiger's right to survive as species overrides the rights of individual men to extirpate them. I believe such preservationism is ethically justifiable under any moral or social code we can think of.

Opposite page: *Gharials bask on the banks of the Ramganga, a river which forms a vital part of the tiger's riverine habitat*

DHOLE, THE WHISTLING HUNTER OF
THE INDIAN JUNGLE

A J T Johnsingh

Thin mist shrouded the forests around Thavarakatte (*katte* or pond) in Bandipur Tiger Reserve, one early morning in November 1977. With great caution against wild elephants, I made my way on foot from Bandipur village to the hide near Thavarakatte, one kilometre away. This shooting hide, built by an earlier Mysore maharaja, is in the middle of dense *lantana*, bamboo and dry deciduous forests which have an abundant population of wild pig, chital and sambar. Tiger, leopard and dhole hunt in this area frequently. The hide has a tin roof and mud walls with several holes designed to shoot through. It stands under a large *Bahera* (*Terminalia bellirica*) tree. Visibility is good from the shooting hide as a road runs in front of the hide for about 200 metres and a ten metre wide view line cuts through the scrub to the left for about 150 metres. I used to sit either inside, on top of the roof or in the tree to wait for dhole and I had discovered that Thavarakatte was the best place in Bandipur to observe large mammals.

Soon after I made myself comfortable on the rooftop, a sambar alarm broke the morning silence of the forest from left of the hide, closer to the view line. This was followed by many more alarm calls of sambar and peafowl — sure signs of a large predator's presence. Verifying that there were no elephants nearby, I jumped down from the rooftop and hurried 100 metres to a large rosewood tree (*Dalbergia latifolia*) closer to the view line.

By the time I was comfortably seated on a large branch about four metres from the ground, the jungle around me was lit by the golden light of the morning sun. A sambar stag in magnificent hard antlers ran from the scrub in front. I could also hear the commotion of several animals running through the undergrowth.

Soon six dhole came trotting onto the view line from my left and when they came closer to my tree they stood spread in a distance of 15 to 20 metres all facing the scrub before me. Their soft whines, restlessness and occasional muscle twitching of their bodies indicated that they were extremely excited about the morning hunt. They were intently watching the scrub in front of me and I also looked in that direction. I could discern the movements of animals walking from the scrub in the direction of my tree.

First to emerge was an adult sambar doe. Meanwhile the dhole had come closer facing the trail along which the sambar was emerging. Excitement ran through every vein of my body and breathing became heavy but I sat without a movement. The sambar doe was already aware of the presence of the dhole. When she came out of the scrub her neck was extended, nostrils dilated and eye-balls rolled back, so that the whites of her eyes were visible; every long hair on her neck was erect. She snorted and stamped her forefeet as she walked. It was a formidable threat display.

Contrary to my expectations, the dhole, instead of pouncing on the doe and tearing her to pieces, split into two groups giving enough space to the doe to walk through safely. The doe was followed by a yearling doe and another adult doe, and all walked through the dhole safely, all with an amazing display of threat. Meanwhile more dhole, which had flushed out these sambar, joined the six on the view line and then entered the scrub behind my tree. A little later, the muffled scream of a fawn, immediately followed by the cracking of bones, indicated that the dhole had eaten a morning snack. After the hunt, the dhole may have gone to the *katte* to drink because when I saw them again they were all coming from that direction. As they came to the dense shade of another rosewood tree, they all lay down to rest. Before long four sambar doe came out of the scrub and, as a team, chased the dhole here and there and the dhole solicited play as if saying 'catch-me-if-you-can'. I thought how inappropriate it was to call these graceful hunters 'bloody killers'.

Dhole, or Asiatic wild dogs as they are also known, are rust-sand coloured, weigh around 16 kilograms and stand approximately 50 centimetres at the shoulder. Their length — including a long black, bushy tail — is about 135 metres. Females are somewhat slighter of build but can not easily be differentiated from males at a distance. The distribution of dhole is extremely broad, extending throughout Eastern and Central Asia.

Dhole occur as far north as the Altai Mountains of the former USSR, perhaps as far north as southern Siberia. From there their range extends radially southward encompassing Mongolia, much of China, Thailand, Indo-China, the Malaya Peninsula, Sumatra and Java. To the east, dhole occur in Tibet, Nepal and India. They are not present in Sri Lanka, Borneo and Japan.

Dhole or wild dog

Of the nine subspecies recognised by Ellerman and Morrison Scott, three subspecies definitely occur in India. They are *Cuon alpinus laniger* in Kashmir and Ladakh, *Cuon alpinus primaevus* in Garhwal, Kumaon, Nepal, Sikkim and Bhutan and *Cuon alpinus dukhunensis* south of the Ganges. The dhole found in the Namdapha area in Arunachal Pradesh could well be the *Cuon alpinus adjusts* from north Burma. Dhole occupy an enormous variety of habitats. In the northern reaches of their range they inhabit dense forests, river gorges and mountainous alpine regions. In Ladakh, as in Tibet, they inhabit the cold windswept deserts. In the rest of India they exist almost exclusively in dense forests and thick scrub jungles where there is sufficient prey and water. Dense montane forests are the preferred habitat in Thailand.

The genus *Cuon* is distinguished from *Canis* by more rounded ears and a proportionately short muzzle, a characteristic that enables dhole to exert an extremely powerful bite. Dhole have only two molars on either side of the lower jaw instead of the usual three. Thus the dental formula for *Cuon* is incisors 3/3, canines 1/1, premolars 4/4, molars 2/2 = 40. The usual pattern in the family Canidae is incisors 3/3, canines 1/1, premolars 4/4 and molars 2/3 = 42.

Many myths are woven around the dhole. One is that dhole attack people if they run away from them. I had an opportunity to explode this myth. One morning, in Bandipur, I observed nine dhole emerging from the jungle onto a forest road and immediately I took cover behind a large tree. The dhole were 50 metres away trotting in my direction. To see their reaction, I came out of the cover and ran in full view of them to an easily climbable tree 30 metres away. The dhole, instead of chasing me, abruptly turned back with a short growl and disappeared into the bush.

Another myth is that dhole hunt their prey in relays. According to this theory one dhole runs after the prey until it becomes tired and then another dhole pursues it and this change of hunters will go on until the prey becomes tired, at which point all the dhole will join together and kill it. I never observed this to happen. Of the 48 chases I witnessed, 44 ended within 500 metres and only twice did the chase go beyond this. Team work and the dhole's speed enabled them to kill their prey within short distances. It would be impossible for one dhole to pursue a particular prey animal through the dense Indian jungle where there are many prey and prey signs to confuse them in their pursuit.

In fact, I observed dhole employ two strategies. One, as I had observed while sitting atop the rosewood tree, was to flush prey to other waiting members of the dhole pack. The other was to go in an extended line through the forest and any dhole that was capable of killing would start the attack once a suitable prey was located. It is possible to identify which strategy dhole will adopt only at the beginning of the hunt as at the end, in the melee, it is impossible to differentiate between the two strategies.

It is also believed that dhole urinate on the eyes of prey to make them blind before killing them. This belief seems to me reminiscent of the technique of keeping butter on the head of a pond-heron and catching the bird when the butter melts and blinds the bird! It is also reported that dhole urinate on leafy branches, force the prey to run into the branches, make them blind and kill them. This again is an impossible technique to use in a dense jungle and I saw no evidence of it.

Not long ago, hunters and foresters thought that dhole were responsible for the decline of deer species which in fact is due to overgrazing, habitat loss and poaching. Lt Col R W Burton, in his article on wild dog in the *Bombay Natural History Journal* of 1940, opined that in those days when the stock of deer in all parts of the country was rapidly lessening, it should be the fixed policy of the Imperial Forest Department to offer government rewards of sufficient amount to encourage the continual destruction of the wild dogs in all Reserve Forests. This was practised throughout India but only certain agencies kept records of how many dhole were killed.

In the 21 years from 1912–13 the average yearly destruction of dhole in the area controlled by the Nilgiri Game Association in south India was 38 and the reward offered for each dhole killed was Rs20, which was a covetable amount in those days. This promotion of killing was continued by the Association and between 1939 and 1964, 309 dhole were killed. Dhole was a much maligned and persecuted species in the Indian jungles and even until 25 years ago it carried this bounty on its head.

Phythian Adams, a retired army officer who lived in the Nilgiris, wrote in a *Bombay Natural History Society Journal* of 1949 that the epithet 'a perfect swine' may with every justification be applied to the wild dog, whose nature and habits may be summed up in a single word — 'bloody'. He concluded that except for its handsome appearance the wild dog has not a single redeeming feature and no effort, fair or foul, should be spared to destroy the pests of the jungle. Even as recently as 1964, E P Gee, spoke only lukewarmly in favour of dhole. His opinion was that dhole play a useful part in the general set up of nature. They keep the deer on the move, and so favourite grazing areas do not become overgrazed and therefore impoverished. But apart from this very little has been said in favour of these animals.

Fortunately for the dhole the tide has changed. The last dhole was shot in Bandipur in 1975 and, being in Schedule II of the Indian Wildlife (Protection) Act 1972, it now enjoys total protection from hunting. Unless there is permission by the Chief Wildlife Warden of the state the dhole cannot be legally shot. Since the inception of Project Tiger many tiger habitats such as Kanha, Melghat, Simlipal, Bandipur and Periyar, which also harbour dhole, have shown a significant increase in tiger numbers which would not have happened had the dhole been containing tiger numbers as was once thought.

This accusation against dhole, that a high density of their population can suppress tiger and leopard abundance, need

A pack of dhole feed on a chital kill

not be true also as there are several behavioural and ecological parameters which help these predators to avoid conflict with one another. There is temporal and spatial variation in use of habitat. Dhole are largely diurnal while tigers and leopards prefer to be nocturnal. Open habitats are generally avoided by the shy tiger but leopard and dhole use them without any inhibition. Tigers generally prefer prey heavier than 100 kilograms while leopard and dhole largely kill prey around and less than 50 kilograms. Dr Ullas Karanth has also observed a similar prey selection in the adjacent Nagarahole National Park. Besides, in Bandipur, dhole showed a preference for male sambar and male chital and my limited sambar and chital kills of tiger and leopard seemed to suggest their preference for female sambar and chital. Females, who spend considerable time in cover to give birth and nurse fawns, are more prone to stalking predators. In addition, the kill data also suggest that since the dhole is a coursing predator, they kill more young and old animals while the tiger and leopard, as they hunt by stealth and surprise, kill prey of all age classes.

The reason for dhole being called 'bloody' is that they kill larger prey by biting off chunks of meat and by evisceration. Often their killing occurs in daytime, so it may be more easily witnessed by people. One March evening, darkness was gathering and I was atop the shooting hide. My attention was abruptly drawn to a silent struggle between a large chital stag with a fine set of hard antlers and a group of seven dhole. Two or three of the dhole were biting, and hanging onto the rump of the stag, thereby rendering it completely immobile, while the others attacked on its flanks. The stag was vainly trying to fight off the dhole by swinging his great antlers but they never made contact with the dogs. Throughout the struggle the dhole remained silent and the deer vocalised its agony three times.

Suddenly one dhole caught the snout of the stag and pulled it forward while those at the rump continued to bite and pull him backwards. Eventually the helpless stag was dragged down and the dhole started eating even before he had died. Although predation is as much a biological process as grazing, such incidents often appear gory and repugnant. However, in defence of dhole, the following could be said: Since dhole lack the killing bite of the large cats they can best kill prey larger than themselves by biting off chunks of meat. An animal thus weakened obviously becomes easier to overcome as blood loss and shock progressively lower its resistance. Close examination of numerous fresh kills clearly showed that dhole are particular about holding onto the nose of stags sporting hard antlers — presumably to prevent themselves from being stabbed by these lethal weapons. Often, while in the process of biting off chunks of meat from the rump of adult stags, dhole bite off the scrotum and this has led to the belief that dhole intentionally emasculate their prey. Dhole, however, are very efficient in killing smaller prey like hare and chital fawns which are instantaneously killed with one bite and a vigorous head shake.

Although I had numerous observations of this type of killing behaviour, the one I observed on a cloudy evening from the shooting hide is worth mentioning. Around 16.30 hrs repeated chital alarm calls and the sounds of animals running, drew me to peep through a hole. Three dhole stood there facing west, as if to intercept an animal. Soon a big chital fawn, chased by another dhole, ran in their direction. The fawn, when it saw the dhole, veered to the right but the dhole also moved swiftly as if to block its way. Then the fawn leaped across the dhole but when it landed six to eight metres away from the dhole, all the four fell on it almost simultaneously and there was only a short muffled scream. Within a minute the entrails were thrown out and by this time the entire pack was on the kill.

Dhole, though they look like dogs, do not bark. Their most interesting call is the whistle, although how they produce the sound is an enigma. The whistling call can be imitated by blowing into a medium-bore empty rifle cartridge and in the past hunters used this trick to draw dhole closer in order to shoot them. Dhole separated from the rest of their pack whistle to reassemble after an unsuccessful hunt and even lone dhole whistle to discover the whereabouts of its pack members. However, I never observed dhole whistling to maintain the cohesiveness of their pack while the hunt was in progress. Sounds play an important role in the lives of dhole and they can be attracted, not only by imitating their whistle, but also by blowing air out through a leaf thus producing a shrill note similar to the distress call of a deer fawn.

Like most other large carnivores, dhole have an amazing ability to consume large quantities of meat. A pack of 15 can easily eat a yearling sambar male of 90 to 100 kilograms, each dhole consuming about five kilograms of meat, which is a little over one-fourth of its body weight. This capacity to gorge can enable them to live without food for a few days although this has not been verified in the field. During one 15 day period, I collected almost all the kills made by my study pack and calculated, that during this period, on average, each dhole ate 1.8 kilograms meat per day. One of the benefits of pack life, in addition to providing the capability to bring down large prey several times heavier than a single dhole, is the efficiency with which kills are eaten. Even the bones and skin of young and smaller prey are fully eaten. When larger kills are made the dhole may come back even to scavenge on the dry skin. This habit of scavenging also enables dhole to appropriate leopard and tiger kills and on many occasions leopards have actually lost their kills to dhole. This stealing of kills from other large sympatric predators can be dangerous. I once saw a dhole pup, nearly six months old, killed and partly eaten by a leopard; the potential robber had become an unsavoured prey.

All dhole look alike to a casual observer. A careful prolonged observation, however, can help an attentive observer to differentiate a few individuals based on the variations in colour and in the shape of the ear and tail. 'Bent Ear' was one such individual I grew to recognise. My first prolonged meeting with him was on January 4, 1977, when I went to the den around 11.00 hrs. Bent Ear had already returned from the hunt and was lying in front of the den. The leaf litter was so dry that I found it difficult to walk without making noise. My approach had alerted him and, pricking up his left ear, he watched the direction of the sound. I crawled to the cover of a rock 40 metres from the den, and, lying comfortably under a bush, observed him.

He had an unusually thick neck and a pale white throat, chest and belly. His tail had a bend as if it had been broken. His scrotum hung loosely showing he was aged. Throughout the three hours of observation he was suspicious of my presence but never came close to investigate. This was probably because of his dislike for the hot sun which scorched the shadeless areas. When I left the den he was sleeping in the shade. The rustle in the bush made him raise his head lazily and partly open his eyes before he again fell into a deep slumber to while away the hot afternoon.

Thereafter I observed him several times. He appeared to be the leader of the pack and was extremely fond of the pups. When the pack had made a kill of a small animal the pups would run to him pestering him to regurgitate some extra meat. I soon developed a strange affection for this aged hunter who flitted freely through the forest. He led a daring life. Alone and unafraid he slipped without any hesitation through thickets which I entered only with much reluctance, bated breath and a tense body. When he suddenly disappeared in April 1978 I felt a pang of sadness which remained for a long time.

During my study in Bandipur I learnt to understand the mechanisms of pack size regulation. In November of the first year of my study, the study pack of 15 was suddenly reduced to seven or eight animals. This was unexpected. The diminished pack had three females but one gave birth to eight pups. At no time were two packs seen operating in the same area, which suggests that the dhole could be territorial. Thus I realised that mortality, emigration of a part of the pack before the arrival of the pups, breeding by one female and the territorial nature may be the mechanisms that regulate pack and population size of dhole in an area. In spite of these mechanisms sometimes pack sizes of 20 to 25 dhole are reported. The possible explanation for this is given by Dr Arun Venkataraman who has done a four year study on dhole in the nearby Mudumalai Wildlife Sanctuary. He opines that such large packs are due to the absence of suitable areas nearby for the emigrants to occupy.

In Bandipur, the pups remained in the den until they were 70 to 80 days old and during this time they did not visit the nearby waterholes. They possibly got enough water from the mother's milk and the meat regurgitated by several of the pack members. I also observed that pups were shifted from one den to another when the den sites were disturbed by people.

The pack cared for the pups even after they had left the den and the adults treated them with special concern and solicitude until they were four to five months old. During this period the adults would hunt either very early in the morning or late in the evening to avoid both the presence of man and the heat of the day. The pups were left in hiding during these hunts and the absence of a couple of adults in the hunting party even suggested that some adults may have stayed behind to guard them. Even when the pups started following the pack on hunts, young stragglers were escorted by one or two adults. Pups were permitted to monopolise small kills like chital fawns and when food was insufficient the adults, who had eaten earlier, would regurgitate meat for them. When the pups were about seven months old, on occasions when food was insufficient, the adults were reluctant to regurgitate meat. The pups, however, chased them and appealingly nibbled at the corners of the adults' mouths until the food was regurgitated.

Even tigers are sometimes threatened by dhole packs

One winter morning I made my way through the thick fog to a large tamarind tree about 500 metres southeast of Bandipur. While perched on the tree I heard the hushed scream of a sambar fawn 150 to 200 metres close to Bandipur. An obvious sign of a kill. I hurried to the place which had already been reached by a flock of jungle crow. In Bandipur, these birds tenaciously follow dhole to feed on kill remains and were of immense help to me in locating dhole. I waited to give sufficient time for the dhole to settle on the kill as I had the intention of approaching them and taking some photographs. The crows were sitting on the top of a dead tree and looking down cawing. Minutes ticked by and abruptly the dhole growled and ran in different directions. For a moment I thought that perhaps a fight among themselves had made them disperse but as I waited for them to reassemble the crows landed on the kill site. As this was evidence that the dhole were not at the kill, I went ahead cautiously. The crows flew to the dead tree when I approached. On the short green grass, except for the splattered blood and hair and a few splinters of bone, there was no sign of the kill. I walked around the site and found tracks on the dew-covered grass of two persons who had come from, and gone back to, Bandipur. The clearly visible tracks led me to a Kuruba tribal hut on the outskirts of Bandipur.

One of the major objectives of my study was to evaluate the impact of dhole predation on chital and sambar and therefore every kill was valuable. The problem of local people taking the kills, if unabated, could seriously affect my study. I also believed that it could disturb the delicate prey-predator balance that exists in Bandipur. In view of this, I returned to the hut with the Bandipur Range Forest Officer and two guards and we rescued the 30 kilogram sambar fawn which was wrapped in sacks and hidden in one corner of the hut. I removed the jaw of the fawn for ageing it by studying tooth eruption, pieces of lung and liver for investigation of parasitism, and the carcass was left at the kill site with the hope that the dhole would come back to feed on it. This incident reveals one more form of association between dhole and man. Regretfully, since time immemorial, in almost every association with man, dhole has been the loser.

For ages, jungle tribes all over the range of dhole have been following them and appropriating their kills. But it is due to this association that tribes, such as the Gonds in Madhya Pradesh, never harm dhole. However, one way people do destroy dhole is by digging their dens and killing the pups. This particularly happens in areas where dhole prey on livestock.

Nearly 20 years have passed since my study and there are many questions that still need to be answered to fully understand dhole biology and ecology. Some of them are: What prevents *Cuon alpinus primaevus* from staging a comeback in prey rich areas like Corbett Tiger Reserve? What diseases periodically wipe out dhole in reserves like Kanha and how are these diseases transmitted? What happens to the emigrants and what is the social status of the emigrants? What is the genetic status of the different dhole populations? Short—term studies focusing on different populations of dhole and a long—term study on three or four neighbouring packs in an expansive dhole habitat, with several dhole individually marked and some radio-collared, are urgently required to unravel many of the existing mysteries about the dhole.

The Western Ghats, a 1,400 kilometre stretch of hills which hug India's western coastline from the Dangs in Gujarat to the Mahendragiri Hills in Tamil Nadu, are second only to the Himalaya in diversity of species. Listed internationally as one of the world's 18 hot spots of

biodiversity under serious threat, the rich evergreen forests of the Western Ghats have suffered hugely from over-exploitation. Many of the species of fauna and flora are endemic to the region and much of it is now highly endangered. The **Nilgiri langur** Semnopithecus johnii (left) is one species that is seriously affected by the severe shrinkage and fragmentation of forest. The **Nilgiri tahr** Hemitragus hylocrius (above) is endemic to this region and survives in the high grassland slopes and cliffs. It shares a common ancestor with its northern relative, the **Himalayan tahr** Hemitragus jemlahicus. (above left)

THE LION-TAILED MACAQUE

Ajith Kumar

In the six years from 1978 to 1984 that I spent studying a group of lion-tailed macaques *Macaca silenus* in the Indira Gandhi Wildlife Sanctuary (previously the Anamalai Wildlife Sanctuary) in Tamil Nadu, there were many interesting events — 12 births and a few deaths; I had seen the only adult male of the group (and my favourite) being harassed and finally thrown out of the group in disgrace by another male in a coup; fights between Nilgiri langur and my study group (of which I was often a silent supporter) ending in the deaths of Nilgiri langurs; the females ganging up against the usually unchallenged male and chasing him for more than a kilometre when he threatened an infant; the adult male eating more than ten giant squirrel nestlings in a week; the group feeding a few feet above wild elephants; the adult male trying to chase away crested hawk eagles harassing the juveniles; bitter fights between females of the neighbouring groups.

What struck me, however, was the absence of any spectacular events on most days as the group went about getting food; up in the morning at the first stroke of sunlight, to the nearest feeding tree, out of it after a couple of hours to look for insects till noon, on to another fruiting tree for an hour, sometimes followed by a short rest, then again looking for insects till evening, and then on to another fruiting tree till they retire for the night to a neighbouring large tree. The same routine for 365 days in a year. Only the heavy showers of the southwest monsoon could break this monotony and force them into inactivity, that too only for a few hours. Fruits, seeds and insects — the life of a lion-tailed macaque revolves around them.

The lion-tailed macaque is endemic to the tropical rain forests or wet evergreen forests in the Western Ghats. It feeds exclusively on ripe fruits, seeds, nectar, gums and resins which are rich in simple carbohydrates or lipids, and invertebrates, which are rich in proteins. They also feed on birds' eggs and nestlings, and giant squirrels. They feed on more than 100 plant species — mostly for the ripe fruit flesh. Some of these are drupes (eg, mango *Mangifera indica*) but the majority are small berries. Many species are used for their seeds, a few for nectar (eg, the silk cotton *Bombax malabarica*), and others for their gums or resins (eg, *Gnetum ulae* and *Vepris bilocularis*). Flowers, mushrooms, lichens and mosses make up the rest. About ten to 25 plant species are used every month, and about eight to ten species every day. Not all of them provide large quantities of food. Some, such as fig *Ficus*, mango and *Bischofia javanica*, are large trees and provide great quantities of fruits and seeds, but for a short period. Many species are small understorey trees, climbers or shrubs which provide small quantities of fruits or seeds; eg, *Psychotria favida*, *Smilax zeylanica*, many *Annona* spp. An interesting food item is the flower of *Xanthophyllum flavescens*, the only flower eaten. In Malaysia, the gibbons feed extensively only on this genus, which has very high concentrations of the amino acid, phenylalanine.

The diet of ripe fruits and seeds is very deficient in protein necessary for growth and reproduction. The lion-tailed macaque obtains protein largely from invertebrates. They spend nearly half the time looking for them. Foliage insects, caterpillars, pupae, spiders and various bark insects such as termites, provide the bulk of the protein requirement. Nearly three-fourths of the invertebrates are provided by the green foliage. They do, however, also feed on bird eggs and nestlings, land snails and lizards opportunistically. The adult males even feed on the young onces of giant and flying squirrels! The lion-tailed macaque is perhaps the most meat eating macaque.

The digestion of fruits, seeds and insects requires only a simple stomach, like the human stomach. This is what the lion-tailed macaque has evolved over the years and its stomach today is the simplest among all the macaques. The digestion of leaves on the contrary requires a complicated stomach, much like that of a ruminant, for breaking down the cellulose using microbes. Many of the leaf eating monkeys such as the common langur and Nilgiri langur have such stomachs. In its adaptation to a diet of simple sugars and carbohydrates, the lion-tailed macaque has lost its ability to digest even leaf buds that other macaques such as the bonnet macaques can digest.

This adaptation has tied down the lion-tailed macaque to a habitat, the tropical rain forest, in which fruits, seeds and foliage insects are available throughout the year. Other forest types such as deciduous forests provide fruits only during some months of the year, and also shed their leaves during part of the year. The nearly 5,000 species of flowering plants in the rain forests of the Western Ghats ensure a constant supply of fruits and seeds, across the seasons and years. Many of these

Habitat of the lion-tailed macaque in the Anamalai

are tuned to fruit just before or during the southwest monsoon beginning in June, many others do so in tune with the second northeast monsoon. Some, because of the ideal conditions prevailing in the rain forest, fruit during other months, ensuring fruit supply throughout the year. Many species of *Ficus* are aseasonal in fruiting and are critical in providing food when no other species are in fruit. Trees of some species, such as *Bischofia javanica,* provide small quantities of fruits over long periods of time and thus help in overcoming temporary shortages of food. Since most plant species are also evergreen, foliage invertebrates are also ensured throughout the year. The high plant species diversity also buffers against variations between years in the availability of fruits, seeds and invertebrates.

Many factors have contributed to the evolution of the amazingly rich species diversity in rain forests. The moderately high temperature of the tropics, the high rainfall and the many wet months in a year which keep conditions ideal for plant growth are the most important of these. The rain forest of the Western Ghats is among those areas richest in biodiversity. Of the 15,000 flowering plants reported from India, the Western Ghats, although geographically covering only about five percent of the country, has more than 30 percent and about 1,200 species are endemic. The rich plant species diversity in turn supports an extraordinarily rich faunal assemblage. Among the vertebrates, species richness and endemism are the highest among fish, amphibians and reptiles. Among the 158 species of fish in the area more than 30 percent are endemic. Of the 205 species of amphibians in India no less than 120 are from the Western Ghats, of which 75 percent are endemic, notably the limbless amphibians or caecilians. Among the reptiles, all the 33 species of shield-tails or uropeltid burrowing snakes are endemic to the Western Ghats; so are eight of the 14 pit-vipers in India, and many of the 60 species of lizards. Among the mammals also, endemism is high, especially the smaller mammals: the lion-tailed macaque, Nilgiri langur *Semnopithecus johnii*, Travancore flying squirrel *Petinomys fuscocapillus*, Brown palm civet *Paradoxurus jerdoni*, brown mongoose *Herpestes fuscus*, stripe-necked mongoose *H. vitticollis*, Nilgiri marten *Martes gwatkinsi*, the nearly extinct Malabar civet *Viverra civettina* and Nilgiri tahr *Hemitragus hylocrius*. Endemism is also high among invertebrates such as butterflies and moths. The avifauna also shows species richness with nearly 500 species, although endemism is low with only 14 species.

It is doubtful whether the lion-tailed macaque faces any significant competition from the other arboreal mammals and birds in its habitat. The bonnet macaque *Macaca radiata* visits the rain forest only when fruit abundance is very high, thus avoiding competition. The other species such as flying squirrels, giant squirrels and birds also overlap the lion-tailed macaque's diet, but mostly when the food is abundant. The Nilgiri langur is by and large a leaf eater.

However, it was not unusual for my study group and the Nilgiri langur to pick a fight. Since there were ten groups of Nilgiri langur within the home range of my study group, they bumped into each other very often every day. As the lion-tailed macaque is a fruit eater and the Nilgiri langur, a leaf eater, they seldom fought over food. Instead, fighting often started when they came together on the same tree and an infant or juvenile of either species felt threatened by the other species. The adults would immediately join in kicking up a fight. Often the fight ended quickly after an exchange of growls, and with the Nilgiri langur retreating. One day, however, the fight became particularly intense with the adults chasing each other. What drew my attention was the sound of something falling to the ground. Turning around I saw the adult male hurrying to the ground and disappearing among the thick undergrowth, while the other monkeys of the group stood staring down, growling and wailing. Within seconds, the male was going up the same tree but with a Nilgiri langur infant clutched in his mouth. While the other monkeys growled and wailed even more excitedly, he went up about five metres, stood with the infant in his mouth for a couple of minutes, then dropped it to the ground. I could see drops of blood on his white mane. As the male sat down licking his bloody hand, two adult females came running to him excitedly and started grooming him. The growling and wailing continued for a few seconds more, then there was only the sound of the cicadas. The Nilgiri langurs looked on from a distance of about 50 metres before slowly moving away. About five minutes later, the lion-tailed macaques also started drifting away. When we examined the infant langur on the ground, it was dead, but still warm and had deep canine marks on its chest and neck.

This incident is interesting because the lion-tailed macaque, especially the adult male, often kill birds and small mammals for eating. The adult females and males often raid bird nests in tree holes and devour eggs and nestlings. The adult males would examine giant squirrel nests to get infants. In one week in March 1983, I counted at least ten giant squirrel infants eaten by the adult male of my study group. In one incident the male captured a big juvenile giant squirrel from the nest, killed it with a single bite on the neck but discarded it after keeping it for a few minutes. Even flying squirrels, captured from tree holes, are eaten. It is thus evident that the lion-tailed macaque is a major predator of small arboreal mammals and hole nesting birds. Only the adult and sub–adult males, however, seem to prey on the small mammals.

It is not as if the lion-tailed macaque is merely a consumer of the biodiversity of its habitat. Through selective dispersal of seeds of some species, predation of the seeds of some, and neither dispersal nor predation of many others, the lion-tailed macaque should be playing a role in the vegetation dynamics of its species rich habitat, a role that has not been studied. Similarly, through intensive feeding on foliage insects, they also play a significant, but unknown, role in the ecology of the insects.

Over thousands of years the life history of the lion-tailed macaque has become highly adapted to the relative stability of its habitat, particularly the stability of food resources guaranteed by the rich floral and faunal diversity. This is reflected in density, group size and composition, and the demographic parameters. The abundance of fruits, seeds and insects is always low, for example compared to leaves. The lion-tailed macaque is thus found in low densities. The home range of lion-tailed macaque is about 1.25 square kilometres in the lower elevation forests in the Anamalais and about five square kilometres in the higher elevation forests of the southern Ashambu Hills. In contrast, as many as ten to 20 groups of Nilgiri langur may occur within that area. Since most of the fruits, seeds and insects are highly dispersed, in order to harvest them efficiently the lion-tailed macaque forms relatively smaller groups, compared to other macaques. The group ranges from ten to 40 animals with an average of about 20 animals. In other macaques the group size may exceed 60 animals! Another notable feature is that most groups contain only one adult male, while other macaques often have more than one.

The stability of its habitat allows the population to be maintained at the carrying capacity of the habitat (ie, the maximum population that can be sustained by the habitat). The population parameters have evolved in order to maintain populations at this level. More importantly, in the process the lion-tailed macaque has lost its ability to respond quickly to population perturbations that are now being caused by human impacts, but were never expected in its habitat. The characteristic features of its life history are a low birth rate, high age at first birth, and high pre-adult and adult survival rates. A female gives birth only once in three years, compared to at least twice in three years by the other macaques. The births are also more aseasonal compared to other macaques, although more common during early monsoon when food is abundant. Even in the best captive colonies, the birth rate is lower than in other macaques. It is likely that the lion-tailed macaques have even evolved behavioural mechanisms to control birth rate by the dominant females suppressing the mating of ovulating subordinate ones.

In most species it is common to find males fighting over females, even disrupting a male while he is mating. It is uncommon to find females doing this. But this is what occurs in the lion-tailed macaque.

Female macaques have menstrual cycles very similar to human females, with a cycle length of about 28 to 30 days. Mating is confined to a period of about 14 to 16 days, preceding ovulation, often called the oestrus period. This receptive phase of the female is indicated in the lion-tailed macaque by a lemon-sized swelling at the base of the tail. The perineal area also gets slightly swollen. Female and male consort during this period and copulation occurs frequently throughout the day, especially in the morning and evening. Once pregnant, the female does not come into oestrus and stops mating for nearly 20 months — the time required for pregnancy (six months) and lactation (15 months). The male lion-tailed macaque is a multiple-mount ejaculator, ie, it ejaculates at the end of a series of mounts (from one to six), the interval between mounts being shorter within the series (five to 30 seconds) than between them (30 minutes or longer).

Most of the groups have only one adult male, but several (four to seven) adult females. When some of these females come into oestrus together, there is some competition among them for access to the adult male. Dominance among the females decides as to which female gets access. If a subdominant female in oestrus tries to mate with the adult male, it is often subject to harassment by one or more of the dominant females who are also in oestrus. The most typical behaviour is to chase away the subordinate female whenever she tries to approach the male to mate. If the male mounts, the female is often chased away ending the mating prematurely. Sometimes the attack is turned to the male, by slapping him on the face or pulling him by the tail while he is mounted on another female. After terminating the mounting, the dominant female will present before the male, inviting him to mate. It is difficult for a subordinate female to disrupt the mating of a dominant female. She would often try nevertheless, by standing between the adult male and female. When there are four to five females in oestrus in the group, the mutual disruption can be so high that more than 90 percent of the matings attempted by the male end in vain! The multiple-mounting behaviour of the male makes the problem even more serious, since a series of mounting is required before ejaculation.

It is very likely that this behaviour plays some role in suppressing population growth. This can happen when due to harassment the subordinate females fail to conceive for one year. Most females come into oestrus together in June, but often only one would conceive, most probably the dominant female. The rest would come into oestrus the next month but again often only one of them would conceive and so on. This is why the births in the lion-tailed macaque are spread over most months of the year, although females often come into oestrus together.

The females give birth for the first time only when they are about six and half years of age, compared to four to five years in other macaques. The females continue to give birth till about 18 years of age. Giving birth at an interval of about three years, from six to 18 years of age means that each female would give birth only four times! A redeeming feature is the remarkably high survival rate, both at the preadult and adult stages of life. Nearly 80 percent of the infants born reach adulthood and more than 90 percent of the adults survive every year. In other macaques living in more variable habitats, the preadult survival could be as low as 40 percent and adult survival about 70 to 80 percent. Assuming equal sex ratio at birth and 20 percent mortality before they become adult, it becomes clear that each female only replaces herself in the population during her life! The male has a different life history. It does not become an adult until about eight years of age, spending about three years in the sub–adulthood stage when they move from one group to another to find a group which

The future of the lion-tailed macaque is seriously threatened as the Western Ghats reel under the heavy onslaught of economic pressure

they can take over. Often travelling alone, the sub–adult male suffers from a higher mortality, probably from predation. In the population, therefore, adult females outnumber adult males.

When we examine the history of the distribution of lion-tailed macaque and its habitat, it appears as though there has been a conspiracy between nature and man against them. What nature began, man is about to complete. Much of peninsular India, up to about 20,000 years ago, enjoyed a very humid climate in which the tropical rain forest thrived. Pollens of many rain forest plants have been recovered from the eastern coast as well as central India. These forests were the pathway for the spread of the ancestral macaque from Africa to South-East Asia, where it speciated repeatedly into more than 17 species including the six other macaques in India. The loss of these forests had nothing to do with man, instead nature was the culprit. The tectonic plate movements in the late Pleistocene, not only pushed peninsular India further north and away from the equator making conditions less ideal for the rain forest, but also set in the monsoon regime that we experience today. The reason was the uplift of the Himalaya, and even the Western Ghats to some extent. Starved of rain, the rain forest quickly disappeared from east of the Western Ghats, and was replaced by drier forests. The ancestral macaque, which later evolved into the lion-tailed macaque, along with its habitat, was progressively confined to the Western Ghats. Over time the rhesus and bonnet macaques speciated to colonise the newly spreading drier forests, excluding the lion-tailed macaque from them.

Favoured by the heavy monsoon rain, the forest would perhaps have been safe in the Western Ghats if man had not resumed what nature had left incomplete. The history of forest loss on the western coast is not well documented, but must have had an early start along with human colonisation. It is nonetheless true that most of the Western Ghats proper was covered with rain forest when the British influence began in this region, in the late 18th century. What followed over the next two centuries was what nature could achieve only in thousands of years. Large areas of virgin forests were lost when these were given away virtually free (or were taken away from the native people) to Europeans for growing tea and coffee, and for teak plantations, beginning from as recently as the 1860s. The tea and coffee estates attracted a flood of labour from the plains, clearing more forests for settlement, agriculture and to meet fuel wood needs. In the Nilgiris, for example, 500 square kilometres were given away to the Kannan Devan Tea Company at one-and-a-half rupees per acre! And the human population in the Nilgiris increased from about 3,000 in 1812, to 700,000 in 1991. Vast areas of rain forests were cleared in a similar way in the Anamalais, which had the largest extent of rain forest in the Western Ghats, and in Cardamom Hills and Ashambu Hills. Vast stretches of rain forest were also given away to settlers under the Wynad Settlement Programme in late 1960s. A series of reservoirs in the Western Ghats for power generation submerged large areas of rain forest, and cleared more for labour colonies. A series of roads and railway lines cut across the forest in

The Malabar or Indian giant squirrel Ratufa indica

many places. The most notable feature in this holocaust is that it was done or sponsored mostly by the state.

This then has been the history of the lion-tailed macaque and its habitat. A progressive loss from most of peninsular India and its confinement to the Western Ghats due entirely to natural causes, followed by rapid loss and fragmentation due entirely to human activities, mostly state sponsored.

CURRENT THREATS

Large scale loss of habitat is not a serious threat to the lion-tailed macaque at present since clear felling and selective logging of rain forests in the Western Ghats have been stopped since the late 1970s. A large proportion of the habitat is covered by protected areas, even though some important areas still remain outside. In this scenario, the major threat facing the lion-tailed macaque is, in fact, a legacy from habitat loss in the past, habitat and population fragmentation. The IV International Symposium on the lion-tailed macaque identified at least 40 isolated populations, of which 26 had less than two groups each, nine had between three and ten groups, and only five had more than ten groups. The areas with substantial, but fragmented, populations are Anamalai Hills and Cardamon Hills. Chamundi Hills in Karnataka and north of Nilambur population in Kerala, also have a few small populations that are confined to small patches of habitat. In the Kodagu area, a small population is confined to a large stretch of habitat, a consequence of many years of hunting pressure. South of Achankoil also there might be small isolated populations in Kerala.

The threats facing such small populations are now well–known. A run of either all females or males in a generation would make the population extinct and this is very likely to occur in small populations. Small populations in small forest fragments are also more susceptible to environmental changes which cause abrupt changes in food supply. This is particularly true of the lion-tailed macaque because its food supply is dependent on a large number of plant species which in turn is dependent on a large area. Diseases and catastrophes such as fire could wipe out small populations. It is also well known that small isolated populations are affected by inbreeding which cause reduced fertility and disease resistance. Thus, about 50 percent of the lion-tailed macaque population, which occur as small sub-populations, are currently under threat.

The above threats are exacerbated further by human activities which cause habitat degradation. A large number of forest fragments are underplanted with cardamom, either by their private owners or by the state. This causes further reduction in plant species richness through selective removal of trees and lopping for meeting the fuel wood needs or for providing appropriate light conditions for the growing of cardamom and coffee. Removal of climbers and undergrowth, many of which are important food resources for lion-tailed macaque is another major problem.

In the Western Ghats, the labour force required for working in the tea and coffee estates, and the government colonies required to run hydel projects and even small townships often occur close to the forest fragments. The fuel wood and timber needs of these people are mostly met from the forest fragments leading to further degradation. Given the inherent problems of small populations and the continuing degradation of their habitat, the future of many of the small populations is indeed bleak; they may more appropriately be called the 'living dead'.

It should be noted that even most of the contiguous forests have been selectively logged until the late 1970s, and are subject to habitat degradation from fuel wood and small timber removal.

Poaching has been a major problem for many species in India, increasingly so in recent years. It had been thought though that monkeys were not under this threat except perhaps in the northeast. But the Nilgiri langur and lion-tailed macaque have been hunted for many years in the Western Ghats. The meat and blood of the Nilgiri langur have been used for the treatment of asthma and many other ailments. Hunting had severely depleted the Nilgiri langur population almost throughout its range in the Western Ghats. Since the Wildlife (Protection) Act 1972, the Nilgiri langur has staged a dramatic recovery. This recovery has been partly due to greater protection, but also due to its ability to recover quickly from population crashes and to colonise unoccupied areas. The lion-tailed macaques are often hunted incidentally along with other animals, by tribals and other people in Kerala who have recently encroached and settled in forest land especially in northern Kerala. Given the low population density, the number of lion-tailed macaques hunted is often low, but the inability of lion-tailed macaques to recover quickly from the population crashes make it very vulnerable even to low levels of poaching. Computer simulation has shown that removal of even two animals once in two years can drive a population of up to 50 animals to extinction. It can suppress a much a larger population as well.

The strategy adopted by the poachers is very simple; make a hide near a fruiting tree such as *Ficus*. Many animals come to such fruiting trees — monkeys and giant squirrels above, sambar and barking deer below, to feed on the fallen fruits. When a whole group of lion-tailed macaques is on the tree, it is easy to shoot down quite a few before the group flees. It is not necessary that this should happen every year. Hunting of four to six animals once in two years can drive a population to extinction or keep it at very low densities. Last year, for example, we had reports of nine animals being poached near Silent Valley in one incident. Areas which have been subject to such poaching have low densities. Typical example are the forests in Makut, Mandrote and Srimangala forest ranges of the Coorg district in Karnataka. These forests are some of the best habitats for the lion-tailed macaques but on the east are the people in Coorg who have had a tradition of hunting and on the west are the largely Christian population in Kerala, who settled down in the area during the late 1960s and are not restrained from hunting by Hindu mythologies. As a result these forests have a very low density of lion-tailed macaques, and the Nilgiri langur has almost been hunted to extinction.

Given the adaptation of the lion-tailed macaque to the biodiversity of its habitat, its inability to respond quickly to population perturbations and the present highly fragmented state of its population and habitat, the management of lion-tailed macaque is not an easy task. The two areas with the largest population — Ashambu Hills and Silent Valley area — perhaps require only protection from further habitat loss and poaching. Other areas require more interventionist measures than mere protection. The population size and structure, and the status of the habitat need to be estimated for each population as baseline data. These need to be then monitored on a long-term basis. The corridors through which animals can move between fragments need to be identified and protected. Any distorted age/sex ratios (eg death of the single adult male) need to be detected and set right through introduction or translocation. Given the long period of isolation, it is likely that many of the small populations are already suffering from the ill effects of inbreeding. We need, therefore, to estimate the extent of inbreeding in the isolated small populations so that new genes can be introduced through translocation of individuals. Similarly, the status of the vegetation of the fragments need to be monitored and action taken in order to ensure that plant species diversity is restored. This obviously requires not only protection, but also systematic assisted regeneration, especially of species with food value for the lion-tailed macaque. It is here that the management of a large number of fragments, now under coffee or cardamom plantation, need to be reconciled to lion-tailed macaque conservation. Many of these are with private owners who have considerable financial stake in them. While fuel wood and logging to meet light requirements are genuine needs, both are often used as pretexts to harvest timber. It is necessary, therefore, that the management of such privately owned forests are integrated with lion-tailed macaque conservation, and that guidelines for the removal of trees are redefined.

In spite of our best efforts, it is very likely that lion-tailed macaques in some fragments have little scope for long-term survival, either because the habitat is very small, highly degraded, or subject to poaching. We should perhaps start thinking of translocating these animals to other patches (eg, for managing genetic variability) or to other contiguous forest where poaching has suppressed population or to zoos to enhance the genetic variability in the captive colony.

In most areas where such rain forest fragments exist, their value is not merely that of lion-tailed macaque, but also other components of biodiversity. Many contain endangered and rare plants, a large assemblage of the rich and endemic herpetofauna and are the feeding ground for many birds such as hornbills. Many large mammals, such as elephants, gaur and tiger often use such fragments as refuge as they move from one part of the landscape to another, whether they are protected areas, reserved forests or private forests. Forest fragments therefore play a critical role in maintaining the genetic flow of mobile animals across the landscape. A proper appreciation of the role of forest fragments, in addition to their importance in harbouring lion-tailed macaque, is yet to take place. Forest fragments, therefore, receive little attention from park managers.

PRESENT DISTRIBUTION

It is only during this century that the distribution range of the lion-tailed macaque in the north shrunk to the Sharavati River in Karnataka, as most of the rain forests in Maharashtra and Goa were wiped out. Similarly, the lowland rain forests was also wiped out, thus confining the lion-tailed macaque to the higher elevation of the Western Ghats. Human activities in the last 200 years or so, not only reduced the extent of the rain forest further, but also fragmented the remaining forests into numerous small isolated patches. Presently, therefore, the lion-tailed macaque occurs as numerous small populations.

Steven Green of Miami University conducted the first survey of the lion-tailed macaque in 1976-77. G U Kurup of the Zoological Survey of India repeated it in the following year. Their estimate of a wild population of less than 1,000 animals painted a grim picture. Surveys conducted since then indicate a substantially higher population. The Census and Distribution Group of the IVth International Symposium on the lion-tailed macaque held in Madras in October 1993 estimated the total population to be about 4,000 animals, with about 1,000 animals each in Karnataka and Tamil Nadu and 2,000 animals in Kerala. This followed higher population estimates for Karnataka, Anamalai Hills and Cardamom Hills, after detailed surveys in these areas.

The lion-tailed macaque is presently distributed from almost the southern tip of the Western Ghats in the Ashambu Hills in Tamil Nadu up to slightly north of the River Sharavati in Karnataka. The first detailed assessment of the status of lion-tailed macaque and its habitat in Karnataka was carried out by Ullas Karanth in 1984.

Most lion-tailed macaque groups contain only one adult male

In Karnataka, the rain forest is mostly confined to the steep western face of the Western Ghats, below 700m msl. This narrow band of forest is discontiguous at some places, and at least four isolated populations can be recognised.

Compared to Karnataka the rain forests in Tamil Nadu and Kerala, occur at a higher elevation mostly above 700 metres. The best quality low elevation habitats have all been lost to plantations and encroachment. An assessment in these two states is severely handicapped by the lack of a vegetation map, comparable to the one available for Karnataka. Although Kerala accounts for nearly 50 percent of the population and Tamil Nadu for 25 percent, in both these states the habitat and population have been severely fragmented. The only exceptions are Silent Valley-New Amarambalam area, Ashambu Hills, and, to some extent, the Cardamom Hills. There are about seven populations in these two states together, but except in the three areas just mentioned, the other populations are further fragmented into smaller isolated sub-populations.

Following spread: The habitat of Kalakad-Mundanthurai, one of India's 23 tiger reserves

ARE WARBLERS LESS IMPORTANT THAN TIGERS?

Madhusudan Katti

Now what kind of a stupid question is that?! Everyone knows that tigers are more important, being large predators, as apex species, at the top of the food chain, flagship species for conservation... etc. ... etc. ... etc.! These are arguments I have to face often enough when I tell people I am studying warblers — in Kalakad-Mundanthurai Tiger Reserve! For some reason, studying these tiny, nondescript, common birds is thought to be an entirely trivial, indeed arcane, academic pursuit of little practical or conservation value. 'What can studying little birds tell me about the habitat of large mammals, which are my primary concern?' asks the reserve manager. On the other hand, if we focus on the larger mammals — the apex species philosophy of Project Tiger — and do our best to improve their habitat, other species will also naturally benefit. Given limited funds and manpower for conservation (research and action), is it not better to focus on the mega-fauna and let the mini- and micro-fauna take care of itself? The only small creatures one should worry about then are those that may form part of the food chain leading up to the larger focal species.

Before you accuse me of a biased perspective (which is undoubtedly true, for I make my living watching little warblers!), let me state that, in defending these little creatures, I am also arguing in favour of a broader ecological perspective in conservation, one that goes beyond the charismatic mega-fauna, and starts looking at species more in terms of their ecological role in the system, rather than their appearance/charisma or tourism potential! So what is the ecological role of my favoured little leaf warblers?

Leaf warblers (genus *Phylloscopus*) must surely rank among the least glamorous vertebrates, so utterly lacking in charisma that even many diehard birdwatchers dismiss them lightly, scarcely bothering to try and even identify them to species level. Part of the problem is, of course, the fact that they are all small, dull-green coloured, and highly active in the forest canopy, making identification in the field difficult. It is only rarely — either when one is truly nuts about birds or when the fate of one's PhD thesis hangs on such identification — that one develops the eye for the subtle morphological, auditory and behavioural differences between species. These difficulties in identifying species, however, need not bother our busy manager too much, since the leaf warblers are all pretty similar ecologically as well — their role in the forest is largely independent of their taxonomic status, except insofar as structural aspects of their foraging microhabitat within the forest canopy are concerned.

All 18 species leaf warblers occurring in the Indian subcontinent are migratory. They breed during the temperate summers from the Himalaya north to the Arctic Circle, and take over the peninsular forests, including those in the Himalayan foothills and much of northeast India, from September through May. While each individual may weigh only seven to 11 grams (this range includes all species, give or take a gram), one may still emphasise the term take-over when describing their relationship to their forest habitats: they number in the billions and form probably the most abundant avian guild in the subcontinental forests during our tropical winter. My study at Mundanthurai (in the southern Western Ghats) records a density of six to eight leaf warblers (of two species) per hectare of forest — usually any given patch of forest may have two to three species, depending on the type of forest. I doubt whether there is any forest habitat in India that does not host at least one species some time of year. Picking a random hectare from my 20 hectare study plot at Mundanthurai, I find six leaf warblers (of two species) making it their home for seven to eight months — for these are territorial individuals that remain on site for much of the winter. And what do they do during this period? Eat insects, mostly! Humdrum as their lives may sound, they spend over 75 percent of their waking hours foraging for insects (and other arthropods, but insects predominate) in the foliage. Since they are not concerned about finding mates or raising young during this season, and want merely to survive in good shape for the next summer, their other activities — preening and maintaining territories through vocal and visual dialogue with neighbours — does not take much time. Hmm... a bunch of small, dull birds spending most of their day peering at leaves in search of insects — do I seem to be only weakening the defence? Not really...

Consider the fact that each leaf warbler, on average, eats three insects every waking minute (this is averaging over all their activities throughout the day). Since they forage by picking prey off a substrata — mostly leaf, sometimes also twigs and flowers — the prey largely consists of herbivorous insects. In the case of my one hectare on Mundanthurai, it is mostly leaf-eating caterpillars. A single leaf warbler thus eats an average of 180 insects every hour, or about 1,980 per day (assuming an average 11 hour working-day from dawn to dusk). The six individuals on our plot thus rid the plants of almost 12,000 insect pests every day!! Multiply that with the number of days (200 to 250) that they are in residence on that one hectare plot and you may begin to appreciate the service they render to all the plants. Now I ask you to consider removing these warblers from the study plot, since they seem to take away so much research and conservation energy from your more favoured mammals, and picture the forest as it may appear in a few weeks' time...! The scenario could become even more dramatic if you (in your large-mammal chauvinism) remove all the other insectivorous birds from the plot as well: I estimate each hectare of Mundanthurai's forest has at least 40 insectivorous birds, including other warblers and flycatchers (both resident and migrant), minivets, shrikes, drongos, babblers etc. The average number of prey may come down to just over two per bird per minute — which gives a total of about 5,000 insects per hour, or 55,000 per day in every hectare of forest! Remove those insectivores: ...and don't be surprised if in a few weeks

The green leaf warbler

your plants start to appear ragged with their foliage tattered... and your endangered langurs become unhappy because so many leaves are now packed with toxic anti-herbivore compounds produced in response to caterpillar nibbling... and the plants make fewer flowers and fruits as they are forced to spend too much energy in self defence... in turn making the nectarivores and frugivores unhappy... and regeneration of the forest slows down as fewer seeds get produced and dispersed... and the ground starts to dry faster because the canopy is thinner and more sunlight gets in... I leave you to work out the rest of the ecological cascade effects on your own!! For now, I'd be happy if you simply pause to appreciate the job done by the nondescript little green jobs — the leaf warblers — and their insectivore colleagues that travel thousands of kilometres every year to eat all those insects.

Before you start protesting that you will never contemplate removing all those birds, and that I am just another doomsayer, consider the fact that 80 percent of the warblers (especially the green leaf warbler, which is the most common one here) as well as the next most abundant migrant (Blyth's reed warbler) spending each winter at Mundanthurai come from the forests of the hill regions around the Caspian Sea, from Turkey east through Kashmir, including bits of southern Russia and Afghanistan. Now imagine that these hills — breeding grounds for so many migrant insectivores — are deforested on a large scale (either directly by us or through effects of global climate change) cutting down the bird population by 90 percent. Such a decline is not very unrealistic, as those studying migrant forest birds in the Americas will tell you — though they worry more about forests in the wintering areas being cut down rather than in the breeding grounds. In fact, over the past two decades, Americans and Europeans are increasingly facing the prospect of another Silent Spring. Not, this time, due to the factors mentioned in Rachel Carson's clarion call in the 1960s — overuse of chemicals in agriculture at the height of the green revolution — but to a suite of other human activities that have hit the habitat of avian migrants in both their northern breeding grounds and southern wintering grounds. Many species of migrant songbirds, which enliven the northern spring after the dreary and silent winters, have been pushed to the brink of extinction — some, like the Kirtland's warbler, down to a few scores of breeding pairs — over the past two decades, even as my ornithologist comrades in the West are racing against time to figure out the causes of these declines, so that we may try to reverse the process! The culprits are, of course, us humans: deforesting the tropical wintering grounds, fragmenting the temperate forests into suburban woodlots more accessible to human subsidised nest-predators such as domestic cats and other small carnivores (wild or feral) thriving on our garbage and directly subsidising populations of non-migratory nest-parasites like the North American cowbird through backyard bird feeders, enabling them to survive the harsh winter, and fool over 200 gullible species of songbirds into raising their offspring! We seem to be particularly adept at causing damage to the ecological fabric of this planet, even when we mean well — feed them poor little birdies in the winter, or the cute raccoons at night!

Getting back to our continent, where we have no information on population trends of forest birds at all — whether resident or migratory, in tropical South and South-East Asia or temperate Russia, Mongolia and Siberia — declines paralleling those on the other continents are very much on the cards, if, indeed, they haven't occurred already! Given the contempt that these migrants have for human geopolitical boundaries, their populations are subject to forces beyond the control of any one national conservation agency, let alone the manager of a single tiger reserve. If their populations are found to be declining as drastically as many New World migrants have over the past several decades, mammal chauvinists may be reduced to haplessly watching the habitats of their favourite creatures getting degraded.

Do you think even the tigers might get worried about such a scenario? Is it worth studying these warblers, trying to figure out what makes their populations tick, and how to save them and ensure they continue to keep all those insects down?

Are warblers less important than tigers? Isn't the question itself meaningless?

A VILLAGE OF STORKS

Gerard Busquet

At first glance the village of Jagyanagar, with its thatched mud huts and its tree-lined ponds, appears similar to countless other Bengali villages scattered across the fertile Gangetic plain. But a closer look reveals the difference — the unusual 'guests' which inhabit it during the summer months.

Before seeing them we can hear them. It is a distant hum which grows noticeably louder as we approach Jagyanagar along a narrow path winding through emerald green paddy fields. What appeared from a distance like huge flowering trees turn out at closer range to be old tamarinds, crowned with dozens of storks sitting atop big nests made out of twigs. All the trees lining the three ponds found in the village are inhabited by large colonies of openbill storks. Last autumn, the villagers counted as many as 8,000 storks — almost three times the human population of Jagyanagar which has only 3,000 inhabitants. Parents feed their young by regurgitating food into the hungry open gullets and are constantly taking off and landing with a heavy flapping of wings. The adult storks go to neighbouring or distant marshes and ponds to feed. They usually eat big snails (ampullaria), crabs, frogs and insects. The storks do not seem frightened by our movements, even when we stand close to their nests as they obviously feel quite secure in this village, where they have traditionally enjoyed a total immunity from human predators.

Jagyanagar embodies the age-old tradition of conservation of nature. In the 18th and 19th century, European travellers were greatly astonished to see wild animals like deer and blackbuck wandering fearlessly through Indian villages. Even at the end of the last century, the British ornithologist, T C Jerdon, mentioned innumerable colonies of storks, egrets and herons nesting in numerous villages of Bengal. However, with the extension of cultivation and the drying up of marshes all across Bengal, Jagyanagar remains today one of the last natural shelters of aquatic birds. Jagyanagar has a mixed population of Hindus, Muslims and tribals — mostly Santals and Baoris. All live peacefully side by side and share the same concern and attitudes towards their 'guests'.

A bearded villager rushes out of his mud hut to greet us and offer us tea. The air is vibrating with the constant chattering of the storks surrounding us. I ask Nasiruddin Ahmed, our host, if there are other villages sheltering storks. 'Yes, there are a few in neighbouring hamlets like Islampur, Khetiya and Usho but nothing on the same scale as here'. Two young girls, Shiuli and Meena, bring out two small storks which they have been looking after since they fell from their nests. Like other openbill storks, they have the distinctive greyish-white feathers streaked with black on the wings and tail and a long curved reddish-brown beak with an opening in the middle. A villager sets down a dish filled with big snails in front of the birds. With a few strokes they tear them apart and swallow the flesh greedily.

We call on the village headmaster. Abdul Halim, a man in his fifties, welcomes us and ushers us into his drawing room with an earthen floor. This room, although spartan, boasts an electric fan activated by a small generator — a real luxury in this village without electricity.

I express my admiration for his fellow villagers who have kept this age-old tradition of giving shelter to birds. He replies with a smile: 'They do it mainly out of affection. The birds bring more disturbance to the villagers than real benefits. Besides the constant noise and foul smell of their droppings, they also have to protect them against poachers. Sometimes they keep vigil at night near the trees where the storks live so as to prevent outsiders from killing them. They recently started a lawsuit against local farmers who had killed storks in our village. The only direct benefit they get from them is the guano they collect but it is hardly more that the contents of two bullock carts. Basically the farmers welcome the birds because they believe their lands would become unproductive if the storks stopped coming. So they will do everything in their power to keep them here and make them feel secure'.

Do the young have the same respect and affection for the birds as their elders? 'The children rescue the young storks which have fallen from their nest or have become orphaned. They will bring them up. If a boy from the village hurts or kills a bird, wilfully or accidentally, his parents will have to pay a fine of Rs50 or Rs60'.

What do the storks mean to the village? 'Our life and agricultural cycle are determined by the seasonal movement of the birds which form an integral part of our lives. They come during the month of *Asarh*, prior to the monsoon and leave

The village is surrounded by nesting storks

A boy rescues a fallen chick

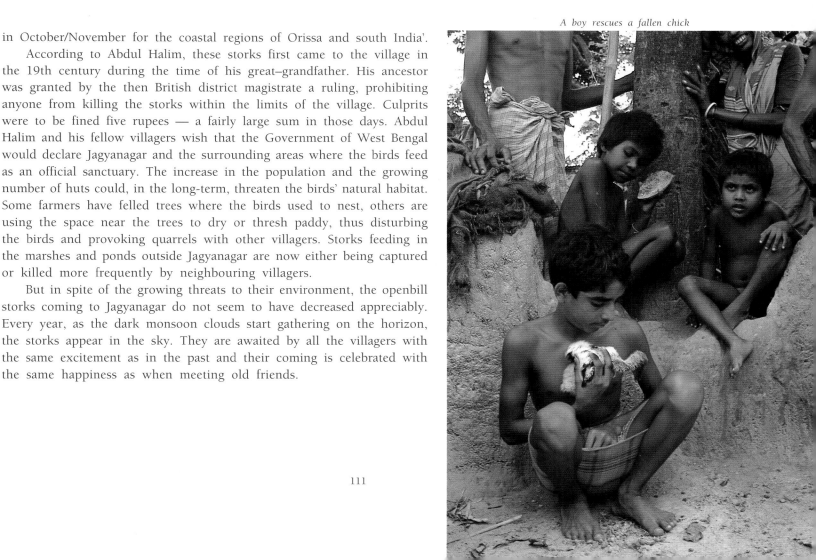

A boy rescues a fallen chick

in October/November for the coastal regions of Orissa and south India'.

According to Abdul Halim, these storks first came to the village in the 19th century during the time of his great–grandfather. His ancestor was granted by the then British district magistrate a ruling, prohibiting anyone from killing the storks within the limits of the village. Culprits were to be fined five rupees — a fairly large sum in those days. Abdul Halim and his fellow villagers wish that the Government of West Bengal would declare Jagyanagar and the surrounding areas where the birds feed as an official sanctuary. The increase in the population and the growing number of huts could, in the long-term, threaten the birds' natural habitat. Some farmers have felled trees where the birds used to nest, others are using the space near the trees to dry or thresh paddy, thus disturbing the birds and provoking quarrels with other villagers. Storks feeding in the marshes and ponds outside Jagyanagar are now either being captured or killed more frequently by neighbouring villagers.

But in spite of the growing threats to their environment, the openbill storks coming to Jagyanagar do not seem to have decreased appreciably. Every year, as the dark monsoon clouds start gathering on the horizon, the storks appear in the sky. They are awaited by all the villagers with the same excitement as in the past and their coming is celebrated with the same happiness as when meeting old friends.

111

FORESTS AND SETTLEMENTS

Romila Thapar

It is possible to trace through Indian history a changing attitude on the part of the Indian towards his forests. This change is reflected in the texts in Sanskrit, Prakrit, Tamil and other languages as well as in the oral tradition. There is gradually a self-consciousness and a distancing from the forest, especially in the culture of high literacy. The distancing takes the form of romanticising the forest at a time when some forests are being cleared and the forest people living there being forced to change their lifestyle. Often the oral tradition is more sympathetic to the forest.

The gradual clearing of forests over the centuries has changed the ecology of certain regions. The pace of change was not uniform. It was slower in earlier times and more limited in its geographical area, but as the demand for land increased, the clearing of the forests became faster and the area so cleared, larger. Seals from the Indus civilisation depict a variety of animals, of which the tiger, the rhinoceros and the elephant are the most frequent. These are all animals which require a reasonable forest cover and it is not surprising that with the present desiccation of the Indus plain, it no longer remains the habitat of these animals. It has been suggested that in the past there were forest galleries where these animals made a home but which have disappeared in the last couple of centuries. The climate and ecology of the region are being further investigated by archaeologists, some of whom maintain that the climate was wetter at that time. The historical study of the ecology of the Indus region and Gujarat is especially important because it is being argued that the decline of the Indus cities was substantially due to their inability to check the degradation of their environment.

Some categories of literature are very aware of ecological differences and their links to culture. Thus the *tinnai* concept of Tamil Shangam texts, composed around the start of the Christian era, is a fascinating example of a detailed and early perception of the significance of eco-zones. The landscape has been classified by five types of eco-zones and these in turn are co-related to other activities, and to cultural articulation. The zones are listed as the littoral, the wetlands, the pastoral tracts, the dry zone and the hilly backwoods. Occupations are said to differ in each of these. Fishing and the making of salt was important to the coastal area, the cultivation of rice in the wetlands, the breeding of livestock and practice of shifting cultivation in the pastoral tracts, which were subject to cattle-lifting from those who lived in the dry zone, and hunting and gathering was associated with those who lived in the backwoods. There are descriptions therefore of the way of life in each of these and their interactions. Wetlands, for example, were extremely limited as compared to the non-cultivated tracts, but over a period of time this changed. There was some interaction through the exchange of paddy and salt for other products, generally at places which remained constant and grew to become exchange centres. There have been some historical studies attempting to trace the process by which these micro eco-zones gradually evolved into macro-zones.

Early Sanskrit texts such as the Vedas make a distinction between what they call *grama* and *aranya*. These categories are generally seen as confrontational, but it is a confrontation which is sometimes used to highlight social perceptions. The *grama* is the settlement and is therefore orderly, disciplined, known, predictable and the location of what came to be called civilisation. It is the place where Vedic rituals can be performed. It is basic to agriculture, urban living, exchange, government, the arts and the culture of elite groups (often referred to as high culture these days). The *aranya* is the forest, disorderly, unknown, unpredictable and inhabited by predators and strange creatures, different from those living in the *grama*. This fantasy of associating the unknown with the dark depths of the forest is common to all societies which begin to view the forest from the settlement, as is evident from folk tales and children's stories. As the lifestyle of those who live in the settlement evolves into urban centres, the distancing from the people of the forest becomes greater. They are regarded as less civilised and because their social mores are different, they come to be treated as the backward peoples of society relegated to the lowest rungs of the social hierarchy.

This dichotomy between *grama* and *aranya* is generic to the narratives of the two epics, the *Mahabharata* and the *Ramayana*. The forest is the habitat of those who are sent into exile. But gradually the forest comes to be appropriated in the epics and there is to some degree an identifying with the forest. But this identity is kept distinct from that of the settlement. In

Orchha battlements with the forest in the background

Several thousand year old rock paintings in the Satpura

in which the social mores of the *grama* can be and are, transgressed. The explanations given for these transgressions are fascinating. One wonders for example, whether the marriage of Draupadi to the five Pandava brothers would have been feasible in a setting untouched by the fact of exile.

Among the more graphic descriptions of the deliberate destruction of the forest and forest life are incidents narrated in the *Mahabharata*. Dusyanta goes on a hunt, deep into the forest which brings him to the *ashrama* where he meets Shakuntala. The hunt is a campaign against nature. He is accompanied by a large band of warriors and they indiscriminately kill the animals. Herds of deer, families of tigers and elephants are mowed down and trees are devastated in this process. The people of the settlement are demonstrating their power over nature. Elsewhere in the epic we are told that when the Pandavas were given half the kingdom, they had to build their capital, Indraprastha. This required the clearing of the forest and in order to do this effectively the god Agni came into action and the forest was burnt. Descriptions of the burning of trees and of animals attempting to flee the flames provide a glimpse of the destruction of the forest prior to establishing a settlement. The *grama* is again projected as triumphant, irrespective of what may have been involved in the building of the new city.

Exiles from the *grama* are different from the people of the forest, because for the former the forest remains a wild habitat which has to be tamed, whereas for the latter the forest is the natural habitat. Forest people are said to live on gathering roots and fruit and on hunting wild animals and this is a different culture from the cultivators and traders who constitute the settled society. The life of the forest people is seen as antithetical to the evolution of civilisation if civilisation is defined as the activities of the settled society.

But the concession to the forest was made in various ways. The most obvious is the continuing worship of trees. This was in the form of either the veneration of particular trees, such as *Ficus religiosa*, which has perhaps the longest continuity of a sacred tree in India. It occurs on the seals from the Indus civilisation, it is associated with Buddhism and is depicted in the sculpture from Buddhist places of worship and it continues to be venerated in association with religious shrines of Hindus and Muslims.

Texts associated with Buddhism and Jainism refer to sacred groves, some maintained by the people of a city, others by a monastery and still others by the wider community who lived on the edge of the forest. Thus the cities of Vaisali, Kushinara and Champa, all maintained sacred groves. The importance of the forest had not disappeared as yet. The groves may even have been specially planted as they are often described as being of specific kinds of trees, such as the *banyan* or the *sala*. Individual trees under worship, sometimes referred to as a *chaitya* or a sacred enclosure, were cordoned off in various ways. The tree had platforms around it for offerings and the placing of ritual pitchers, the area being enclosed by a railing with doorways. The railings appear to have been decorated with sculpted reliefs. Sometimes the individual tree was located in the midst of a sacred grove. A platform, believed to be of Mauryan times, was excavated near the Bo-tree at Bodh Gaya, constructed of brick and stone and decorated with sculpted human and animal forms.

The worship of trees as part of a fertility cult has remained a constant feature of the religion of pastoralists, peasants and those of lesser status among urbanites; an undercurrent which from time to time enters and suffuses even the more sophisticated expression of belief and practice. The frequency of sacred groves, some enchanted and magical and some inhabited by deities, is a common theme in Indian narratives. The tree was and is, personified as a deity and some trees are sacred in their association with deity. The spirit of the tree mingled with the spirit of the cults of water and mountains as well as those of animals — the *naga* and the tiger, for instance. These were not just mystical manifestations, but represented a sense of integration with the world of plant and animal life, where the sensitivity of the human merged awe with affection, very different from what has eventually become the insistence on dominating nature.

Ritual vessels used in the Vedic sacrifices had specific functions and were only to be made of specific kinds of wood, which suggests a symbolism regarding trees and wood which was far more complex than in many other societies. The incorporation of the people of the forest into the society of the settlement required the accommodation of the deities of each to the other, in a process of acculturation. Of those that perform their rituals diligently, very few realise that there is much of the forest embedded in their rituals.

Pastoral groups form a kind of grey area, since they are people who live in the settled society but graze their animals in the forest. They are familiar with only the edge of the forest. But the fact that they have been so important to Indian culture means that the forest was not seen as altogether hostile or distant. The cycle of Krishna legends draw from both the pastoral and the more gentle forest associated with the grazing of cattle.

Not surprisingly when a person decided to opt out of the *grama* he became an ascetic and went to live in the forest which represented the opposite pole from the *grama*. For him the forest was not alien but was an avenue to the discarding of the mantle of civilisation and the discovery of the self. Buddhist monks who were renouncers from society lived either near the *grama* from where they got alms, or the more respected ones lived in the forest away from civilisation. The forest also curiously becomes the location for the salvaging of the highest ethical qualities which are associated with the settlement. The Chinese Buddhist pilgrim, Fa-hien, who visited India in the fifth century AD, tells us that one of the current beliefs concerned the future of the Buddha's teachings. He relates that when these teachings will decline, which they will because of the increase of evil in the world, then those who are still virtuous will flee into the forest. They will live there until the coming of the Buddha Maitreya — the future Buddha — who will restore the world to virtue and those who had escaped to the forest will return once more to live in the settlement.

The closeness of man to the forest through asceticism is also demonstrated in the idyllic picture which is often constructed of life in an *ashrama* in a forest. For example, the setting of the play on Shakuntala by Kalidasa emphasises the dichotomy. The forest hermitage is a place of gentleness, peace and closeness to nature, where even the plants and the deer reach out to Shakuntala. This is contrasted with the court in the capital and its hostility and violence. The romanticisation of the forest is subsequent to its being the habitat of exiles and renouncers and reflects less a fear of the forest and more a familiarity with it. It could be argued that the romanticisation of the forest begins when it is thought that Culture is superseding Nature. The forest of epic literature is a different kind of forest and has quite another place in the imagination from the forest of Kalidasa.

Perhaps this image was exaggerated and the forest treated as a kind of imagined alternative, a fictive paradise, when the complexities of civilised life became overwhelming. The symbolism of *grama* and *aranya* are marked in early Indian culture and possibly this enabled the two categories to live co-existentially for many centuries, where the characteristics of the one did not impinge on the other. There was also in earlier times, enough forest available for it to remain a distant habitat. But today, the attempt that is being made is to insist that the *grama* subordinate the *aranya* to its needs — hence the exploitation of the forests.

The importance of forest wealth is recognised in the *Arthashastra* of Kautilya who states that no one is permitted to cut any part of the forest without the permission of the state. This was to ensure a control over revenue both from the produce of the forest and from the land cleared and brought under cultivation. Kautilya is also very precise in describing how the state should clear wasteland and settle families of agriculturalists on it as part of the process of extending agriculture and enhancing revenue. Emperor Asoka took pride in the roads which were constructed by his administration and these he states were lined with shade-giving trees and with wells. The building of *baolis* at intervals along the major roads characterises road construction at many points in history. These were mainly small structures with wells, often set in a garden. The more elaborate ones elsewhere were virtually underground places and a thick growth of trees in the vicinity added to keeping the place cool.

Sometime after the fourth century AD when agriculture was extended, both to bring in greater revenue and perhaps to support a larger population, there appears to have been a greater encroachment on the forests. There are references to violence against forest tribes in a Gupta period inscription and the need to subordinate the dwellers of the forest in inscriptions of a slightly later period — and inscriptions in those days were the official statements. Forest dwellers were brought under control, their forest resources — timber,

Memories of man, a sati stone in Panna

mines, gem-stones — appropriated, and they were then converted into the lower castes of the area and established on the edges of towns or in separate settlements in the forest. This was a process of marginalising those who lived and worked with the produce of the forest.

The clearing of wastelands which was substantially jungle and converting it to cultivated land, was necessary to the creation of the many small states which emerged at the time, dependent on agriculture for revenue, and which continued gradually to increase in number. Shifting cultivation lets the forest reclaim what is cleared. Settled cultivation means losing the forest altogether and it was revenue from the settled cultivation that maintained the new states. The expansion of trade and the opening up of new areas to commercial exchange also resulted in routes cutting through forests and the conversion of some forest settlements into markets. The establishing of monasteries and *ashramas* in the forest meant clearing the forest, and unless they were maintained as inaccessible to the rest of society (which was rare), there was gradually a building up of settlements around these institutions, particularly where they became the nucleus of a new settlement which worked to support the monastery or the *ashrama*. Religious interests, therefore, also sometimes coincided with economic interests in converting the forest into a settlement.

Significantly, the forest people play a central role in the origin myths of many dynasties in every part of the subcontinent and this role cannot be ignored. Most dynasties were of humble or obscure origin and their mythologies in which they legitimised their coming to power provide clues to this origin. Yet there are some Brahmanical myths with a clear contempt for the forest dweller. One of the most powerful myths is that of the first ruler, Prithu. The original king, Vena, turned against the Brahmans and therefore, the Brahmans killed him. In the absence of a king there was the threat of chaos and disorder. Therefore, the Brahmans churned the left thigh of the body of Vena and out of it sprang a short, dark man, whom they banished to the forest and called him Nishada — which became the generic name for the forest people. They then churned the right arm of Vena and from it sprang a tall, fair, handsome man whom they made the king and who was responsible for introducing cattle-keeping and agriculture. So pleased was the earth with him that she bestowed her own name on him and he was called Prithu.

Has there always been in Indian culture a contempt for the forest dweller? It was one thing to set up an *ashrama* in the forest but it was another to mingle with the forest people. The latter were looked upon as beyond the social pale, in spite of the romanticising of life in the *ashrama*. Even to this day they are described as 'backward' and needing to be 'assimilated' into the mainstream of Hindu society. Even benign official policy gets vitiated by such attitudes. Yet it is the people of the forest who are closest to the forest and more in harmony with it than the others. Their knowledge of the forest is different from that of the officials who are supposed to be their benefactors or that of the environmentalists who are concerned about the forest and its people. The people living in the forests were in the past subordinated, but as yet, the forests were not destroyed. The pressure on the land was less since the pressure of population was not so great. Today, the problem is that not only are there few forest people left, for most are being brought into the net of 'modernisation', but the forests themselves are being destroyed.

Another dichotomy lies in the terms *Prakriti*, that which is natural, and *Sanskriti*, that which is created by man, self-consciously cultured and to that degree, artificial. This becomes apparent in all activities where things naturally existing are differentiated from those which are artificially created. Here the forest would be the natural unit and the settlement, the created one. Gradually over time, it is the latter, *Sanskriti*, which comes to be equated with civilisation. This dichotomy continues into later literatures in other languages of India, such as the regional languages, Turkish and Persian. The forest is the retreat of recluses and holy men and even the princes of the royal court have to go there to meet them — as many Mughal miniatures depict. This is again a form of turning away from the settlement.

The old ambiguity of using the forest for royal hunts also continues. The dichotomy of Nature and Culture is interestingly reflected in the activity of hunting. Those who live by hunting are treated as uncouth, looked down upon and subordinated to outcaste status. Yet princes and kings frequently go on hunts, which are meant to be a sport but which can sometimes be described as a ferocious destruction of nature and animals. These activities do not affect the high status of royalty, even when they behave in a manner far more gruesome than the actions of professional hunters.

The earlier suspicion of the forest and contempt for the people of the forest was reinforced by colonial rule, when forests became an area to be exploited for their wealth — particularly timber — and the people were dismissed as backward and primitive in the worst 19th century sense of the word. Some were seen as wild tribes and some even as criminal tribes where their moral codes were different from those of the colonisers. The somewhat more ameliorating position of romanticising the forest or treating it as the habitat of the renouncer, which softened the hostility to the forest, was no longer encouraged in colonial attitudes to the forest. The philosophy of colonialism was based on man's necessity to control nature at all costs, even if it meant destroying the forest. Hunting became a sport open to all and the target was the biggest and the best of the species. With the extensive availability of firearms, the sporting element of the hunt was changed to a carnage of animals.

A quantitative change came about with the colonial decision to build railway lines. This has been seen as one of the most destructive acts in the clearing of forests. Routes had to be cut through all kinds of terrain and if there were forests

The Ken River in Panna Tiger Reserve

on the way, they were destroyed. The routes were originally located to serve the economic demands of carrying resources to the markets and the ports, to enhance the growth of industrialisation. Inevitably the introduction of the railway had other results. Access to new lands through rail communication led to migrations and new settlements. These were not limited to land along the rail tracks but often took settlers into the interior of forests where land was cleared for cultivation. Railways brought communities closer together but they were also responsible for changing the environmental conditions in many areas. The building of an extensive canal network in the 19th century had much the same effect, for large tracts of jungle had to be cleared for canals to pass through and canal colonies to be established. What started as an attempt to improve and increase agriculture through providing irrigation facilities, is now seen in many areas as terminating agriculture because of the ensuing salination of the soil.

In looking critically at these changes, the intention is not to suggest that all technical innovation has to be brushed aside. But now that there is a greater awareness of the crucial role of environmental conditions, innovations have to be examined more carefully to assess the alterations that they will introduce in the interaction of man, nature and culture. The change is not even restricted to the environment, for, attitudes of mind change as do attitudes to other human beings. If a technological innovation in an area is imperative, then the first concern should be that the least damage be done to those who live there and their environment. The point of having the capacity to plan and to project the effect of a plan, is to ensure the minimum devastation. But it is this which we have moved away from in the claim that development is ultimately all to the good.

The colonial interlude has taken us even further away from what might have been a holistic understanding of Nature and Culture. The pressure of population in the past has been encroachments into forest lands but the forests were plentiful enough to meet this pressure. Now this is coupled with the ruthless middle class determination to wrench the maximum revenue out of the forest. In the formidable alliance of the politician, the contractor, the bureaucrat and the industrialist, there is little hope for the forest and the people of the forest, for they are not permitted even to denounce, let alone stop, the desecration. We are all now silent witnesses to the holocaust of the forest in India.

MAN AND ANIMAL IN INDIA

Paola Manfredi

Sacred cows wandering undisturbed through the busy streets of the Indian metropolis; Ganesha, the god with an elephant head; the Naga whose hood protects Vishnu lying asleep amidst its coils; Jain devotees offering food to ants and to the other insects in the early hours of the day; images of Durga riding the tiger or the lion; monkeys somersaulting around temples or on the roofs of houses; animal hospitals or temples where rats are fed and protected; blackbucks who are allowed by the Bishnois to feed on crops if they want to... wherever one turns in India, the presence of animals, real or mythical, is everywhere.

Images of animals pervade Indian myth, art, literature and religion. Attitudes towards animals can bear very definite social implications and sanctions: the killing of a spider or a snake will be regarded with reprobation, as well as the eating of meat which will generally qualify a person, one way or another.

It would be only natural to think of India as a Garden of Eden, as a place where humans and animals peacefully coexist within the same space, be it urban, rural or even within the forest. Instead the reality is that the niches in which animals are safe are shrinking everyday and with the same accelerated speed everything is changing in today's race to **modernise** India.

Soon many of the species that have been so important for the development of India's diverse cultures will find no place to live and will disappear forever.

The special place occupied by animals in Indian art, culture, religion and society have amazed foreign travellers to India since Greek and Roman times. Such a special relationship with animals has contributed to the propagation across the world of the most marvellous, incredible and fantastic stories about India, its people and its animal species. 'It is said that in India, in one valley called Iordia, certain kind of snakes are born, and the most precious stones grow around their necks ...' [Liber Monstruorum] ...*

The belief, in Western medieval culture, that the Garden of Eden was 'in India or just beyond it...' had something to do with tales carried for centuries about the peaceful coexistence in India between humans and animals.

The old travellers' accounts can sometimes be very imaginative and truly fantastic. Yet in describing the peculiarities and uniqueness of the interactions between people and animals in the old days in India, they suggested the extent to which Indian people were perceived as having developed unique ways to understand a 'language' of nature and to interact with the animal species, some of which have survived to this day with amazing similarities.

Marco Polo, travelling in India in the 13th century, talks about 'fish charmers'. There were said to be people in south India who specialised in accompanying the pearl fishermen on the boats. Their job was to charm the dangerous fish so that they would do no harm to the fishermen who could, therefore, safely plunge into the deep sea to collect the pearls. However, incredible this practice may be, we have all seen so called snake-charmers on the roads of India or at local fairs and festivals where they exhibit snakes. Snake-charmers are tribals, some of them simply buy snakes from tribal snake-catchers, others also catch them. To do this they obviously require a remarkable knowledge of natural history : 'they [the Irulas/snake-catcher from Andhra Pradesh and Tamil Nadu] identify the species from tracks, droppings and shed skins, trace it to its burrow and dig it out with uncanny precision.' [R.Whitaker: 85]

Marco Polo also gives an interesting description — whose accuracy or truthfulness I leave for others to judge — of a very ingenious method to collect diamonds. On the *Multiphili* plateau, in remote and steep valleys, there were diamonds in great quantity, unfortunately along with poisonous and ferocious snakes. The local people, from the top of the ravines, would then throw chunks of meat on the diamonds below, so that the diamonds would get studded in them. White eagles, living in these regions, drawn by the smell of flesh, would fly deep into the ravines, catch the meat along with the diamonds and take it to the top of the ravines to eat it. The people could thus safely collect the diamonds by scaring the eagles away.

Marco Polo, as any other traveller in India throughout the ages, was equally amazed by the fact that nobody in India would dare kill a cow and eat its meat.

*To which legend, the Irula snake-catcher replies, 'If it was so we would be rajas, not snake-catachers'.

A tribal chief in Nagaland on an elephant skull throne

In much more recent times, in the 19th century, when the inventories of the natural resources of the world were being drawn, various Western naturalists and travellers in India were reporting the incredible difficulties they encountered in collecting animals' specimens since Indians objected to the killing of animals.

'The banks of the ravines are full of cavities which afford safe retreats to a number of wolves. The inhabitants have however, a superstitious prejudice against killing wolves. They believe that wherever the blood of the wolf is shed, several other wolves of a peculiarly fierce quality will be produced from it, and will make it their special business to avenge the slaughtered wolf by preying on the aggressor or his family. Many children and some women are carried off every year from Futtehghur by the wolves, which come after dark into the very houses; and the people are always satisfied that some individual of the family, in which the calamity occurs, must have provoked their vengeance by killing a wolf somewhere. I had orders given to my *shikaree* (keeper) to shoot a wolf for me, as I wanted to see if there were any difference between it and the wolf of Europe. He answered that if he could get a shot at a wolf while it was passing a piece of water he would certainly try to kill one for me, but that he did not dare to attempt it where the blood would fall on land'. [M.Hastings:1858:41-42]

India is a vast country where all kinds of ecosystems are present and where different racial groups, religions, cultures, languages and social organisations have developed and coexisted for millennia. It is obvious that within this context the spectrum of attitudes towards wildlife is as wide ranging and diverse as are the different groups that live in India. Yet, despite such extreme differences, as those existing between tribals hunters or meat eaters living in the forests of central India and some south Indian strictly orthodox vegetarian Brahmans, the respect towards the life of an animal was a value absorbed since childhood throughout Indian communities.

'No boy in India has the slightest wish to molest birds in their nests; it enters not into their pastimes, and they have no feeling of pride or pleasure in it. With us [European] it is different — to discover birds' nests is one of the first modes in which a boy exercises his powers...The same feeling of desire to display their skill and enterprise in search after birds' nests in early life renders the youth of England the enemy almost of the whole animal creation throughout their after career [...].

'Among the people of India it is very different. Children do not learn to exercise their powers either in discovering and robbing the nests of birds, or in knocking them down with stones and staves; and, as they grow up, they hardly ever think of hunting or shooting for mere amusement. It is with them a matter of business; the animal they cannot eat they seldom think of molesting'. [Heber:218]

It is interesting also to note how no animal species was perceived as intrinsically dangerous or harmful, even the tiger: 'He is not fierce, but very civil when he is not provoked or very hungry; he then meddles with nobody'. [Sherwood:1910:270]

'The mountaineers, it is said, formerly used to think that they had entered into a treaty with them [the tigers] and in consequence, they never killed any of those beast unless there had been any infraction of the treaty on the part of the tiger themselves, manifested by an injurious act, such as the destruction of an individual; on an occasion of this kind the villagers were wont to arise in a body and to hunt the enemy, until the full price of the mischief had, as they calculated, been paid by the death of one or more of the savage beasts, after which the tigers were supposed to have got their lesson, the treaty was put in force again, and every one returned to his hut under a comfortable sense of present security. The English, however, have turned the tide greatly against the tigers within the last few years by promising a reward of ten rupees for every tiger's head brought to a collector, and it is wonderful how many are now killed'. [Sleeman:1915:117]

It is a fact that under British rule totally alien attitudes towards nature and wild animals were introduced into India : nature and wildlife became, according to the circumstances, a commodity, a sport for enjoyment, a subject of study, a pest, etc..., and natural resources were at their disposal for unlimited exploitation and use.

When I had thought, in the context of this project, to look at today's interactions between human communities and wild animals, I did not anticipate the extent to which information would be scarce, scattered and difficult to find. It is a topic that does not appear to have stimulated much focused attention, therefore the information is more often than not found in the form of casual or passing remarks or as a picturesque anecdote, more or less pervaded with superstition or religious zeal.

Yet to explore the world of perceptions and attitudes towards wild animals by the different tribal and rural communities would be an extremely interesting approach to the study of both the species themselves as well as the communities, their traditional knowledge and their relationship to the environment. This would not just be an academic exercise. Its relevance is actually far reaching and its implications stretch in many different directions. All this would certainly be an essential prerequisite to any conservation effort.

A recurring feature that emerges from various data collected is how people have been able to take advantage of some aspect of the animal species that share the same habitat, thus looking at them more like allies and partners than enemies and competitors. Obviously this implies a deep knowledge and understanding of the ecosystem, its cycles, and of what keeps it in balance.

Strikingly in contrast with the commonly accepted image of the big carnivores as ferocious beasts and pests, even today the tribal communities in India perceive them as quite friendly towards humans. One of the reasons, according to their perception, is that the carnivores help in providing food. This happens among the Konds who would take the kill that the tiger has left

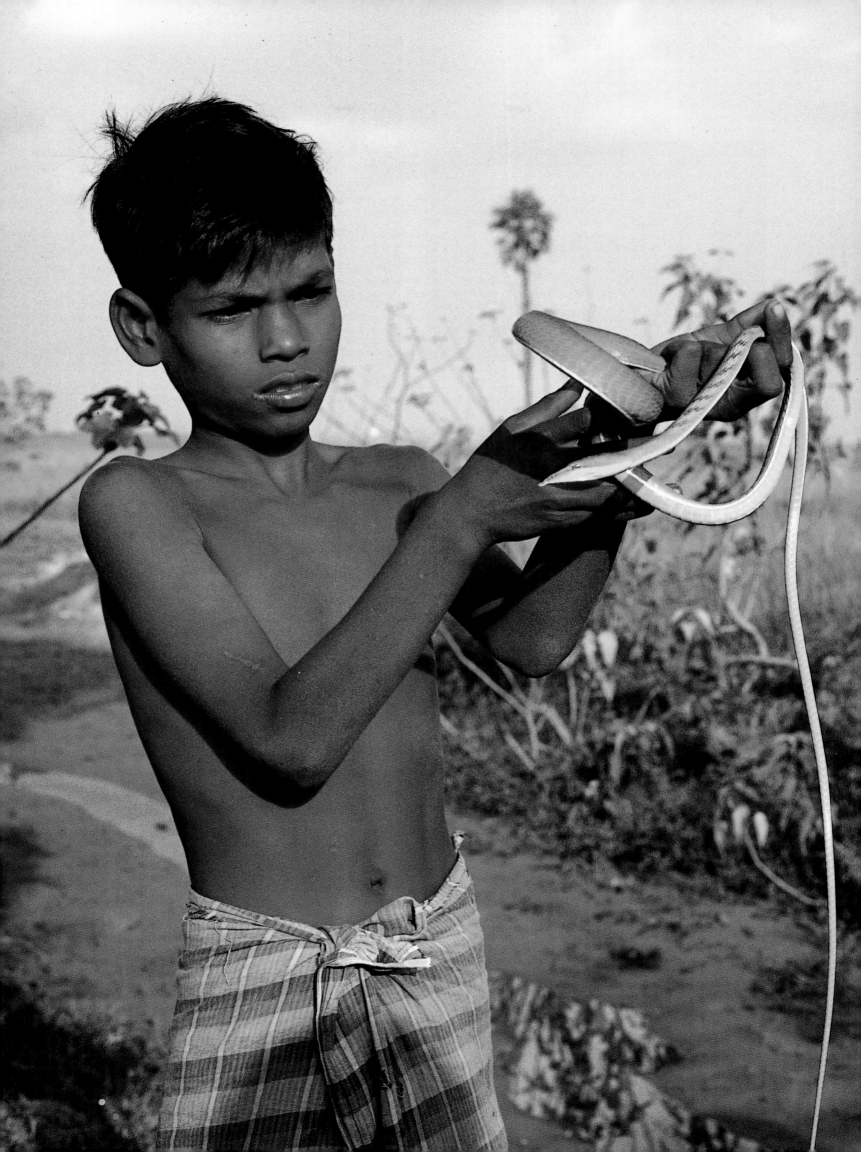

Propitiating the spirit of the tiger

unfinished. Similarly, among Ladakhi communities, who, being Buddhist, do not kill animals, but they do not mind eating the meat when it is the snow leopard who has acted as the butcher, even when the victim is one of their own goat or sheep. Similar situations occur with the kills of the dhole or wild dogs in other parts of the country.

The big carnivores are also often perceived as essential to keep ungulates and herbivores away from the ripening crops, thus protecting their fields.

The Warlis have even made the tiger into a god. Pug marks in the soil will be given offerings of coconut and will be smeared with red lead powder, so that the harvest will be abundant. This does not mean that nobody is scared of tigers, or that tigers are regarded as some sort of glorified pets!

The perception of the **sacredness** of the tiger which can be easily dismissed as 'blind faith' or superstition, actually holds many interesting elements and concepts that it would be worth exploring further! The sacred is, by definition, intrinsically ambivalent, it inspires fear as much as a sense of security. The deity — presiding over the order of the beings and of the 'things' — provides a rationale for the way 'things' are in this world. It prescribes, therefore, to the human being how to deal with the things of the world, so that the order and the cycle of life can continue.

The perception of the tiger as a god, as an incredibly powerful being that can, under certain given circumstances, become fearful and dangerous, but that in itself it is not an unpredictable roaming monster, has certainly induced, beside rituals, very practical attitudes and behaviours as well. A sort of 'directions for use', unconsciously absorbed since childhood, which must have made the coexistence of man and tiger safe enough. This can only be possible through a deep knowledge of the natural history of the species, yet there was no harm in a little sacrifice to the deities to avoid any encounter to make life even safer, like among the Nagas.

The perception of the tiger as the protector is widely represented in the traditional iconographies throughout the area where the tiger roamed, and it is certainly significant that the tiger is depicted more often than not peacefully merging with man, be it with a saint in the forest, be it in the paintings of the Warlis or in popular images of the heroes of the Shan tribes of Myanmar.

The rationale about man-eating tigers has again amazingly common features among the tribal communities across the entire tiger-range countries, from India to South-East Asia. Even in Siberia the tiger is called Amba, much the same way as it is in India. Such common features mainly concern the belief that a tiger would only attack a man if possessed or ridden by supernatural powers, destructive spirits or malicious human enemies, and that the human soul will be transferred into a tiger when the person is attacked and killed by a tiger, becoming, for example, as the Konds believe, a *bagoleenju* [female *bogoleeri*]. The event being of an extremely serious nature, it requires elaborate and powerful rituals of purification.

Hunters in the last century often mentioned how local people hired for hunting expeditions would make offerings and would ask forgiveness from the spirit of the tiger whenever one was killed. This again has been recorded not only in India but in distant Vietnam as well.

Some populations in West Sumatra, instead, think that a tiger inhabited by a human soul is a friend of the people, and that it accompanies them in their trips into the forest protecting them from danger and helping them to overcome difficulties!

In Gir, Gujarat, the last population of Asiatic lions has managed to survive basically because the Maldharis, in the past, 'had learned to live peaceably with the great cats and were even sometimes beholden to them for the protection they afforded the simple herdsmen from roving bands of trespassers and wood-poachers'. 'Because he [the lion] has learnt to know that man seldom has evil intentions towards him, he has become used to the presence of human habitations. The lion of Kathiawar, unlike some African lions, does not look on man as his enemy, except when he is hunted with the gun, and therefore one does not (nowdays) meet with man-eating lions. Moreover, decrepit lions and lionesses seem to die a natural death in solitude when their powers of hunting fail rather than attack man towards whom they have a natural fear', K S Dharmakumarsinhji wrote in 1955.

Throughout the world, science and its approach and methodologies have become, in the last 150 years, the only accepted way 'to know' the natural world around us. Every other approach has been dismissed as unscientific or as a childish superstition. Unfortunately, in the process, an incredible amount of information has been lost. Many of the so-called superstitions contain elements of knowledge that are perfectly compatible with science.

Among the Naga : 'The Ao group, for example, believe that in ancient times both man and monkey were covered with hair and that man has been able to shed them after having stolen the fire from the monkey. As far as the Konyaks are concerned, they perceive the monkey as an inferior clan of humans. Monkey skulls were decorated with the same ornaments of human skulls or of their representations. Thus they often have eyes made of glass beads, seeds, fragments of metals or mirror. They have been decorated with tattoos, wigs and earrings made of red goat hair like the ones that warriors wear and that sometimes are put on the cut heads ... The British, in their endeavour to suppress head-hunting among the hill tribes, used this belief to shift the attention on the monkey skulls and the rituals normally revolving around human heads. But the unsatisfactory results proved that monkey heads emanated an energy that was too weak for the earth and the villages to benefit from it. Even if monkey skulls could be symbols of human heads, yet they could not fully replace them'. [Vigorelli:1992]

In northwestern India people believe that the krait, the dangerous snake, sucks a man's breath away while he is asleep. It is a fact that the krait's bite provokes a paralysis of the lungs.

A myriad languages of nature — each one appropriate to its own area — with which the local communities were familiar have now to be rediscovered, if we want the last remaining patches of forest to be saved and some of the pressure on them relieved. In the area around Ranthambhore National Park, in Rajasthan, the villagers express weariness towards the introduction of agro-forestry techniques because they fear that the trees planted amidst the cultivated fields will attract birds which will destroy the crops.

Among the Warlis in Maharashtra, on the contrary, the pests of crops are controlled by 'planting' branches of trees in the paddy fields for birds to perch on, however, 'since they use those of certain tree species only, it is possible that these also possess some pesticidal action'. [Pereira:1992]

Similar attitudes of looking at animal species as allies to control pests is found in Tamil Nadu, where the name of *dhanasu*, 'one who produces wealth', is given by the farmers to the drongo which, perched on the backs of draft animals, swallows insects flushed by their hoofs, that might otherwise have destroyed the crop.

Some traditional farmers believe that 'drongos, hovering over rice-fields, indicate the presence of caseworm pests. According to studies conducted by the Farmers' Training Centre, Lalgudi, Tamil Nadu, these birds are the first to detect the pest and devour the caseworm's larvae as they wriggle out of the eggs'. [Rangaswami:1993:122]

The ability to fly has given birds all over the world a very special place in the cultures and the hearts of the people. Because of this, birds have been generally thought as being in touch with the gods, and in India many species are considered sacred to specific deities. For this also the birds are often looked upon as messengers of the gods, as foretellers of the future, as harbingers of auspicious or inauspicious happenings.

The **peacock** — the vehicle of Kartikeya, god of war, and of Saraswati, goddess of learning — is venarated in India because it is said that it has the ability of scenting the coming rain, and to scream and dance with delight as the rains draw closer.

The **roller**, also called the blue jay in India, is sacred to Vishnu, who once assumed its form. It is caught only to be liberated at the Hindu festival of Dussehra in western India and at Durga Puja in Bengal.

The **pied–crested cuckoo** *Clamator jacobinus* is a migrant species and it appears to move north with the advancing monsoon. Bombayites consider the bird a harbinger of the monsoon, as it times its arrival there within almost 48 hours of the rains. [Rangaswami:1993:104]

The eerie looks of the **barn owl** *Tyto alba*, its ghost-like flight and loud screams and screeches have given rise to the superstitious belief that it is a bird of ill-omen. Its name — bad bird — in several Indian languages, overlooks the role it has as an effective controller of rodents.' [Rangaswami:1993:108]

The **Brahminy kite** is sacred to Vishnu. Within the Islamic tradition the Brahminy kite used to be called 'blessed spirit', because victory was presaged to the army over which it hovered.

In popular belief the kite is considered a notorious thief; 'no other creature is so splendidly equipped for larceny, for no other can snatch so unerringly and escape so securely. The confectioner's tray of sweetmeats, the dishes on their way from kitchen to mess or dining-room, the butcher shop, and the kitchen itself are well liable to his sudden swoop'. [Kipling:1891:40]

Popular beliefs, religious feelings, sacred symbols but also a good sense of humour when one would use the expression 'The saintly heron' or 'saintly as a heron'. 'A heron poised on one leg in a remote corner of a pool is

A traditional Andamanese hunter

the very image of a Hindu Sadhu or Muhammadan faqir, pretending to be absorbed in holy meditation, while all the time he is intent on the next fish or frog that may come within reach...the phrase is common for there is as much of the hypocritical "meditation of the Heron" in India as elsewhere...'[ibid.]

In places as far away from each other as West Bengal and Tamil Nadu there are still villages which enforce a very strict protection towards migratory birds species such as storks, pelicans, etc, though in the past they were many more examples scattered across the entire country. In Koondakulam, Tamil Nadu, birds are treated as important guests whose arrival every year has almost a religious significance. They spell good harvests and prosperity for the village. Everyone in the village, therefore, has to ensure the well-being of the birds which nest in thousands on tops of the trees within and around the village, where few water tanks and depressions ensure the presence of water and aquatic life that the birds need for their survival. The birds supply freely to the villagers tons of guano, part of this get dissolved in the tanks which supply the water for the irrigation of the fields certainly contributing to the abundant harvests. 'The tradition of giving stringent protection to birds has therefore, despite all its religious overtones, a powerful material basis. The villagers protect the birds and the birds in turn make them prosperous. It is this mutual dependence, this almost symbiotic relationship which exists here between man and bird which makes a village heronry like Koondakulam significant from the point of view of conservation'. [S V Kumar:1994:40]

Yet the balance is as usual precarious and can be easily upset as it happened in Aredu, near Kolleru, A P. 'The pelicanry at Aredu was the largest in India. There too the villagers and the birds had been living amicably for centuries. But with the coming of modernity and education, the newer generation of that village apparently learnt to scoff at the silly superstitions of their fathers. They discovered too that there is a good market in the bars and restaurants of nearby towns for "duck meat". In no time the birds and their fledgings were decimated in exchange of cash'.[ibid.]

We found records of how the cycle of the agricultural activities among many traditional communities outside India, eastward as well as westward, was often regulated by the migratory rhythms of different species of birds, with birds playing the role of a sort of yearly cosmic clock. We have not come across any such record in India, yet this widespread practice may induce us to think that deeper and more focused research could reveal different results also among tribal and rural communities.

The sentiment of the sanctity of nature along with the religious feelings is still very deeply rooted in traditional India. Let us never forget that thanks to 'dreaded superstitions', 'blind faith' or animism, the last remaining patches of pristine habitat with their wild inhabitants have survived into today's world. There are few remnants of this today throughout India.

In Kerala, the southwest corner of the gardens are allowed to grow as a natural and wild jungle, the place is dedicated to the snakes, and every tree and bush, every branch and twig is sacred.

Every village used to have a sacred grove in which it enforced total protection of the flora and fauna. There are number of records according to which local communities have fought against governments, rulers and other powerful lobbies to protect their sacred groves as both the symbol and the material basis of their cultural identity.

'The significance of the concept of the sacred grove within each village boundary is two-fold : it speaks of the value system of the tribals who are very close to nature and whose very survival is dependent upon the natural resources around them. Even the uninitiated youngster in a village, is thus taught to respect nature from the very beginning through the sacred groves. Though through superstitious beliefs, the sacred groves have been an effective method for preserving patches of virgin forests, easily accessible to the entire village'. [Gadgil:1992]

Because of their pristine status, the sacred groves have been and still are the big nature book from which any young would learn the essentials of the language of nature and of the traditional knowledge of the community.

The language of nature is sometimes very subtle like a whisper, like the buzz of the honey-bee. The honey-bee is the most reliable indicator of the availability of honey, which is a food as well as a remedy, and it is also an indicator of the health of the forest, since when the vegetation deteriorates, the honey-bee cannot not survive.

'According to the Hill Kharias, there are several honey reservoirs in Simlipal. These are called mahu bhandars. They are spread evenly, cutting across the core, buffer and the periphery areas. Traditionally, each of these reservoirs has been taken care of by Kharia families who collect honey from these bhandars. They point out that only a decade ago, Simlipal was famous for the quantity and variety of honey. Lamenting the loss of honey, an elder said, "these days honey-bees live in the city" [...]

'It is in the nature of things in a forest to ensure the fitness of all as far as possible, and to ensure the production of honey. In this perception the tiger has an important role to play — it protects the forests from intruders who disrupt the production of nectar, aromas and honey. The interdependence of living beings in any ecosystem is such that no one species is dispensable. Thus, it may be stated that a forest rich in honey production must correspondingly be rich in plant diversity. The Kharias maintain that the absence of a honey-bee can affect plant diversity in a forest as well'. [Savyasaachi:1994;33]

The language of nature can also be as unassuming as the small mounds of wet mud that the land crabs excavate and leave around their holes. Warlis locate underground water by searching for them. 'The larger the number of crab holes at a given spot, the greater the availability of water. It is as simple as that; no incantations or mantras, no divining rods or forked twigs, not even magnetic needles or resistivity measurements'. [Pereira:1992:199]

Huli Vesha, the traditional tiger dance performed at Dussehra in Dakshina, Kannada

THE END OF A CENTURY

Bittu Sahgal

Indians have an innate reverence for life. This is one prime reason that a land so densely populated by humans is still able to support such a vast diversity of wild animals. In recent times, however, this live-and-let-live relationship is showing signs of cracking. One reason for this unfortunate development is the fact that forest and wildlife conservation laws passed in recent years have served to alienate local communities by impinging on their traditional rights. Not only has this distanced forest communities, but it has also created a schism between social activists and wildlifers. Yet, ironically, the only place where forest cultures are still relatively safe is in our sanctuaries and parks.

In the shimmering heat of May, I saw two young girls dig a shallow pit in the sandy bed of the Indravati, just away from the waterline of the incredibly blue, slow flowing river. Purposeful, yet patient, the girls sat back under the shade of an overhanging bough till seepage filled their pit. Using a ladle fashioned from an old coconut shell and a bamboo shaft, they scooped the water out and waited for their pit to fill again. Meanwhile they bathed, laughed and seemed so at peace with their surrounds that I was left with little doubt as to my own alien status. When they used the ladles again, they deposited the sparkling water into six gourd containers. Thus laden, they walked back into the thick canopy of the moist deciduous forest from whence they had emerged less than an hour ago. They were Maria Gonds and they lived in one of the smaller villages that dot the Indravati Tiger Reserve. Very detailed documentation exists as to their peaceful ways and advanced culture. Their technology for water filtration had been handed down over several generations. But such technologies may not stand them in good stead in the days to come.

Outside the Reserve, a combination of pollution, urban land grab and rampant deforestation has turned Gond communities into urban migrants, rural workers or marginal farmers. One example of how the tribal heart of India has been ripped asunder can be seen from the adverse effects of the Bailadilla iron ore mines whose produce will enrich distant Iran. The mines have devastated vast portions of Bastar. A 32 kilometre. stretch of the Sankhini River is, in fact, referred to as *lal pani* (red river) by the Gonds who believe that the earth is bleeding from the wounds inflicted on it by the miners. No amount of river bed-filtration can make the Sankhini's water safe to drink. Fortunately, such projects cannot be executed inside the 2,799 square kilometre tiger reserve and in the 1,258 square kilometre core area, no official tree felling can take place either. But the government has the power to denotify the Indravati Tiger Reserve, which amounts to stripping the forest, its wildlife and its tribal communities the protection afforded to them by the Wildlife (Protection) Act 1972.

Confusion prevails about the admittedly complicated issues concerning people and parks. On the one hand, we have blinkered wildlifers who believe that any human being who comes near a wilderness, threatens it. On the other, we have blinkered human rights activists who will not admit their failure in preventing projects such as the Bailadilla mines from destroying tribal cultures... who ask for the only legislation protective of such cultures — the Wildlife Act — to be scrapped.

'Species generally become rare before they become extinct — to feel no surprise at the rarity of a species and yet to marvel greatly when the species ceases to exist, is much the same as to feel no surprise at sickness, but, when the sick man dies, to wonder and to suspect that he dies by some deed of violence.' [Charles Darwin].

As we supervise the extinction of species after species, Darwin's words should ring embarrassingly loud in our ears. The end-game is underway for *Elephans maximus* and *Panthera tigris* as 1995 draws to a close. In fact, the pincer between habitat destruction and poaching has already led to a series of local extinctions of both these charismatic and much loved animals. But the government of India is unmoved. Either the Prime Minister's office does not believe the tiger is in trouble, or, worse, does not care. 'In a land where people are dying, why should we waste energies and resources on saving wild animals?' This refrain is a companion cry to that other shortsighted gem: 'Do you want to keep adivasis as museum pieces?' What follows is an attempt to address these two apparently logical, but hopelessly shortsighted questions.

The wildlife and the tribal cultures of India share a common fate because both depend on the survival of natural India. In April 1960, the President of India, acting under the provisions of Section 339 of the Constitution of India, set up the Scheduled Areas and Scheduled Tribes Commission (SASTC). The purpose was to institutionalise protection for the tribal people,

Wild buffalo in the seriously endangered habitat of Manas, a World Heritage Site

Leopard at home in a tree

who then constituted around 10 percent of the total population of India. It would be an understatement to say that the Commission has failed. Not, I hasten to add, for any lack of effort on the part of its various Commissioners, but rather because the national policy of the Central and State Governments always was (and still is) to deforest natural India, where tribal people live.

With a suspected 500 tigers dying every year, the fate of the tiger is clear. Less clear is the fact that in just over four decades of Independence, 95 percent of tribal cultures which evolved on the Indian subcontinent have become so seriously eroded as to be virtually unrecognisable. Once-proud adivasis are now bonded labour, rural poor, urban migrants and slum-dwellers. This is the heart of the failure of the SASTC. I believe, in fact, that the Tribal Welfare Department is directly responsible for this tragedy as its mandate (like that of the missionaries of yesterday's Africa) is to wean tribal people away from their lifestyles... to 'educate' them and make them 'modern'.

If you superimpose a satellite map of forested India over a map showing the current concentration of tribal settlements, you will see that the only true forest cultures still intact (outside the northeast and the Andaman & Nicobar Islands) are in and around the Protected Area (PA) network of sanctuaries and national parks. Admittedly saving the tribal people was not the intent of those who set up the PA system, but in saving tigers, lions, leopards, elephants and rhinos, forest habitats were saved. And where such forests were saved cultures were saved. Where they were not, the cultures were lost.

THE WILDLIFE (PROTECTION) ACT 1972

Without a shadow of doubt, this one piece of legislation, more than any other — including the Constitution of India itself — has been the most effective instrument in saving the tribal cultures of India in their purest form. Yet, most social activists have not even read the Wildlife Act. This does not, however, prevent them from blindly condemning it as being 'anti-tribal.' There are two reasons for this unfortunate state of affairs:

1. Social activists perceive wildlife protection to be an elitist concern.
2. Some provisions in the Wildlife Act are clearly insensitive to and abusive of the human rights of tribals.

After considered debate, the offensive provisions require to be redrafted. This would, in fact, strengthen protection to the forests and wildlife as well, but some social activists lobby for the Act to be scrapped altogether. Ironically, such activists find their strongest support coming from the industrial lobby! Mines, dams, the timber trade, five star tourism, thermal plants, copper smelters, steel mills and paper factories would all be delighted if the Wildlife Act was scrapped.

Even in its present form there are many provisions in the Wildlife Act which social activists could use to the advantage of communities they wish to champion. Section 17 A, for instance, reads thus: '... nothing in this section shall prevent a member of

Maria Gond woman drying mahua flowers in the Indravati Tiger Reserve

a scheduled tribe; subject to the provisions of Chapter IV, from picking, collecting or possessing in the district he resides any specified plant or part or derivative thereof for his bonafide personal use'. Section 24 C of chapter Chapter IV, which deals with the declaration of Sanctuaries, National Parks and closed areas, rights of residents, powers of the collector etc, reads thus: '... the Collector may... allow, in consultation with the Chief Wildlife Warden, the continuance of any right of any person in or over any lands within the limits of the sanctuary.' Clearly, it was never the intent of the Wildlife (Protection) Act to discriminate against the tribal people. If Section 24 C alone were to be correctly interpreted, or better still redrafted to make it less ambiguous and directly relevant to traditional forest communities, a major lacuna in the Wildlife Act would be plugged.

THE CORE OF THE MATTER

The fact is that none of the forests in which tribal cultures originated were ever planted by humans. This task was accomplished by 'wildlife' including birds, bees, butterflies and even tigers, bears and monkeys. These basic connections elude most urban social activists, though all adivasi communities themselves have understood and respected nature from time immemorial. These forest dwelling communities are our best hope for tomorrow, for they are probably the only mass group which will back our demand for the setting aside of five percent of the Indian landmass for the strictest of protection, away from the exploitative hand of humans. Here, in core forests whose borders should be drawn in consultation with forest dwelling communities, the tiger and the ant must be enabled to continue a genetic chain of life in whose web even the future of human life ultimately lies.

The idea of excluding people from parts of the forest is not new. But we now know the methods employed in the past by Project Tiger were questionable and ineffective, unjust... and as wrong as unworkable. Had those of us involved with Project Tiger been more in touch with people's groups, we might have seen that alienating communities by displacing them for the creation of sanctuaries and parks was as unworkable as displacing them for dams, mines or other mega-projects. Besides, the customs and mores of forest dwellers had always incorporated 'exclusion zones' in the management of their forests. Temple groves, burial grounds, the Van Raja concept where people would religiously avoid lifting even a stick from parts of the forest belonging to the 'Forest King', were all people-created 'core zones'. A result of community decisions, enforced by community laws and taboos, such areas helped the jungle to regenerate as well, if not better, than today's 'scientifically managed' core zones, to which all manner of VIPs, tourists and wildlife researchers have unlimited access. The task on hand today is, clearly, to forge unity between the adivasi and wildlife camps as these are the only two forces asking for the protection of natural, as against, man-made, forests.

Forging unity

The basic position of enlightened wildlifers today is that the PA system cannot survive without the support of the people living in and around the forest. They also know that injustices meted out to forest dwellers by the government agencies, including the forest department, have indeed alienated people who were once in harmony with the forest. They ask, for instance, that Project Tiger institute an urgent survey to establish the conditions in which those ousted from Reserves such as Kanha and Ranthambhore now live. Subsequently, it would be incumbent on us to deliver social and financial justice to such communities. This would be the first step towards restoring the bonds of trust between wildlifers and forest communities.

In a nutshell the issue is as follows: How can we ensure that traditional forest dwellers are enabled to meet their sustenance and survival needs, without creating gaping holes in the protective net which would allow industries, politicians and their camp followers to destroy our last remaining wildernesses?

An environment for violence

Just as saving the elephant, rhino or tiger without simultaneously saving other plants and animals is unthinkable, so too is the idea of saving only the PA system, while ignoring the country at large. A look around reveals, however, that the Himalaya reels under unfettered assault. The north-east is in tatters. From Kutch to Bengal, our coastline lies wounded. The Andaman Islands and their unique tribal cultures are dying. And no one can drink the water of our lakes and rivers without being poisoned. Even our air is pregnant with pollution. Few can now pluck fruit freely from our commons, or take fish from millions of ponds which once dotted our land. As wildlife managers will themselves confirm, even fuel to cook food is now almost impossible to obtain for people living outside protected areas. These were once nature's gifts to our people. No more. They have been snatched away by merchants selling false dreams of development.

In the Nallamalai Hills of Andhra Pradesh a peaceful, semi-nomadic tribal community called the Chenchus lived a hunter-gatherer existence for longer than living memory. Even as recently as the early eighties, their lifestyles remained unchanged, though many now gather to supply medicinal herbs to buyers for pharmaceutical industries. Administrators and forest officers readily admitted that their way of life did not impact adversely on the extensive forests of the region.

In 1980, the government in its wisdom decided to let the Sirpur Paper Mills take bamboo from the forest. This mill was responsible for large-scale destruction in the Adilabad District. Hundreds of contract labourers were trucked in to cut bamboo from the upper Amrabad Plateau. In short order the bamboo forests were pillaged and regeneration was seriously affected. The Chenchus who depended on the bamboo for food, implements, shelter and even containers to carry water and food, were slowly pauperised. Apart from direct use of the bamboo plant, tribal communities suffered domino deprivation as the ecological web built around a bamboo ecosystem collapsed. Chronic hunger is commonplace today and old value systems are being eroded even faster than forest soils.

Though many Chenchu tribal traditions are still alive, young men and women increasingly look to outside opportunities for survival. Cattle are grazed on behalf of outsiders and wood is routinely carried out of the forest for urban consumption. Their knowledge of the forest, it is suspected, is being put to use by poachers and, some reports suggest, even terrorists.

Unlike Bangladesh, West Bengal suffers less intensity and frequency of cyclones and tidal waves. There is one simple reason for this: the mangroves of the Sundarbans are alive and well and are able to protect the coast from the sea. The forests of the tiger reserve form the heart of such protection. They are also the foundation of the economic well–being of lakhs of people whose livelihood is dependent on fish, honey and forest fruit. But in the Sundarbans, because lakhs of people entered the deep forest each day, almost 100 people used to die annually because woodcutters, fishermen and honey tappers had to confront tigers, snakes and sharks in the core area of the swampy habitat at high tide. Project Tiger put the core area out of bounds and suggested that only the buffer area be harvested. After an initial period of protest, people discovered that their fish catch had doubled, even though the core remained inviolate. This was because the biodiversity spilled over into the buffer from the core. The same results were forthcoming where honey-tapping was concerned. Best of all, man-killing incidents dropped by 800 percent. The strategy of maintaining a core and buffer area was, and still largely remains an all-win situation.

In other areas, Project Tiger felt that employment generating activities involving soil and moisture conservation schemes would help restore the land, even as they afforded locals the opportunity to repair their own earth. As the availability of water, grass, fuel and fruit improved, thanks to the expanding productivity of the core areas, the survival requirement of people would be met — just the way it did in the Sundarbans. This, it was felt, would wean them away from carrying headloads of wood to urban centres, or to poach animals and timber for cash. Such creative solutions were based on our own indigenous wisdom and resources.

But now, in the name of biodiversity conservation through eco-development plans to bring in piggeries, poultries, duckeries, tailoring shops, carpentry, and even diamond cutting and lathes in some places have been prepared. These are to replace tribal lifestyles. Such 'we know what is good for you' attitude will thus take ecologically wise people and turn them into

Godwits wheel through the threatened mangroves of Bhitarkanika at sunset

third-rate versions of city dwellers putting the final seal on the fate of India's forests, such plans will destroy the knowledge base of the adivasi people, the only group who have ever exploited our forests sustainably.

After an initial recovery, over a span of a decade, the buffer areas of forests such as the Melghat Tiger Reserve are dying. Why? Because they were never protected as part of any people's movement. MLAs and MPs of all colours are now running riot, flexing their political muscle to extort profit from these protected forests under the guise of ushering in 'development'.

Maharashtra's Vidharbha region is suddenly said to contain 'useless' zudpi jungles where 'not a blade of grass' grows! That these are dry deciduous jungles which will regenerate the moment cattle and fuel pressures lift is not understood. Instead of protecting Vidharbha, therefore, more than 2,000 square kilometres. are to be denotified... against the wishes of the forest department. Who mourns this loss? I have heard some social activists take perverse delight in this tragic turn or events, believing that it 'serves the arrogant wildlife wallahs right'. This is myopia at its worst. They do not see that the death of Vidharbha is foretold if 40 irrigation projects drown the last few scrub jungles.

And what will then happen to the over 1,00,000 people who enjoy *nistaar* rights in such areas? When these forests go, our sanctuaries and parks will certainly suffer additional pressure.

In Melghat, Mahrashtra's only Tiger Reserve, for instance, the Sipna and Dolna rivers nourish thousands of agriculturists when the rest of Maharashtra goes thirsty. The same rain that killed 3,000 people when the Wardha River turned into a killing torrent some years ago also fell in Melghat. But no one died. Because the forest, painstakingly 'manufactured' by its millions of large and small inhabitants, sponged the downpour and moderated its impact.

Similarly, when 500 Korku children died of malnutrition in Dharni outside the Melghat Tiger Reserve, not one child died inside the forested area because communities still had access to tubers, fruit and wild plant materials which they used as medicine and food.

This then is the wildlife connection. While there is no doubt that nature is awe-inspiring and that its wards are beautiful, this in itself, is not reason enough to expend extraordinary human energy, or to make major sacrifices, to protect it.

The real justification is that without wild animals our country would be turned into a hostile desert and we would have to beg for food from other countries — a direction in which I believe we are headed — like Ethiopia, Somalia and other sub-Saharan countries.

133

DEVASTATION

The crisis of species, people and habitats has reached serious proportions. On one hand, urban pressures be it mining, dam projects or other large scale initiatives result in large tracts of forests becoming completely degraded. The increasing pressures of a growing population also add to the burden on our natural resources.

This combination depletes our forests, rapidly causing suffering for forest, rural and urban communities..

Between 1990 and 1995, the Indian Government diverted nearly 200,000 hectares of forest area to meet urban pressures and to legalise encroachments on the forests. The state of Madhya Pradesh has suffered the largest share of this forest decimation) Millions of trees were cut down across India. There are 129,580,000 hectares of wasteland in India of which 35,889,000 are degraded forests land.

Many apparently natural events, eg, floods and famine, are actually caused or aggravated by man's own actions.

Following spread: *Dangerous times — two tigers cuddle in a captive enclosure*

135

RANTHAMBHORE FOUNDATION

WORKING TO SAVE THE TIGER

The **Ranthambhore Foundation (R.F.)** was registered in 1987 as a non profit society with the primary objective to strive for the maintenance of the essential ecological balance necessary for man to live in harmony with nature. The Foundation has been working since 1988 in villages around Ranthambhore Tiger Reserve, situated in Sawai Madhopur District, along the southeastern periphery of Rajasthan.

The 392 sq. km. Ranthambhore National Park is an ecological island surrounded by 91 villages and three townships with a total human population of 1.67,000 and a cattle population of 1.00,000 l.u. In addition to the resident livestock, an estimated 20,000 l.u. of migratory herds pass through the forest in search of fodder every year. The human population's growth rate in the area is 3.2% p.a. Both the cattle and the human populations are either totally or partially dependent on the resources of the park for meeting their basic requirements of fodder, and of firewood, timber, grasses and building materials. It has been estimated that 85% of the population in the villages and 28% in the townships are totally dependent, while the remaining population is partially dependent. In the townships only 15% of the population do not depend on forest resources at all, as primary consumers.

Besides the extraction of forest products for their own consumption, a sizeable population both in the townships and in the villages derive economic benefits by selling products extracted from the forest. The townships are the largest consumers. A research study has calculated that the firewood extracted for the townships' consumption is more than the sum total consumed by all the villages put together. The extraction of grass, fodder and timber is higher in the villages nearer the forest than the villages away from the forest. The dependence on the natural resources of the forest is directly proportional with low economic status.

The buffer zone is in a state of severe degradation because of cutting and grazing pressures. About 75% of the buffer surveyed, explicity indicates the high pressures due to lopping, pollarding, cutting and grazing.

R.F.'s interventions in such a situation have been site-specific, flexible and based to a large extent on ideas and needs of the local people, since it is our firm belief that fragile ecological systems like Ranthambhore can survive only with the active support and participation of the people in the area. R.F.'s approach basically attempts to rally the support of local communities through a variety of activities and facilitates the **creation of green areas outside the National Park** as a viable and sustainable alternative for the procurement of resources to meet the needs of the local communities, thus deflecting the pressure from the protected area.

A special emphasis of all R.F. efforts is to ensure the safety of the tiger in its natural habitat across India and in any other tiger range countries. R.F. believes not only that the tiger is a great living symbol of the natural world, but also that if there is a tiger within a forest, because of the protection given to the tiger, that forest is relatively safe. Unfortunately today the tiger and the forests it lives in, along with all the wildlife, fauna as well as flora, are severely threatened by an ever increasing demand on natural resources mainly by industries and unsustainable commercial exploitations, or for state revenue, by developmental projects, and by poachers.

The problem is that today, with the population's growth and its requirements, whether it is the survival needs or the needs induced by the spreading of the consumer society, the amount of what is extracted from the forest is beyond the forest's own capacity of regeneration, and the forest areas are shrinking at alarming rates.

R.F. believes that it is imperative to increase biomass and to regenerate the forest, as this might also help to reduce the conflicts that are devastating the protected areas, as they are the last remaining fragments of 'untapped' natural wealth.

R.F. believes that saving the tiger and the forest from their present fate is an essential component of the fight for a better world for humankind. R.F. therefore also lobbies, nationally and internationally, to generate the support required to save the tiger and the forest through interventions in meetings, committees, workshops, debates and across a series of field sites in India, that can contribute both to policy and more effective field action. The challenges are enormous but if we fail to save the tiger what can we save?

FIELD ACTIVITIES AROUND RANTHAMBHORE NATIONAL PARK

Healthcare & Family Planning

Working closely with PRAKRATIK Society, R.F implements since 1989 a Health Care and Family Planning programme across 32 villages around the National Park. In 1996 a Village Health Centre and Clinic will commence operations. At least 40,000 people derive benefits of the programme. **Family planning** with the acceptance of various methods has increased by 10%, **immunization** has increased from 25% to 75% with 50% of the children reaching the full immunization at one year, a number of **eye camps**, and many facets of primary health care are the regular components of the programme. This medical facility is deeply entangled in the concept of environment and ecology and its very symbol is a tiger and a tree. It is a vital component of a broad range of activities that integrate together to reduce the pressures on the Park.

Dairy Development & Cattle Breeding Centre

Since one of the critical causes of depletion of the natural resources of the Park is free grazing of livestock, R.F. has focused on this problem in order to minimize the dependency of livestock on the National Park. R.F. promotes home fed, home reared and improved breeds of cattle and buffalo by sponsoring both a **BAIF Cattle Development Centre**, which implements a comprehensive breed improvement programme to increase milk production, thus contributing to the upliftment of the economic standards of the farmers, and a **Cattle Demonstration Farm** that provides improved and tested livestock to the farmers. Fodder development, veterinary care, the support to village milk cooperatives, distribution of cattle feed, training and extension services are only a few of the strategies in place.

137

Afforestation

To address the serious problem of the depletion of wood from the National Park to meet both urban and rural pressures, R.F. has been running since 1988 a **mother nursery** which today has reached a capacity of 65,000 saplings for the afforestation and agroforestry projects. R.F. has been sponsoring several **village nurseries** also. In six years R.F. has been instrumental in the plantation of about 3,00,000 saplings in the area, and about 1,00,000 of these trees survive today. A seed bank, extension services, and the creation of tree compounds adjacent to schools are an integral part of this effort. Since 1994 an intensive **agroforestry project** has started focusing on private land. The project's aim is to encourage the farmers to restore the trees in the agrarian landscape of the area, by planting adequate species amidst their crops. The project has also an experimental component to test a variety of agroforestry technologies and associations. The agroforestry project is meant mainly for the farmers who are dependent on the forest resources.

Alternative energy

Both the above activities have resulted in a small effort in alternative energy by propagating biogas plants in villages where livestock is home reared. The slurry from the biogas is effectively used for natural fertilizer in agricultural fields. Some efforts are also underway to encourage solar energy.

Education

Between 1990-1995, 7,000 children from the villages around Ranthambhore National Park have participated in a non-formal education programme. The activities have been focusing on awareness of land-use practices, and the understanding of water, and soil conservation, tree planting, and alternative energy. The deep entangled link between man and nature was reasserted through jungle camps, forest trips, Park visits and a number of activities such as paintings competitions and exhibitions, theatre plays and skits staged across the villages. A small nature centre is now focusing mainly on extension services with trees. Ranthambhore National Park is nature's own classroom.

Research & Documentation

R.F. has sponsored small research grants for students working on environmental related issues. Scientific research and surveys provide valuable information for the development of the strategies of R.F.'s projects and activities all of which are documented as much as possible by facts, figures, statistics, and by project reports. R.F. has also conducted an important two year research project on the **Park-People Interface** with a view to measure the rate of exploitation of the natural resources with the rate of regeneration. In addition to the above, R.F. tries also to keep an updated and comprehensive information base about the National Park, be it reports, census data, etc.

Satellite imageries of the National Park and R.F.'s work area are undertaken every two years by R.R.S.S.C., Jodhpur, at the request of Ranthambhore Foundation. These land-use and forest maps are vital indicators and assessments of the state of the area.

Village Groups & Meetings

A special effort over the last six years has been towards the creation or catalysation of village groups that could be empowered to act in the Park's interest. Some groups have functioned effectively, some have been paralyzed by government apathy and others have failed. In December 1995, at the request of a group of village elders, R.F. organized a two-day meeting of over 200 people from 55 villages including 16 sarpanches/ex-sarpanches and 44 representatives of village organizations to formulate an action plan to save Ranthambhore National Park. Here are some of the recommendations formulated at the meeting :

The Park must be saved with the participation of the people and Forest Protection Societies must be formed in each village; the Forest Officers should become more responsible and both Forest Officer and people should collaborate to protect the Park. Massive land development initiatives, water conservation measures, etc, should be undertaken in the area. Initiatives to prevent crops' raiding by wild animals, crop insurance and compensation schemes should be available to the local people. Income generated from the tourism in the Park should go towards a village fund managed by representatives of different villages, illegal activities inside the Park should be prevented, especially if it is for commercial purpose.

Support to NGOs and other organizations

R.F. has attempted to harness the expertise of other NGOs by persuading them to undertake field activities in Ranthambhore. R.F. supports and facilitates:

● **Dastkar: Craft Development at Dastkari Kendra**

The Dastkar Ranthambhore Project of income generation through craft was conceived by R.F. as a component of its integrated ecodevelopment programme. The project started in 1989 and in 1994 R.F. has built in Kutalpura village a centre for traditional art and craft development. Over 100 families regularly use the Kendra to propagate, create and market their skills and products. Training courses in new craft skills are also organized at the Kendra. This income generation activity has used the motifs of trees, bird and animals in many of the products that are created, to stress the concern towards the forest and the tiger. The project is self sufficient. The Kendra is also used as a venue for medical camps and for community meetings.

● **Ranthambhore School of Art**

R.F has supported and facilitated a group of painters under the broad banner of a Ranthambhore School of Art. The painters from the nearby town and adjacent villages depict tigers and other wildlife. Over a dozen exhibitions by these painters have resulted in creating awareness both in India and across the world about conserving the tiger and the forests. These painters have also helped in village workshops and in the educational activities by R.F.

● **BAIF Research Foundation**

The Foundation provides full financial support to the BAIF Research Foundation's Artificial Insemination Centre in Kundera village [see *Dairy Development*].

● **Prakratik Society**

The Foundation financially supports Prakratik Society [see *Healthcare & Family Planning*].

● **INTACH**

R.F. has facilitated the Indian National Trust for Art and Cultural Heritage to work in the area by providing necessary supports to take up programmes for cultural and heritage conservation in the region.

● **District Milk Union**

R.F. has been supporting the Sawai Madhopur and Tonk Milk Union since 1991 to promote a viable milkshed in the region. R.F. has provided a series of financial and other inputs to the Union for better services to the farmers.

RANTHAMBHORE FOUNDATION (Delhi) INTERVENTIONS

For all Ranthambhore Foundation (Delhi) interventions in the national and international debate about wildlife conservation policy and all the related issues, a vital root of understanding, learning and awareness has come from R.F.'s field activities, their 'ups' and 'downs', their impact in and around the National Park. R.F. (Delhi) functions as an Information Centre for the Tiger, for other wild cats and for wildlife in general, it is a Data Centre for Natural Resources, Dams, Power Projects and their impacts on the environment. The issue of People and Protected Area is at the core of R.F.'s concerns and activities. Here is a brief outline of R.F.'s (Delhi) activities:

Networking
● Tiger Link
In February 1995, R.F. initiated and coordinated a new initiative for tiger conservation: Tiger Link. At the first meeting over 22 organizations and 70 individuals took part. Tiger Link is a mechanism to network people and organizations to create support for field action in the interest of the tiger. R.F. (Delhi) extends support and assistance to Tiger Link participants as and when requested to strengthen their field actions and try to help in solving some serious problems they might confront in specific situations. Every four months R.F. (Delhi) produces a Tiger Link newsletter which provides all participants in Tiger Link updated information on the tiger and the initiatives to protect it.
● Bagh Bachao Andolan
R. F. has participated in the Bagh Bachao Andolan, a Tiger Link initiative, on 1 October 1995 when a protest meeting has been organized to 'Save the Tiger' at Vishwa Yuvak Kendra, New Delhi.
● Informal networking
Ranthambhore Foundation has been active in linking donors both national and international directly to site specific situations, Park management, and NGOs that genuinely have a need for infrastructural support or financial aid.

Promoting Wildlife Conservation Awareness
● Wildlife Conservation Talks at the I.I.C., New Delhi
R.F. (Delhi) in its efforts to increase awareness has also been organizing monthly talks by leading conservationists and specialists on issues concerned with Wildlife, People and Forests at the India International Centre, New Delhi.

The talks include: The Cult of the Tiger by V. Thapar; The Life of the Tiger by Dr. K.U. Karanth; Tiger Poaching and Trade in Wildlife by A. Kumar; Snow Leopard by Dr R.S. Chundawat; Dholes by Dr A.J.T. Johnsingh; In and Around Water by B.C. Chowdhury; Natural India and the Economics of Destruction by B. Sahgal; The Bustards and Floricans of India by Dr. A.R. Rahmani; The Gir Lion by Dr. R. Chellam; Threatened Birds of India by B. Grewal; The Right to Life by A. Kothari; The Raj and the Natural World by Dr. M. Rangarajan; Himalayan Musk Deer by Sathyakumar; The End of a Trail by Divyabhanusinh.
● Exhibitions of Wildlife Art
Since 1991 Ranthambhore Foundation has helped in organizing 12 Wildlife Art Exhibitions, solo and/or collective, by the artists of the Ranthambhore School of Art in India and abroad.

Committees, Forums, Organisations, Meetings
From 1992 representatives of R.F. have participated, in various capacities, in the following national and state level committees, forums and/or organizations.
- ● Steering Committee of Project Tiger (MOEF)
- ● Tiger Crisis Cell (MOEF).
- ● Cat Specialist Group for Asia of SSC/IUCN.
- ● Commission on National Parks and Protected Areas (CNPPA) of IUCN World Conservation Union.
- ● Environment Appraisal Committee (EAC) — Hydro Electric and River Valley projects, MOEF.
- ● Madhya Pradesh Government Tiger State Committee.
- ● Wildlife Institute of India Society.
- ● Global Tiger Forum, MOEF
- ● Global Tiger Patrol, U.K.
- ● WWF State Committee of Rajasthan.
- ● Delhi High Court Committee on Wildlife
- ● Committee for the Wildlife Sector of the 9th Plan constituted by the Planning Commission.
- ● **Eco-development committee of MOEF, 1993-1994**

R.F.(Delhi) provides the necessary assistance, infrastructure, data and information for an effective participation in the above mentioned committes and organizations.
● Cat Specialist Group-IUCN, Indian Region
Ranthambhore Foundation facilitates and assists in the organization of the meetings of the Cat Specialist Group (Indian Region) of the SSC/IUCN, ten such meetings have been organized so far.
● People and Protected Areas
R.F. supports initiatives whose aim is to identify ways and means through which local communities can be effectively associated in the wildlife conservation efforts, and so that, through this, new strategies for the effective management of protected areas can emerge.

Publications and Papers
- ● Regular publications by the Ranthambhore Foundation include **Poaching Files** and **Tiger Files** which are collections of newspaper clippings bound together on tiger, wildlife and wild habitats' issues such as poaching, trade, management, policy.
- ● Ranthambhore Foundation has published **The Flora of Ranthambhore National Park** and various **Reports** on R.F.'s Health, Dairy, and Research projects.
- ● A document on **The Violation of Environmental Laws and Conservation Policy** by various state governments in their respective Hydro Electric Dams and River Valley Projects all over India has been compiled for wider reference and analysis of the situation. A detailed database on the above is also being set up.
- ● A document with detailed information on the **Diversion of Forest Land for Various Commercial Purposes** with data on the amount of cutting of trees has been compiled for reference and further follow up action.
- ● The book *In Danger* : Endangered Species, People and threatened Natural Habitats has just been published.
- ● A Comprehensive Survey of Tiger Reserves all over India has been undertaken and the report has been submitted to the Ministry of Environment & Forests.
- ● Policy interventions, suggestions and notes on environmental issues and on the necessary actions to save the tiger across India have been prepared and sent regularly to the Ministry of Environment and Forests.

R.F. International Participation
R.F. representatives have participated in a number of international meetings and workshops. R.F. (Delhi) has facilitated the contribution of papers and interventions at such international meetings.

WILDLIFE, PEOPLE, FORESTS AND NON GOVERNMENTAL ORGANIZATIONS
A Survey by Paola Manfredi

The original aim of this section is to provide the reader with basic information about organizations [NGOs] which, in different parts of India, are working with the local communities towards the common goal of protecting both the habitat and the species living in it.

At the Ranthambhore Foundation, we strongly believe that networking with organizations and people across such a vast country as India is an essential component of our work in the field of conservation.

Tiger Link

In February 1995 Ranthambhore Foundation held a two-day meeting in Delhi, Tiger Link, attended by nearly 70 people and 22 organizations. Everyone who participated came at their own expense, since R.F. did not have the financial resources to provide for the travels and/or accommodation of so many people from different parts of India.

People came from as far as Karnataka, Tamil Nadu, West Bengal and Assam, motivated by the belief that it was important to meet, to discuss, to exchange information, experiences, views and problems, and to find in such exchanges both support and renewed energy to continue to work for the protection of the tiger and its habitat.

People and organizations had different backgrounds and approaches in their 'field action'. For some of them the only common point probably was a genuine commitment to the cause of saving the tiger and its habitat! Discussions, therefore, were at times very animated, but also very enriching since every different point of view or approach was a reflection of the many different ground realities of this vast country, where a sensible intervention in one place might be totally inadequate for another. Fortunately the 'my approach is better than yours' attitude did not take over, to jeopardise the main goals of the meeting.

Tiger Link thus succeeded in creating linkages between different organizations. Tiger Link is a support structure to facilitate the work in the field. It offers support by research institutions, by legal aid agencies, by anti-poaching and wildlife trade specialists and by media people. Its effort is to prevent anyone working in the field from feeling isolated or alone. A person or an organization working even in very remote corners of India can now tap into the support structures that Tiger Link has activated, to facilitate better and faster action in the interest of the tiger and its habitat, and all that lives in it. Tiger Link is not a registered organization, nor a centralized mechanism. Every organization or individual in need of help will directly get in touch with the individual or the organization which can best answer their needs.

A **Tiger Link Newsletter** produced every four months by the Ranthambhore Foundation helps to circulate news about Tiger Link participants and their work and problems in the field. It also updates field action.

NGOs working for wildlife conservation

Though on a different scale, the NGO section of this book aims at activating similar kinds of links between organizations which work in the field of environment, with a special focus towards saving wildlife, and India's natural habitats from extinction.

Some 170 organizations, based in every state of India, whose activities include the protection of species, especially fauna, were contacted through a questionnaire, in which they were asked to introduce themselves, the geographical area of their work, the kind of problems that they face and tackle, and to articulate the kind of activities and approaches that they follow. The NGOs were also asked to share some positive experiences that could inspire other organizations to follow in their footsteps!

Nearly 60 organizations from different areas answered the questionnaire, and we feel very grateful to many of them who took the time to give us such detailed information. Moreover, to overcome the problem of the multiple local languages, we requested that, as far as possible, the reply be in English!

The unevenness of the answers does not allow for an extensive presentation of each organization, the outcomes of the questionnaire are, therefore, presented in a general way, except for a few experiences which are related separately **in the NGOs own words**.

The list of the NGOs which answered the questionnaire along with the ones that participated in the first Tiger Link meeting will follow, and others that are concerned with wildlife.

Who are the NGOs who answered?

It appears that quite a few of the major religions (Hinduism, Islam, Christianity) or philosophical schools (Gandhian, J. Krishnamurti, etc.) are the source of inspiration for some NGOs and effect their approach and activities.

By the kind of answers to the questions it appears that all types of groups are represented, rural as well as urban, covering a fair spectrum of the different political stands. The main targets of the NGOs' activities are also wide ranging, from working with tribal communities, and deciding whether to **educate** them or to **be educated** by them, to the urban elite and a middle class audience.

The type of approach seems equally to cover a broad spectrum, from the so-called **top down to bottom up** ones. All NGOs consider the involvement of the local communities as the essential pre-requisite for any wildlife conservation effort.

A few organizations appear to be very specialized in their approach, concentrating, for example, mainly on scientific research or on legal battles.

THE PROBLEMS

Three questions in the questionnaire concerned the problems: problems faced by the wildlife and the habitat in the organization's specific area of intervention, the problems that the NGO is specifically addressing and the problems they encounter in their work.

Poaching

By far the most widespread problem faced by wildlife is poaching, 65% of the answers we received reveal such a sad state of affairs in the specific areas where the NGOs are working : poaching for pleasure, poaching for trade, killing in retaliation for the wild animals' encroachment on man-land, be it villages, or cultivated fields, tribal hunting as a traditional food gathering practice, or as a traditional festival or celebration. Here are few quotes from various NGOs:

'The army: bored army/paramilitary personnel in border areas shoot bharal, musk deer, etc, just for the heck of it. Plenty of ammunitions available!', and also 'Extensive poaching particularly in high altitude for musk deer, leopard pelts, etc. Traffic across the border with Nepal of tiger skins/bones exchanged with/ for *toosh*'.

'The local leaders and the landlords, those who are far beyond the control of the government and the departments, enter the forest area for hunting only for their pleasure'.

'Poaching is widespread and all sections of society are responsible. Rural and urban elite use guns, the poorer villagers or tribals use poison and snares to kill wildlife to meet needs of local, regional or even global markets'.

'Poaching by rich local landowners, film stars and other such persons' says an NGO from Madras.

'Poisoning of animals — particularly tigers and leopards — appears to be a significant threat [...] The sanctuary is also virtually defenceless against the "sport" shikari'.

'Every year there is a local [in Sevapur, T.N.] festival celebrated by the people. On that day, people are encouraged to hunt on the hills [...] Due to this hunting activity bison, pythons, giant squirrels, lizards, mouse deer, fox, etc, are all in an endangered position. By overgrazing of the cows, throughout the year quite large number of plant species are being destroyed. Very recently two bison were hunted by the local people'.

Among the main problems faced by the wildlife of the area there is also the : 'Use of explosives in poaching fish from the Cauvery River — especially Mahseer'.

In addition to this, indirect killing is also widely reported by the NGOs : through poisoning by insecticides, fertilisers, industrial pollution.

'Application of insecticide in the paddy field creates a disturbance of the environment in Lotak Lake, so the wild birds, fish and snails become extinct'.

Habitat degradation

This is the second most important problem faced by wildlife. The definition of habitat degradation here includes deforestation, loss of habitat and extinction of prey species, commercial forestry, introduction of monoculture as well as invasion by exotic species, cutting and uprooting of tree species for making charcoal, habitat fragmentation and destruction of corridors used by wildlife.

'Almost all the big trees are cut for man's greed. The dried branches of living trees are taken for firewood purposes. Birds do not get tall trees and dry branches for construction of their nests. As a result of which so many local birds are on the verge of extinction'.

'Extraction of bamboo by the [...] Paper Mill after construction of a road in the interior forest'.

'A booming trade in hooch and timber during the past ten years on the periphery of Dalma WLS has taken its toll on the elephants of this sanctuary, forcing them to leave their natural habitat in search of food. The problem has been accentuated by the fact that in gross violation of the Forest Act various stone quarries have come up in the area. [...] It has been observed that a general exodus of a herd of more than 60 elephants from Dalma Hills crossed the Subarnarekha and Kansabati rivers and entered the East Midnapore Forest Division during November 1987. Observations state that no such extra-limital movement of elephants from Dalma has been recorded over the last 200 years. Since then this has become an annual event. And the erratic movement of this elephant herd is causing immense damage both to material and human life in the Midnapore, Bankura and partially in Purulia districts'.

One of the reasons for such a seasonal exodus is that 'in the adjoining state of West Bengal forests thriving under JFM through a beneficial sharing system with the FPC's has been restocked with moribund sal forest making it a safe abode for the elephants causing a seasonal man-wildlife conflict.[...] Since the elephant requires a much larger home range than other terrestrial animals, it is really one of the first species to suffer the consequences of habitat fragmentation and destruction'.

Another NGO states: 'Habitats of wildlife are getting degraded due to excessive biomass removal to meet market needs of timber, fuelwood, fruits, fodder, nuts, rattan, leaves, tree bark and a host of other non-timber forest products. Such biomass collection, allegedly for "subsistence" is actually market driven and provides scope for widespread poaching and arson'.

Forest fires are also mentioned as a cause for habitat degradation in a few areas. 'Overgrazing and fire, against which there is no organised protection, are a major cause of degradation and are major inhibitory factors against rehabilitation of forests'.

Water problems are an integral component of habitat degradation.

In the Sunderbans water is polluted by 'hazardous pesticides used in the crop fields', or 'withdrawal of excessive ground water for cultivation results in lowering the water table and in the appearance of arsenic in drinking water'.

Population pressure and encroachments of habitats, often by 'immigrants', are indicated as important causes for the degradation of the environment or for the reduction of the natural habitat needed for the survival of wildlife species.

'Methods of use of forest resources that may have been sustainable in the context of very low population levels are totally unsustainable today. A classic example being the felling of trees for fodder'.

The **negative impact of various kind of developmental projects** such as dams, mining, tourist infrastructures, aquaculture, and industries with their heavy polluting wastes, is often stressed by the NGOs as heavily affecting the natural habitats and with them the wild animals of the area, be it large mammals, fish, amphibians or birds.

Government & Administration

What is startling, but not surprising, is the fact that **the major difficulty** faced by the various NGOs (45%) in their efforts to intervene to redress/address some of the problems mentioned above **is the government itself**, be it the state government, or the forest department and wildlife department, the local politicians, the judiciary system, etc. The difficulties vary and they cover the entire spectrum, from total apathy, disinterest, non-cooperative attitudes to suspicion, direct antagonism and even open conflicts with NGOs.

Sometimes the conflicts arise between different departments of the administration, which is also a clear symptom of the lack of direction within the government and the administration as far as management of wildlife and protection of natural habitats are concerned!

Here are some quotes from the answers to the question: Main problems/difficulties encountered in your work:

'Low morale and motivation of field staff [within a Tiger Reserve] resulting in inadequate patrolling and hence soft target for the organized poaching mafia'.

Or 'Red-tape and the tardy execution of works taken up by government departments. Apathy on the part of the people in and out of government. An enduring and mutual suspicion of public and government staff that surfaces at the barest excuse.'

An NGO, whose members are 'fighting since ten years with local politicians' and are 'after forest/ wildlife officers to do their job', writes to us that: 'Our government pays lip service to wildlife conservation, protection of natural forests but actually nobody gives a damn. Yet there are so many acts and laws that if someone outside government wants to do something, they can't'.

Another one says that: 'The only hurdle is the interference of the politicians and local leaders. We have to face them with courage'.

A problem is also the 'Lack of holistic approach from the state machinery. The work undertaken in this region [Bankura Forest Division, West Bengal] has been entirely of voluntary nature, individually subscribed by members, local people and donors and agencies' own resources. The forest department is reluctant to give any support for the programme not even resource materials'.

The political will to protect the environment and the species is overwhelmingly missing. The lack of comprehensive environmental and wildlife management plans allows all kinds of negative happenings.

An NGO based in the Himalayan region points out also the **lack of transparency** in the administration of matters relating to the environment and specifically the large projects. 'Environment impact assessment reports are done by outside consultant organizations for the project. The consultants get the report cleared with the Ministry of Environment & Forests. Local people and NGOs are not consulted. The report is not even made public by the government'.

Funding

The second major problem faced by the NGOs in the implementation of their activities and objectives to save wildlife and the habitat is a desperate lack of financial means.

Man/Wild animals conflicts

Some NGOs who replied to our questionnaire report from their working area the problem of man/wild animals conflicts, and very often they refer to the problem of elephants.

'Due to mass deforestation of dense forests, cutting of plants and trees by the tribals for their livelihood, chopping of big trees by the big businessmen for earning money, hungry elephants are not getting their green habitats regularly thus killing poor tribals, demolishing their hutments and crops for their own survival. In this Almighty God gifted green earth, tigers and leopards become maneaters due to not getting drinking water and flesh of small animals' to eat'.

Lack of scientific data

An important problem pointed out by an NGO from Kerala, **Niyamavedi** — Progressive Lawyers Forum — is the lack of scientific research or data available for lawyers to prepare writ petitions or public interest litigations:

'Since there is an attitude (from the part of the judiciary as well as the government, both central and state) that environmentalists and their advocates are sentimental and unscientific, it is very difficult to convince the judges of the importance of the issue and prove the case scientifically. Hence we try to get as much scientific reports and data for our case to counter the false and exaggerated reports of the government. To check their counter affidavits, we follow up the case inside and outside the court. But it is a fact that even after obtaining a favourable court order, it does not get implemented fully. So we have to follow-up even after winning a case, to file another contempt petition. Fight should be ongoing...'

THE ACTIVITIES

What do NGOs do to address the various problems which confront both habitat and species?

Education seems to be the most common concern and the most urgent need addressed at various levels by NGOs. As far as the other activities are concerned, they reveal the existence of an extraordinarily active, dynamic, creative, generous and competent world of people and voluntary organizations who do a fantastic job despite or amidst difficulties of all sorts. The lack of financial resources or the opposition by government, by the administration, or by various vested interest groups and lobbies, are very severe hurdles on their path.

Education

Most of the NGOs (80%) pursue educational activities, which include activities with schools, students, organising nature camps, training courses, etc. But more specifically, whose education, about what, and how?

'Education of the people about the need to use the forest resource sustainably' is the objective of the Forest Protection Committee, **Pataur**.

The **Annamalai Reforestation Society**'s 'education programme is specifically aimed at empowering the community to improve the quality and productivity of their lives through understanding basic ecology and how that knowledge can be used to improve the home site, farm and community productivity'. The Society organises permaculture (organic farming and agriculture) residential courses.

Nagarhole Wildlife Conservation Education Project (NAWICOED) 'supported by Wildlife Conservation Society (India Programme) and Global Tiger Patrol, UK, is targeting local youth living in villages around Protected Areas of Karnataka to motivate them to protect wildlife. The activities include slide and video shows, field nature camps and lectures'.

'Training NGOs in bio-diversity conservation, Trainers' training courses' are part of the educational activities of Dr M.S. Swaminathan Research Foundation.

Madras Crocodile Bank is pursuing a programme of public education and specifically has: 'a) Published over 100 popular articles in newspapers and magazines on reptiles, amphibians and conservation in general. b) Collaborated in the production of several documentary films and one children's feature film. c) Over 750,000 visitors to the Crocodile Bank each year are given talks and exposed to information signboards and naturally landscaped, educational exhibits'.

Another NGO, **Niyamavedi**, is adressing an interesting target: 'Environmental illiteracy is prevalent among the judiciary and we plan to bombard them [the judges] with information by mail ... even though they may not read it'.

The **Rishi Valley School** is 'basically an educational institution, yet with the firm belief that education should not take children away from nature, this has inspired the

developmental work, not just in wildlife conservation but regeneration and conservation of the habitat, with the building of a percolate dam to increase ground water table, satellite schools have been set up in various villages of the area, in each school children raise nurseries and plants are distributed to villagers, taking care to raise plants that are indigenous to the region and which would bring benefits to the villagers in future. [...] Continuous efforts by the staff and the students have resulted in substantially greening the hills, winning over the confidence of an otherwise hostile and doubting village populace.

'The approach of the school is towards the principle of co-existence with other natural creatures, and this has lead to conserving the snakes, scorpions and other such fauna generally feared by many [...] Above all we are an educational institution, and every activity is a learning exercise'.

The **Zoological Club of Payyanur College, Kerala,** is focusing on conservation education for school children and college students. 'The work undertaken by the organization is at the grassroot level. The children and youth who have had the opportunity to be associated with the manifold activities of the Club have retained their love for nature. Many of them have taken up careers in fields connected with conservation of nature and natural resources. Even those who have not, continue to be amateur birdwatchers'.

Another NGO suggests that local Natural History Museums should be established to highlight the flora, fauna and culture of the district.

A few organizations advocate the need for changes in the formal education syllabus. **Conservation of Nature Trust** suggests that 'conservation biology should be introduced ... with special reference to wildlife conservation [...] Study of taxonomy should be strengthened in the college curriculum as the present syllabus does not give enough importance to this branch of science and the students are not equipped with enough knowledge to understand or appreciate bio-diversity or diversity of species'.

Such a step towards introducing wildlife conservation courses seems to be even more urgent as, ironically enough, if on one hand education is felt as a must for conservation initiative, on the other, there can be contradictions.

'...another potential threat to wildlife and forest is the large number of educated youth in the area [Corbett]. They have high, unfulfilled aspirations and are virtual misfits in the village since, because of their education, many of them are reluctant to work on the land. This group, it is felt, can be misdirected by mafias. As it stands, liquor and lotteries are creating serious social stress'.

Awareness programmes

Fifty percent of these NGOs are also actively involved with awareness programmes, through lobbying, campaigning and organising events to rally public support for the environmental and wildlife issues that they are specifically addressing. Such efforts create very interesting **Newsletters**. Exhibitions are often chosen as a means to appraise the public of environmental/

wildlife issues along with nature orientation camps for the youth, film shows, video shows, melas, meetings. To appraise the local media of the problems faced by wildlife and sensitive habitats is one of the approaches followed to create awareness.

The **Federation of Societies for Environmental Protection, Darjeeling** has been organising 'An exhibition on the relationship between wildlife and man.'

The **All India Jeev Raksha Bishnoi Sabha** lobby for vegetarianism, they fight against cruelty towards animals, and their awareness programme for the conservation of wildlife and of green trees is conducted through educational institutions, training centres, workshops, libraries, etc.

The **Antyodaya Research and Action Group in Orissa** has been successful in creating: 'adequate awareness among administrators and people so that the rehabilitation in Suneirupei jungle block of Bitarkanika by cutting mangrove has been pushed back by about 1,000 acres ...

'People consciousness has developed, number of crocodiles has been increased, sea turtles coming to nesting ground has been raised, research on horseshoe crab restarted'.

The **Bharat Sevak Samaj** appeals 'to the people not to kill wild animals and birds.'

The **Good Shepherd Rural Development Trust** has conducted a 'national environmental awareness campaign 1989, with the following activities: a) Integrated environmental campaign on water conservation in Tiruchy and Salem region; b) Workshop on environmental education for students; c) Save the Karaivetti Lake's birds campaign to declare the lake a Bird Sanctuary; d) Water pollution; e) Save the Pachaimalais Padayatra; f) To promote awareness about the degradation of Kolli Hills in Salem District which harbours many herbal medicinal plants and wildlife... After seven years, the Bird Sanctuary has finally been notified'.

Wildlife protection schemes and interventions

Twenty-five percent of the NGOs who answered R.F.'s questionnaire are also directly involved in wildlife support and/ or management schemes, or in physically saving or protecting wild animals through all kinds of initiatives, like the patrolling of the forest or checking on forest fires.

Gram Seva Sangha has taken up 'The programme of artificial nesting for birds [...] — with the aim to maintain the birds' population on one hand and to combat the use of hazardous pesticides on the crop field — which ultimately affects the general health, particularly the children's health by consuming such vegetables. Maintenance of sustainable population of birds by artificial nesting helps farmers indirectly by eating various insects and larva in large quantities of which many are harmful to the crops. It is estimated that each bird eats 10-15 gms of insects and larva per day. A population of 1,000 birds keeps in balance the growth of insects'.

Imba Seva Sangam, a community living in Tamil Nadu, is trying to achieve 'a new way of life, based on love, non-violence and service' and whose lifestyle is as close as possible to nature has been conducting surveys on endangered local flora

and fauna. The Sangam has organised on five acres of land the Annai Genetic Garden to preserve endangered and medicinally valuable plants of the region: 'endangered species are propagated in the nurseries and then reintroduced in their own habitat', and 'in order to expose our activity to the public we have conducted two camps for students and cultural programmes on environment for the local people'.

The **Lok Biradari Prakalp** has 'started an orphanage for all varieties of wildlife'. Such a 'wildlife orphanage encourage people in the area not to kill and eat the animals but to take care of them'.

The **Alipurduar Nature Club, West Bengal** is 'Physically saving and retrieving fauna and returning it to the forest department'.

The **All India Jeev Raksha Bishnoi Sabha** has recognised a Bishnoi lady, because she saved a baby blackbuck. A female blackbuck, fleeing from a horde of wild dogs, sought protection near the lady working in the fields. On reaching her reassuring presence, the female gave birth to a baby and then died. In order to save the baby blackbuck, the lady, who also had a small child, took care of it by breast feeding it.

WWF-Tamil Nadu State Office has initiated a project for sea turtle conservation and has a project for conserving wetlands and the ecosystem.

Wildlife Association of South India has taken on long lease the Nelliguda Lake (360 acre spread) and they have started to protect 'the ecosystem of selected areas with the active participation of the people living in that area. The main focus of the approach of the organization is: a) To enlist the active support and cooperation of the people living near the rivers, lakes and ponds in conserving the wildlife/forest life; b) To provide them with alternative sources of power-energy; c) To initiate self-help employment opportunities; d) To include the locals in patrolling the river and anti-poaching activities [...].Till the year 1987 experts were considering the Mahseer extinct in the Cauvery River. These same experts are now happy to state that the giant Mahseer is proliferating in large numbers in the Cauvery and Kabini rivers'.

'**Wildlife First!** focuses on enhancing the protection status of nature reserves and endangered species in the state of Karnataka. Its activities include supporting field protection with the donation of vehicles and other equipment that might be needed by the park's staff in difficult circumstances. It also lobbies government to solve the crisis that afflict protected areas. Wildlife First! acts like a watchdog to protect the interests of wildlife through positive action and when necessary critical opposition to government machinery depending on the circumstances'.

Few other NGOs have also specific activities to support forest guards.

Nature Conservation Society, for example, has distributed incentives and small awards in order to motivate the field staff/ forest guards.

In 1994 the **Ranthambhore Foundation** made a comprehensive offer to the Chief Wildlife Warden of Rajasthan to provide forest staff with medicare, award schemes, educational facilities for the family, etc. But till today there has been no response to the offer, on the other hand representation of the Foundation has initiated an annual award scheme for excellence in tiger conservation at Panna Tiger Reserve in Madhya Pradesh.

Man/Wild Animal Conflicts

The conflicts between man and wild animals witnessed by the NGOs which answered the questionnaire are mainly due to the loss or to the encroachement and, therefore, the fragmentation and degradation of the natural habitats for the wild species.

In an attempt to mitigate the conflicts between local people and wildlife encroaching on 'man-land' or attacking human population, quite a few voluntary organizations have developed compensation schemes in favour of the local people for the losses caused by wildlife, or are trying to alleviate the greviance of people in a conflict situation — such as cattle lifting — by getting the government to speed up the payment of compensation or are active in designing measures for better protection of humans and their properties without damage to wildlife.

Speedy compensation helps greatly to reduce poaching which can be the response of the community or the individual in retaliation against a loss suffered.

The **Indian Society for Wildlife Research** is trying to 'mitigate the problems of crop raiding and human killings by elephants. To prevent elephants from straying into agricultural fields, live fences energised by solar cells or 12 volt batteries have been used effectively in some areas of Midnapore [...] To reduce crop damage the farmers are encouraged to grow cash crops that yield good economic returns but are not consumed by elephants like oil-seeds, etc. [...] The nature of damage caused by elephants depredation here [in Krishnapur village under Simlipal P.S.] is mainly in the form of crop raid. In order to motivate the villagers in Krishnapur the Society has taken up an Integrated Development Programme which includes agro-forestry based self-employment programmes as well as supportive programmes like free medical camps has also been introduced... The Forest Protection Committees can be the most effective tool in implementing such extension programmes.

'The Society with the FPCs has specifically been organising: a) Village level workshops to highlight the do's and don'ts in combating elephant depredation; b) Workshops about the do's and don'ts in combating elephants depredation with schools. A seminar which was organised by the Society in August 1994 got a tremendous response; c) A long march from Bishnapur Range in Bankura to Bagmundi in Purulia along the elephant route interacting with the people on the way and making them aware about the do's and don'ts in combating elephants depredation'.

The **Jan Jagaran Samiti** has 'got the government to pay compensation for all domestic animals killed by leopards in and around Binsar Sanctuary on regular basis'.

The **Tirunelveli Wildlife Association** states that: 'Villagers who lost their cattle used to apply folidal poison on the carcass and thus the tiger or panther which would eat the carcass, would die immediately. We took steps to pay compensation for the lost cattle. In the last ten years there has been no case of death of tiger or panther due to folidol poisoning. Illicit poachers were identified and handed over to the forest/police department for action.'

The **Corbett Foundation** states 'in case of any kills of human beings or cattle, we give interim relief to the victim's family/ owners such as financial grants and guidance to obtain government compensation'.

In order to save wild animals which could otherwise be killed: 'the volunteers of the **Wildlife Conservation Society** in Bhavnagar are taking care of wounded animals or birds'. They also 'catch snakes wherever they become a nuisance in urban areas and release the snakes in their natural environment.'

Anti-poaching and forest protection

About 20% of the NGOs have anti-poaching programmes and intelligence gathering activities to try and stop illegal hunting or trade in wildlife derivatives. Many NGOs also organise groups to fight forest fires, wood smugglers, etc...

The **Jan Jagaran Samiti** 'organise local fire fighting units every summer'.

Forest Protection Committee, Pataur organise: 'Physical protection of forests by regularly patrolling against illicit felling, poaching and for fire protection. There is no budget for proper fire-protection work and the committees provide the forest department staff with volunteers for fire fighting work [...] The committes have also moved to ban the entry of migratory cattle herds which has served to greatly reduce the pressure on the forests'.

The Committee has also been active in an anti-poaching awareness campaign among the villagers: 'To educate people about the consequences of poaching and the seriousness with which these cases are being viewed by the judiciary — something that many villagers are unaware of and often mislead by interested parties'.

The Bishnoi community is very well known for its peaceful, non-violent attitude towards every form of life, be it human, animal or plant. Their attitude of caring and co-existing with wild animals, to the extent that a Bishnoi will not chase away the wild animals raiding his fields, is legendary. The **All India Jeev Raksha Bishnoi Sabha** has therefore been fighting poaching, hunting and killing of wildlife and 'Many hunters have been got arrested and the cases are in courts'.

In late 1978 there was a party of Arab hunters who had come to Ramsar near Jaisalmer to hunt the great Indian bustard, with the permission from the Indian government in exchange for oil trade facilities. But the opposition generated among the local population through Bishnois campaigning was so strong that the party was eventually forced to flee.

In the brochures that the Sabha sent to us there is a long, startling list of people who have sacrified their own life in their endeavour to save wildlife from poachers. The Sabha has special schemes to support the families of these people.

The **Conservation of Nature Trust**, Calicut organises 'distribution of shark oil to the fishermen of the Brahmaputra who kill the river dolphins for its oil for the preparation of fish bait'. Such an initiative has reduced the killing of the river dolphins. The Trust also believes that: 'a wildlife protection volunteer force should be formed including NGOs, committed citizens, students and Kani tribals [...] Kani tribal, who live in the Hills in the Kanyakumari District, should be involved in the conservation efforts and monitoring to alert the Forest Department and NGO's about the illegal activities in the forest, they should also be appointed as forest guards'.

Bird Protection Committees in and around Vettakkudi Tank have been organised by the **Environmental Conservation Group**, Tamil Nadu 'At Vettakudi Tank every year thousands and thousands of migratory birds congregate. Illegal poaching is the major threat for birds such as the darter, spoonbills, grey pelican, barheaded goose'.

A rural based organization, which 'has the mass appreciation... is organising teams of young boys for the preservation of wildlife in Muthur forest area, facing with courage powerful people who indulge in poaching for sport'.

WWF-Tamil Nadu State Office has been conducting investigations into poaching and deforestation activities by private organizations or by government departments.

The **Nature Conservation Society** has been organising a network of informers for anti-poaching purpose.

The Junglees from Calcutta: 'To combat the dreaded poaching menace, we offered an alternate economics by launching a disciplined eco-tourism project in the area. The entire populace has now become beneficiary of the project : the local panchayat, boatmen, traders, weavers, railways and local unemployed youth (as trained nature guides)'.

Wildlife First! has donated a vehicle for anti-poaching to Nagarhole National Park. Their activities now encompass most of Karnataka's protected areas.

Wildlife Protection Society of India 'aims to avert the Indian wildlife crisis through: a) Investigation and enforcement to bring about seizures of illegal wildlife products and the arrests of poachers and traders. Trade routes and modus operandi of traders and poachers one also continually studied and information passed on to government authorities; b) The compilation of a comprehensive data base on Indian wildlife crimes; c) A WPSI cell of lawyers has been formed to greatly increase bail levels and to accelerate prompt prosecution; d) Conservation projects with local communtities [...] WPSI has also been active in the training and introduction of sniffer dogs for customs to detect widlife products at airports, railway stations and sea ports. WPSI has been investigating the musk deer trade'.

Legal Cells

Twenty percent of the NGOs are fighting the battle for wildlife and habitat conservation at a legal level, and luckily quite a few of these battles seem to have succeded in stopping major projects or so-called developmental interventions which would

have resulted in further damaging the habitat and shrinking the space for wildlife.

The **Nature Conservation Society**, Daltonganj has organised a legal cell to help in wildlife court cases.

Niyamavedi concentrates its activities for wildlife conservation at a legal level. Niyamavedi 'has filed a number of environmental/ pollution cases and the same is done with the help and participation of the local people as well as activists and experts'.

They have obtained 'a number of stay orders in environmental cases, in a case against quarrying operations, interim order against black wattle plantations at Eravikulam National Park. The cases are fought with the support and the active help/information provided by the local communities, and by the NGOs.[...] It is a fact that even after obtaining a favourable court order, it does not get implemented fully. So we have to follow-up even after winning a case — to file another contempt petition. Fight should be ongoing. We also deal with other issues like women, tribal, labourers and other civil and criminal cases.[...] A case cannot be won without the support of the people's struggle'.

Bombay Environment Action Group have filed a case against the denotification of Melghat Tiger Reserve and **Legal Action for Wildlife and the Environment (LAW-E)** and **Vanya** have filed a case against the collection of MFP from P.A.s in Madhya Pradesh.

Viswadarsanam in Kerala acts and activates pressure-groups against governmental laws concerning forests and wildlife

WWF-TNSO has conducted environmental investigations into endangered forests and polluted areas.

Battles against Big Developmental Projects

'We [**The High Range Wildlife Preservation Association**] as an environment association were able to convince the commission on environment from the central government who came in 1988 to inspect the Munnar area for approving the proposed Munnar Dam for electricity, of the environment hazards it would cause and finally the project was shelved'.

Due to pressure spearheaded by **WWF-Tamil Nadu State Office** 'three major ecologically dangerous developments which would have spelled disaster for wildlife (and people) of Mudumalai and its surrounding areas were stopped:

a) The Masinagudi Needle Industries electro-plating plant project which would utilise and pollute huge quantities of water in this rain shadow region just outside Mudumalai;

b) The Rotary Club sponsored tribal vegetable farms at Mavinahalla which was to block an already bottlenecked elephant migration path near Mudumalai;

c) The Tourism Department sponsored a multistoreyed tourist complex at Thepakadu inside Mudumalai which was to greatly increase the tourist load and associate disturbances at this already besieged sanctuary.

In addition to the above, WWF-TNSO "obtained a stay order on the proposed destruction of some 3,000 hectares of prime secondary chincona plantation forests which were to be razed for the growing of tea[...] These forests which are adjacent to the Eravikulam National Park in Tamil Nadu and Kerala respectively, support a good population of wildlife besides forming a part of an elephant migration path. Part of this forest had already been destroyed but the major portion is under the court stay order'.

The **Himalayan Nature & Environment Preservation Society**, Shimla, has 'saved vital natural forest around Shimla from the Stadium Complex'.

Nature Conservation Society's 'collaboration with Forest Department has resulted in raising the various issues, ie, Kutku Dam, Oranga Dam, Field Firing range of Netarhai, etc.'

The **Nilgiri Wildlife & Environment Association** has been fighting against a destructive hydro-electric project which resulted in its cancellation.

Tarun Bharat Sangh has been fighting and eventually won the case against mining in Sariska National Park. This victory is historic since the matter was decided by the Supreme Court.

The **Wildlife Protection Society of India** is engaged in protecting the Balpakram National Park from the impact of a vast cement plant. Balpakram is in the sensitive North-Eastern State of Meghalaya.

Eco-development

Eco-development, in the sense of regeneration of natural habitats, afforestation, water management initiatives, promotion of alternative energy along with income generation activities, education and health care programmes, is a strategy which is followed by 50% of the NGOs in their endeavour to protect wildlife and their habitats.

Jan Jagaran Samiti has worked 'on eco-development projects for the villages around Binsar Sanctuary for five years. Binsar was notified in 1988, and since then no commercial felling or resin trapping, no poaching has occurred in the sanctuary but there are village rights to fuel and fodder". The Society got the wildlife department to give solar energy devices, bee-keeping tools to the villages inside or on the fringes of the Sanctuary. It got alternative employment for resin workers who, because of the ban on resin trapping, lost their jobs.

The Society has also organised 'a rehabilitation centre for leprosy cured people in Almora, it is managing a programme for self-employement for tribal women weaving wool in Pithoragarh district, and it supports 24 grassroot groups for eco-development work in Almora district'.

Nature Conservation Society has undertaken eco-development initiatives and states that 'the wildlife and the forests can be saved only by the will and with the help of the villagers living inside and on the fringes of the Palamau Tiger Reserve. The main activities [undertaken by the organization] are tree plantations, seed distribution, tassar silk and lac industry, cottage industries for women, adult education activities, welfare activities like medical camps, drinking water, immunisation, etc, have also helped in creating confidence in the NGO among the villages'.

The **Forest Protection Committee, Pataur** has been active in the 'Creation of fodder farms, multi-use plantations protected by the villages — linked to fodder protection is an effort at improving animal husbandry, introduction of silk production, popularising biogas'.

The **Corbett Foundation** has initiated a series of welfare and income generation activities which enable the C.F. to become 'closer to menfolks thereby enabling us to understand their problems in relation to Corbett Tiger Reserve and to put matters in perspective through giving them the macro picture of the urgent requirement to preserve and conserve the beauty of nature and bringing to their notice the consequences that other regions have suffered by not doing so'.

Ranthambhore Foundation eco-development initiatives have been detailed separately.

A number of Joint Forest Management initiatives are also reported such as JFM at Roughoug, or at Buchampeta (Andhra Pradesh) by **Gandhi Marg** 'We are fully involved in mobilizing people towards protecting the forests, in turn conserving the flora-fauna including wildlife... through people participatory approach called JFM.'

The **Good Shepherd Rural Development Trust** is working for the 'Promotion of flora and fauna on 80 acres of land alloted for this purpose with the participation of the rural community.'

The **Himalayan Science Association** has been 'asking the Forest Department to provide alternative energy' in order to reduce the wood consumption and therefore the forest depletion.

The **High Range Wildlife Preservation Association** has been introducing smokeless *chulas* to reduce wood consumption.

The **Integrated Rural Peoples' Development Organization**, Imphal has designed a program for alternative occupation: 'The occupation of rickshaw pulling is arranged for a poor *jhum* cultivator or woodcutter, shrinkage of wildlife habitat is avoided, on the other hand, the poor man is also able to earn enough for living. Thus we can save the wildlife as well as the poor man simply by changing his occupation. Thus a woman woodcutter or *jhum* cultivator can also be changed into a weaver by giving her training and loom along with necessary raw materials to save the environment and wildlife'.

Tarun Bharat Sangh has launched massive soil and water conservation works around Sariska Tiger Reserve.

The support and the active involvement of the local communities to protect the habitat and the wildlife is considered the essential prerequisite of any conservation strategy. Depending on the site specific NGOs which have responded to our **mini-survey**, such support is either there, as part of the community's value system or way of life, or it is actively pursued, with different level of success. A few NGOs work very specifically towards the empowerment of the local communities to control and to manage their habitat and the natural resources of the area. Other NGOs try to involve mainly the women in their efforts to protect the habitat and the wildlife.

Traditional Knowledge

A number of conservation initiatives have also been able to integrate the traditional knowledge of tribal/local communities, turning it into an asset beneficial both for the conservation initiatives as well as for the tribal themselves.

The **Madras Crocodile Bank** is the site of the Irula Snake Catchers Cooperative Society, established in 1978.

'The Irula tribal people are the aboriginal inhabitants of the plain and scrub forest of Chinlepet District near Madras. Most of them still subsist to a large extent on hunting and gathering and their expertise in hunting deadly snakes is almost legendary locally [...] The initial primary objective of the cooperative was to establish a venom centre [...] Irulas would bring freshly caught snakes to the centre for venom extraction. The venom would be dried and sold to Indian manufacturers of anti–venom serum and the snakes released back to the wild after three weeks in captivity. The Irula Cooperative is a small but flourishing example of how a tribal community can maintain its traditional skills and lifestyle through the sustained yield use of wildlife'.

Save the Eastern Ghats Organization is conducting research on traditional knowledge systems.

The **Eastern Region Office of WWF-India** has conducted a survey on five communities of Midnapore District of West Bengal and 'the study has showed that a large spectrum of wildlife is protected by a ring of socio-religious rites. Numerous totemic species are not destroyed, there was a sacred grove, from which no living thing is extracted, even during periods of wood famine.'

Tarun Bharat Sangh has also been very active in reviving traditional water management systems, such as the *johads*.

'Tarun Bharat Sangh's volunteers during the last ten years have observed that the older villagers are still aware of the traditional ways of management of common property resources (CPRs). But along with the decline and degradation of CPRs, the knowledge of traditional systems is also declining and may soon be completely obliterated. [...] Hence TBS volunteers strongly feel the need to educate and train more and more village youth in reviving the traditional methods of CPRs management. [...] The overall aim of such a training is regeneration of natural resources and eco-restoration based on people's traditional knowledge and people's participation'.

'*Johad* is an earthen wall built along the contour of the mountain slope to arrest and store rainwater run-off. Sometimes series of *johads* are built so that water from the overflow of one *johad* goes to the next one below and so on. The water irrigates the fields through unlined canals or through pumps.'

Dr M.S. Swaminathan Research Foundation is following 'a holistic - human participatory approach - focusing on traditional knowledge'.

Gandhi Marg from Jangareddigudem states :

'Our area (Buchampeta, Andhra Pradesh) is richly populated with tribal people...The elders knew that most of their life and livelihood was related to the forest directly or undirectly, income, living, housing, shelters, food... We are disseminating this information again through the elder to the younger generation [...]. Even their original names were the names of fauna and flora of the forest'.

The knowledge of the tribals of the area is appreciated by the management of Eravikulam National Park who integrates them as watchers inside the Park.

Lobbying to notify Sanctuaries and Protected Areas

In a few cases NGOs' active lobbying and campaigning appear to have been instrumental in the notification of protected areas as sanctuaries, as biosphere reserves or national parks. More specifically :

Notification of the Western Himalayan Cold Desert Biosphere Reserve through the lobbying of the **Himalayan Nature and Environment Preservation Society**.

Jan Jagran Samiti 'had Binsar forest notified a sanctuary by the U.P. government despite threats and pressure by vested interests and inactivity of government and saw to it that adequate staff was posted. The Samiti is now lobbying for the notification of a sanctuary in the High Altitude Forest of Kalamuni near Munsyari in Pithoragarh District. Any help in this direction is welcome'.

Orissa Environmental Society has been actively pursuing the notification of the Simlipal forest as a Biosphere Reserve.

The **Rishi Valley School** has been working for the regeneration and conservation of the habitat in and around the valley. 'The valley has been declared a private bird preserve and we are preserving and planting trees to let the bird population increase'.

'The Government of Tamil Nadu has announced in the assembly Vettakudi-Kairavetti Tank as a Bird Sanctuary for Tiruchy District. This announcement was made after the repeated requests from **Environmental Conservation Group** for more than seven consecutive years. This is one of the major impacts of E.C.G. environmental awareness programme'.

The **High Range Game Preservation Association** (today known as The High Range Wildlife and Environment Preservation Association) in 1975 got the Eravikulam/Rajamalley area declared as a sanctuary later on in 1978 it was upgraded as National Park.

The **Nilgiri Wildlife & Environment Association** has been working for the structure and the implementation of the Mukerti Wildlife Sanctuary.

The **Eastern Region Office of WWF-India** has been lobbying to notify : Gautam Buddha Wildlife Sanctuary in Bihar, Buxa Tiger Reserve, Neora Valley, the small wooded area in the suburbs of Calcutta as Narendrapur Bird Sanctuary, the ERO has also been appealing for the sanctuary of Balphakram's final notification.

The **Jodhpur Divisional Committe of WWF-India** 'is making attempts to establish Machia Nature Reserve at Jodhpur, and the Desert Biosphere Reserve in Jaisalmer and Barmer districts'.

Research — Surveys — Census — Workshops

The **Madras Crocodile Bank** is mainly conducting scientific research both within its premises which functions as 'a large outdoor laboratory in which over 10,000 reptiles of 38 different taxa live and breed'. Research focus on conservation of endangered species of reptiles.

The **Himalayan Nature and Environment Preservation Society**, Shimla 'is conducting extensive surveys of wildlife in Himachal Pradesh, it has done an intensive study on the ecology of kalij pheasant, an analysis of the past records of cheer pheasant compared with recent site records, and also surveys remote locations of Himachal Pradesh'.

The **Conservation of Nature Trust**, which regrets that there is so little of scientific research in the Kanyakumari District, proposes that 'Free access should be given to scientists to study wildlife'.

According to **Wildlife Society of India** 'there is a need for systemic documentation and conservation of biodiversity resources in India through well coordinated research and by conservation education for the better appreciation of biodiversity resources. There is also a need for a forum for researchers of wildlife and environmental sciences'. W.S.I. of Aligarh University is trying to address such a need. They have just adressed an issue concerning tourism in Corbett.

Wildlife Conservation Society (India Programme) 'is involved in sample survey of tigers and prey at several sites spanning a diversity of habitats in India. In addition it supports research projects on several endangered species in the Western Ghats and North-East India'.

Promoting research in the field of environmental protection and initiating action for environmentally sound and sustainable development is also the prime objective of the **Environmental Conservation Group.**

WWF - Eastern Region has been active in a number of surveys, census and wildlife conservation projects as well as in the formulation of an eco-development project for Manas National Park.

Ranthambhore Foundation has over the last six years conducted and supported socio-economic surveys and scientific research around Ranthambhore National Park and has also participated in the estimate of tiger density in 1992 and 1993 which revealed the sharp decline in tiger numbers within the Park.

Other organizations which support or undertake research in ecology, species, and related topics :
Dr M.S. Swaminathan Research Foundation, Madras
Centre for Ecological Sciences, Bangalore

Nilgiri Wildlife & Environment Association
Wildlife Institute of India, Dehra Dun
Bombay Natural History Society
Surveys, seminars and workshops :
Alipurduar Nature Club
Antyodaya Research and Action Group
Bharat Sevak Samaj
Conservation of Nature Trust
Nature Environment & Wildlife Society, Calcutta
Orissa Environmental Society, Bhubaneswar
The Junglees, Calcutta
Wildlife Conservation Society of India
WWF- Eastern Region
WWF- Tamil Nadu State Office
Census
Nature Environment & Wildlife Society, Calcutta

Eco-tourism

The Junglees 'to combat the dreaded poaching menace, offered an alternative by launching a disciplined eco-tourism project in the area of Shankarpur, West Bengal'. Shankarpur Gangetic Riverine Isles Complex is the wintering ground for migratory waterfowls, due to great quantities of food available, the number of waterfowls is the highest in West Bengal. The Junglees 'decided to start a biological research station and an eco-tourism centre there. The local *panchayat* donated a *bigha* of prime river front land... For Shankarpur project, we addressed and convinced the local people (with leaflets, campaign and rally) on the economic prospects of this habitat and bird conservation. We educated them to treat the isles complex as their outdoor heritage. Thus in offering protection to the waterfowl and to the habitat, the tourists are visiting instead of the poachers'. The Junglees' programme also includes guided field trips into the Indian forests.

How would you assess the impact of your activity?

'As far as I am concerned I suppose that saving a forest, the only natural oak and rhodo forest in central Kumaon from being tapped, felled, poached and converted into a tourist resort is enough!' says Mukti Datta from **Jan Jagran Samiti**.

A DIRECTORY OF NGOs CONCERNED WITH WILDLIFE

A list of NGOs to whom the Ranthambhore Foundation's questionnaire was mailed and/or with whom R.F. is networking through Tiger Link. The NGOs' names with a mark are the ones who answered the questionnaire. The names have been grouped according to the geographical area.

DELHI BASED

CENTRE FOR ENVIRONMENT LAW (WWF-INDIA)
Chhatrapati Singh, Director
172-B, Lodhi Estate
New Delhi - 110 003
Tel: 4627586, 4693744 Fax: (011) 4626837

CENTRE FOR SCIENCE & ENVIRONMENT
Neena Singh, Program Associate
41, Tughlaqabad Institutional Area
New Delhi - 110 062
Tel: 6981110, 6981124 Fax: (011) 6985879

DEVELOPMENT RESEARCH & ACTION GROUP (DRAG)
Gautam Vohra
75, Paschimi Marg
Vasant Vihar
New Delhi - 110 057
Tel: 602383, 674146

INDIAN INSTITUTE OF PUBLIC ADMINISTRATION
Ashish Kothari, Project Director
I.P. Estate
New Delhi - 110 002
Tel: 3317309

INTACH
Amitabha Pande
Bharatiyam, Near Humayun Tomb
Nizamuddin
New Delhi - 110 013
Tel: 4631818, 4632267 Fax: (011) 4611290

KALPAVRIKSH
Sunita Rao
C-17A, Munirka
New Delhi - 110 067
Tel: 2518377

KINDNESS TO ANIMALS & RESPECT FOR ENVIRONMENT
Camellia Satija
M-39, Main Market
Greater Kailash-I
New Delhi 110 048

LAW-E (LEGAL ACTION FOR WILDLIFE AND ENVIRONMENT)
Mahendra Vyas
C/o H-53-D Saket
New Delhi - 110 017
Tel: 3782492

PEOPLE COMMISSION ON ENVIRONMENT AND DEVELOPMENT INDIA
Ajoy Bagchi, Executive Director
15 Institutional Area, Lodi Road
New Delhi - 110 003
Tel: 4627102 Fax: (011) 4631124

PUBLIC INTEREST LEGAL SUPPORT & RESEARCH CENTRE
Ruchi Pant
C-569, New Friends Colony
New Delhi

RANTHAMBHORE FOUNDATION
Valmik Thapar, Executive Director
19, Kautilya Marg
Chanakyapuri
New Delhi - 110 021
Tel: 3016261 Fax: (011) 3019457

WILDLIFE PROTECTION SOCIETY OF INDIA
Ashok Kumar, Vice-President
Thapar House, 124 Janpath
New Delhi - 110 001
Tel: 3320573 Fax: (011) 3327729

WORLD WIDE FUND FOR NATURE-INDIA
Mr. Samar Singh, Secretary General
172-B, Lodhi Estate
New Delhi - 110 003
Tel: 463 34 73   Fax: (011) 462 68 37

NORTHERN REGIONS
Himachal Pradesh, Uttar Pradesh, Haryana, Punjab, Jammu & Kashmir

ALL INDIA ENVIRONMENTAL SOCIETY
S.P. Grover, Honorary Secretary
3 Nehru Road
Dehra Dun
Uttar Pradesh - 248 001
Tel: (0135) 22426

● ALL INDIA JEEV RAKSHA BISHNOI SABHA
Sant Kumar Bishnoi, President
Street N. 13
Abohar Punjab - 152 116
Tel: (01634) 2774

BALRAMPUR ENVIRONMENTAL ACTION GROUP
A.K. Singh, President
Department of Botany, MLK (PG) College
Balrampur Uttar Pradesh - 271 201
Tel: (05263) 268 (PP)

BERINAG GRAM SWARAJYA MANDAL
Sadan Mishra, Secretary
P.O. Kandey
Pithoragarh District
Uttar Pradesh - 262 531

BILLY ARJUN SINGH TIGER FOUNDATION
Billy Arjun Singh
Tiger Haven, P.O. Pallia
Kheri District Uttar Pradesh - 262 902

CENTRE FOR HIMALAYAN ENVIRONMENT AND DEVELOPMENT
B. S. Rawat, Secretary
Halda-pani Near Akashvani Kendra
Gopeshwar, Chamoli District
Uttar Pradesh - 246 401
Tel: (01372) 2366

● CORBETT FOUNDATION
Pritam Singh, Administrative Officer
PO Dhikuli, Ram Nagar
Nainital District
Uttar Pradesh
Tel: (011) 6444016 (Delhi)

DR. SALIM ALI MEMORIAL NATURE CLUB
Awdhesh Kumar Sharma, Secretary
C/o Sita Ram Sahu
Bari Hat, Mahoba
Hamirpur District
Uttar Pradesh - 210 427

ECOLOGY CONSERVATION ORGANIZATION
(ECO-NATURE CLUB)
S.P. Sharma
Biology Department
Government College for Women
Shimla
Himachal Pradesh - 171 001
Tel: (0177) 2015

GONDA ENVIRONMENT POPULATION AND WILDLIFE AWARENESS ASSOCIATION
Department of Physics and Electronics
LBS Post-Graduate College
Gonda
Uttar Pradesh - 271 001
Tel: (05262) 22994 (PP)

GREEN HIMALAYA CLUB
J.S. Mehta, Hon. Secretary
Oak Ghar
East Pokherkhali
Almora District
Uttar Pradesh - 263 601
Tel: (05962) 23273

HIMACHAL ENVIRONMENT AND LANDSCAPE PROTECTION SOCIETY
G.S. Shah, Hon. Secretary
Village & P.O.Dari
Dharmshala
Kangra District
Himachal Pradesh - 176 057
Tel: (01892) 23212 (PP)

● HIMALAYA VANYA JEEV SANSTHAN
Sarvodaya Bhavan Gopeshwar
Chamoli, Uttarkhand
Uttar Pradesh - 246 401
Tel: (01372) 2526

● HIMALAYAN NATURE AND ENVIRONMENT PRESERVATION SOCIETY
Virinder Sharma, Secretary
Om Bhawan
Chaura Maidan
Shimla
Himachal Pradesh - 171 004
Tel: (0177) 5771 Fax. 211485

INDIAN SOCIETY FOR NATURE VOLUNTEERS
Suresh C. Sharma
Gokal Nagar Rohtak Road
Sonepat Haryana - 131 001

INDIAN SOCIETY OF ENVIRONMENT
P.K. Mathur, General Secretary
7/183 Swarup Nagar
Kanpur Uttar Pradesh - 208 002
Tel: (0512) 214797, 314919

● JAN JAGRAN SAMITI
Mukti Datta, Secretary
Binsar Sanctuary
P.O. Ayarpani
Almora District
Uttar Pradesh - 263 601
Tel: (05962) 22783

● MOUNTAIN ECO-CONSERVATION AND
WILDLIFE SOCIETY OF INDIA
B.D. Sharma
PO Box 78
Jammu
Jammu and Kashmir - 180 001
Tel: (0191) 42277

NATURE CONSERVATION SOCIETY
A.H. Musavi, President
Bengali Kothi
2, Fort Road
Aligarh
Uttar Pradesh - 202 001

● ORNITHOLOGICAL SOCIETY OF INDIA
Asha Chandola Saklani, General Secretary
P.O. Box 3
Srinagar
Pauri Garhwal District
Uttar Pradesh - 246 174
Tel: (01388) 2407

PARVATIYA PARYAVARAN SANRAKSHAN
SAMITI
Sadan Mishra, Secretary
Himdarshan Kutir
P.O. Dharamghar
Pithoragarh District
Uttar Pradesh - 262 571

PRAKRITI MITRA
Divaker Sharma, Director
7, Civil Lines
New Hardwar Road
Roorkee
Uttar Pradesh - 247 667
Tel: (01332) 72334 Fax: 72410

REPRODUCTIVE AND WILDLIFE BIOLOGY
UNIT
Asha Chandola Saklani, Coordinator
PO Box 45
Srinagar
Pauri Garhwal District
Uttar Pradesh - 246 174
Tel: (01388) 2407 Fax: 2174

SIDH BABA BALAK NATH
P.C. Sharma, Project Director
Sidh Baba Balak Nath Temple
Deotsidh
Hamirpur District
Himachal Pradesh - 176 039
Tel: (01978) 7754

SOCIETY OF APPEAL FOR VANISHING
ENVIRONMENTS
P.O. Box 5
Bhimtal
Nainital District
Uttar Pradesh - 263 136
Tel: (05942) 47043

SRUSTI
Vinod Pande, Coordinator
North View
Rattan Cottage
Nainital District
Uttar Pradesh - 263 002

THE WILDLIFE PRESERVATION SOCIETY
OF INDIA
R.N. Mishra, Hon. Secretary
7, Astley Hall
Dehra Dun
Uttar Pradesh - 248 001

UTTAR PRADESH VIGYAN LEKHAKA VAM
SAMVADDATA SAMITI
J.C. Ranjan, President
F-34, Sarvodaya Nagar
Lucknow
Uttar Pradesh - 226 016
Tel: (0522) 380746

WILDLIFE INSTITUTE OF INDIA
PO Box 18, Chandrabani
Dehra Dun
Uttar Pradesh - 248 001
Tel: (0135) 640112/5 Fax: 640117

● WILDLIFE SOCIETY OF INDIA
Jamal A. Khan, Secretary
C/o Centre of Wildlife and Ornithology
Aligarh Muslim University
Aligarh
Uttar Pradesh - 202 002
Tel: (0571) 401052

WOMEN'S ASSOCIATION FOR
DEVELOPMENT
Zarina Hamid, President
Parigam, Yaripora
Kulgam,
Anantnag District
Jammu and Kashmir - 192 232

WORLD PHEASANT ASSOCIATION-INDIA
A.H. Musavi, Secretary
Centre of Wildlife and Ornithology
Aligarh Muslim University
Aligarh
Uttar Pradesh - 202002
Tel: (0571) 401052

WORLD WIDE FUND FOR NATURE-INDIA
U.P. State Office
Newal Kishore Residence,
75, Hazratganj
Lucknow
Uttar Pradesh - 226 001
Tel: (0522) 245190, 249067

WORLD WIDE FUND FOR NATURE-INDIA
Agra Brajbhoomi Divisional Office
Mahinderu Villa,
41, O.P. Mahinderu Marg
Agra Cantt.
Uttar Pradesh
Tel: (0562) 363731

EASTERN REGIONS
Bihar, West Bengal

● ALIPURDUAR NATURE CLUB
Amal Dutta, Chairman
New Town
P.O. Alipurduar Court
Jalpaiguri District
West Bengal - 736 122
Tel: (03572) 2264

AURANGA GRAMIN VIKAS SAMITI
Bhola Prasad, Secretary
At Tumbagara
P.O. Rankikala
Palamau District
Bihar - 814 822

BASIRHAT BIJNAN SANSTHA
N. Das, President
C/o Dept. of Zoology,
Basirhat College
P.O. Basirhat College
North 24 Parganas
West Bengal - 743 412
Tel: (031762) 225, 267

CITIZENS VOLUNTEERS FORCE
P.K. Das, Commandant
2/1A Sidheswar Chandra Lane
Calcutta
West Bengal - 700 012

● ENVIRONMENT PROTECTION SOCIETY
Umesh Dwivedi
C/o St. Paul's School
Darjeeling
West Bengal
Tel: (0354) 2840, 3457

FLORA AND FAUNA-INDIA
Andrew Arunava Rao, President
10 Col. Biswas Road
Calcutta
West Bengal - 700 019
Tel: (033) 435266

● GRAM SEVA SANGHA
D.C. Pal, Secretary
Sachindra Kargupta Path
P.O. Hatthuba, Habra
North 24 Parganas
West Bengal - 743 269
Tel: (03216) 52167

GRAMIN JYOTI
P.O. Sirdalla
Nawadha District
Bihar

GRAM VIKAS SEVA MANDAL
Sidheshwar Singh, Secretary
Bhumihar Mohalla
Giridih
Bihar

● HIMALAYAN SCIENCE ASSOCIATION
G.S. Yonzone, General Secretary
3B Kutchery Road
Darjeeling
West Bengal - 734 101
Tel: (0354) 55486, 55231

● HUMAN RIGHTS ASSOCIATION
Ranjit Kumar Roy, President
Tara Villa Indira Path
Hinoo, Ranchi District
Bihar - 834 002
Tel: (0651) 500576, 500527

INTERNATIONAL DATA MANAGEMENT
CONSULTANCY ON ENVIRONMENTAL
AND SOCIOECONOMIC RESOURCES.
A.B Chaudhuri, Chief Consultant
131 Netaji Subhas Chandra Bose Road
Block 10, Flat 4 Calcutta
West Bengal - 700 040
Tel: (033) 4736734

● INDIAN NATIONAL TRUST FOR ART
AND CULTURAL HERITAGE (INTACH)
Bulu Imam, Director
The Grove
P.O. Hazaribagh
Bihar - 825 301
Tel: (06546) 4793

● INDIAN SOCIETY FOR WILDLIFE
RESEARCH
Tathagata Bhattacharya, Secretary
122 B Southern Avenue, 3rd Floor
Calcutta
West Bengal - 700 029
Tel: (033) 743963, 743417 Fax: 203459

INSTITUTE OF CLIMBERS AND NATURE
LOVERS
M. Chatterjee
17, New Santoshpur Main Road
Santoshpur, Calcutta
West Bengal - 700 019
Tel: (033) 4407527

KISAN MAZDUR SANGHATAN
George Monipally
P.O. Garo
Palamau District
Bihar - 829 204

MANDAR NATURE CLUB
Sunil K. Choudhary, President
Anand Chikitsalaya Road
Bhagalpur
Bihar - 812 002
Tel: (0641) 23479

NATURE AND TREKKERS' CLUB OF
JALPAIGURI
Souren Sen, Assistant Secretary
Nayabasti
Jalpaiguri District
West Bengal - 735 101
Tel: (03561) 22321 (PP)

NATURE CONSERVATION SOCIETY
Ashok Sinha, Chairman
Chandrawati, 1st Street
Hindpiri, Ranchi District
Bihar - 834 001
Tel: (0651) 306514, 36566, 206403

● NATURE CONSERVATION SOCIETY
D.S. Srivastava, Secretary
Ranchi Road
Redma, Daltonganj
Palamau District
Bihar - 822 101
Tel: (06562) 22722

● NATURE ENVIRONMENT & WILDLIFE
SOCIETY
Biswajit Roy Chowdhury
10, Chowringhee Terrace
Calcutta
West Bengal - 700 020
Tel: (033) 2488224

● RANCHI ZILA NAGRIK KALYAN SAMITI
Ranjit Kumar Roy, Organising Secretary
Tala Village
Jai Prakash Path, Shukla Colony
Hinoo
Ranchi District
Bihar - 834 002
Tel: (0651) 408061, 408841

THE HIMALAYAN LOVERS
A.K. Ghosh, Secretary
Aurobindo Road
P.O. Habra
North 24 Parganas District
West Bengal - 743 263
Tel: (031782) 2458 (PP)

● THE JUNGLEES
Raja Chatterjee, Secretary
78 Brahma Samaj Road
Behala
Calcutta
West Bengal - 700 034
Tel: (033) 4680271 Fax: (033) 292897

THE SCIENCE ASSOCIATION OF BENGAL
Subhabrata Roychaudhury, Convenor
104 Diamond Harbour Road
P.O. Barisha
Calcutta
West Bengal - 700 008
Tel: (033) 772312

● WORLD WIDE FUND FOR NATURE -
INDIA
Eastern Regional Office
Tata Centre, 5th Floor,
43 Chowringhee
Calcutta
West Bengal - 700 071
Tel: (033) 247361

WORLD WIDE FUND FOR NATURE-
INDIA
Bihar State Office
DAV Jawahar Vidya Mandir
Shyamali, Ranchi
Bihar - 834 002

NORTH-EASTERN REGIONS
Manipur, Assam, Nagaland

ALL INDIA WOMEN'S CONFERENCE
K. Binapani Devi, President
State Branch
Keishampat, Sega Road
Imphal Manipur - 795 001

ASSAM SCIENCE SOCIETY
P.K. Deka, General Secretary
Latasil
Lamb Road
Guwahati
Assam - 781 001

ASSAM VALLEY WILDLIFE SOCIETY
A.M. Khan, Chairman
Pertabghur Tea Estate
P.O. Chariali
Sonitpur District
Assam - 784 176

● BHARAT SEVAK SAMAJ, MANIPUR
H. Kangjamba Singh, Chairman
141, Mass Hotel Building
Assembly Road
Imphal
Manipur - 795 001
Tel: (0385) 222797

INTEGRATED RURAL DEVELOPMENT &
EDUCATIONAL ORGANISATION
Kh. Kumar Singh, Secretary
Wangbal Palli P.O.
Thoubal District Manipur - 795 138
Tel: (038537) 397

● INTEGRATED RURAL PEOPLE'S
DEVELOPMENT ORGANISATION
B.B. Sharma, Assistant Secretary
Keibi, B.P.O. Taretkhul
S.P.O. Lamlong Imphal East
Manipur - 795 010

● JAMIA EDUCATIONAL SOCIETY
Abdul Hamid, Secretary
Sangaiyumpham Cherapur
P.O. Wangjing Thoubal District
Manipur - 795 148

NATURE BECKON
Soumyadeep Datta, Director
Datta Bari Ward N.1
Dubri
Assam - 783 301
Tel: (03662) 21067 Fax: (03662) 200076

NORTH EAST INDIA GEOGRAPHICAL
SOCIETY
H.N. Sharma
Department of Geography
Guwahati University
Guwahati
Assam - 781 014
Tel: (0361) 88372

NOURHEVI SOCIETY
Shurhozelie
Kohima Village
P.O. Kohima
Nagaland - 797 001
Tel: (03866) 21545

● THE GREENS
Sankar Chakravarty, Secretary
Ekdalia Road (College Road)
P.O. Silchar
Cachar District
Assam - 788 004
Tel: (03842) 31185

WESTERN REGIONS
Rajasthan, Gujarat, Maharashtra

AGA KHAN RURAL SUPPORT PROGRAMME
Shankar Narayanan
Choice Premises
Swastik Cross Roads Navarangpura
Ahmedabad
Gujarat - 380 009
Tel: (079) 427729, 464730 Fax: (079) 464862

ARAVALI VOLUNTEERS SOCIETY
RAJASTHAN
S.K. Yusufzai, Coordinator
P.O. Kherwara
Udaipur District
Rajasthan - 313 803
Tel: (029071) 6228

BOMBAY ENVIRONMENTAL ACTION
GROUP
Debi Goenka
Kalbadevi Municipal School, 2nd Fl., R. 54
Mumbai
Maharashtra - 400 002
Tel: (022) 5122973, 259343

BOMBAY NATURAL HISTORY SOCIETY
Jay S. Samant, Director
Hornbill House, Dr Salim Ali Chowk
Shahid Bhagat Singh Marg
Mumbai
Maharashtra - 400 023
Tel: (022) 243421, 244085 Fax: (022) 2837615

CENTRE FOR ENVIRONMENT EDUCATION
Thaltej Tekra
Ahmedabad Gujarat - 380 054
Tel: (079) 442642 Fax: (079) 420242

DARBAR SHRI ALAKACHAR NATURAL
HISTORY & ENVIRONMENT PUBLIC
CHARITABLE TRUST
D.S. Satyajit, S. Khachar
Darbargadh Jasdan
Gujarat - 360 050

ECOLOGICAL SOCIETY
P. Gole, Executive Director
1B, Abhimanshree Society
Pashan Road
Pune
Maharashtra - 411 008
Tel: (0212) 336408

EK JOOT SANGHATAN
Anand Kapoor
P.O. Narodi
Tal Ambegaon
Pune District
Maharashtra - 410 503

ENVIRONMENT PRESERVATION
SOCIETY
Ashutosh Upadhyaya, Adviser
Vidhyaniketan
4 Station Plot
Gondal
Gujarat - 360 311
Tel: (02825) 20357, 20336

GREEN EARTH FOUNDATION
K.P. Sharma, Chairman
C-141 A Mahavir Marg
Malviya Nagar
Jaipur
Rajasthan - 302 018

● GUJARAT ECOLOGICAL EDUCATION &
RESEARCH FOUNDATION
R.S. Pathan, Director
G1,194/3, Sector 30
Gandhinagar
Gujarat - 382 030
Tel: (02712) 21385, 20560

GUJARAT NATURE CONSERVATION
SOCIETY
Indubhai C. Patel, Chairman
C/o Sayaji Iron and Engg. Co.
Chhani Road
Baroda - 390 002
Gujarat
Tel: (0265) 23791-6

HINGOLGADH NATURE CONSERVATION
EDUCATION PROGRAMME
Nrupendra L. Kachar, Director
646 Vastunirman Society
Sector XXII
Gandhinagar - 382 022
Gujarat

INDIAN PEOPLE TRIBUNAL ON
ENVIRONMENT AND HUMAN RIGHTS
Bittu Sahgal
C/o 602 Maker Chambers V, Nariman Point
Mumbai, Maharashtra - 400 021
Tel: (022) 2830061   Fax: (022) 2874380

INDIAN SOCIETY OF NATURALISTS
G.M. Oza, General Secretary
Maharaja Fatehsingh Zoo Trust
Indumati Mahal, Jawaharlal Nehru Marg
Vadodara, Gujarat - 390 001
Tel: (0265) 558759

INTERNATIONAL TREE CROPS INSTITUTE-
INDIA
S.A. Shah, Hon. Secretary
1 Jesal Apartments
Abhishek Colony, Race Course
Vadodara
Gujarat - 390 071
Tel: (0265) 322950

● LOK BIRADARI PRAKALP-HEMALKASA
Prakash   Amte
Hemalkasa
P.O. Bhamragad, Etappalli Tehsil
Gadchiroli
Maharashtra

NISARGA SEVA SANGH
Ramesh   Ladkhedkar, Secretary
152 Lendra (West)
Ramdaspeth
Nagpur
Maharashtra
Tel: (0712) 523662

PRAKRATIK SOCIETY
10, Bal Mandir Colony
Mantown
Sawai Madhopur
Rajasthan - 322 001
Tel: (07462) 20811, 21123

PRAKRUTI PREMI SANGH
Secretary
CM-23/2, Sector 29
Gandhinagar
Gujarat - 382029
Tel: (02712) 2960

● RANTHAMBHORE FOUNDATION
10, Bal Mandir Colony
Mantown
Sawai Madhopur
Rajasthan - 322 001
Tel: (07462) 20286

● SAHYADRI NISARG MITRA
Vishwas Katdare, Secretary
Near Laxminarayan Temple
Chiplun
Ratnagiri District
Maharashtra - 415 605

SAMVARDHAN
Korah Mathen, Secretary
D-1 Aurobindo Society
Mridul Citadel 1, Near Vastrapur Talavadi
Ahmedabad
Gujarat - 280 015
Tel: (079) 464774

SANCTUARY ASIA
Bittu Sahgal, Editor
602 Maker Chambers V
Nariman Point
Maharashtra - 400 021
Tel: (022) 2830061, 2830081 Fax: 2874380

SOCIETY FOR CONSERVATION OF
FOREST AND WILDLIFE
Shekhar Nanajkar, President
21/A, Asmita, Swanand Society
Sahakar Nagar 1, Parwati
Pune
Maharashtra - 411 009
Tel: (0212) 430877, 450741

● TARUN BHARAT SANGH
Rajendra Singh, General Secretary
Bheekampura
P.O. Kishore,
Thanagazi Tehsil
Alwar District
Rajasthan - 301 022
Tel: (014562) 4443

UDAIPUR ENVIRONMENTAL GROUP
L.L. Sharma, President
P.N. 206, Road 13
Ashok Nagar
Udaipur
Rajasthan - 313 001

VIDARBHA NATURE CONSERVATION
SOCIETY
Dilip Gode, Hon. Secretary
Tidke Ashram
Near Ganeshpeth Police Station, Ganeshpeth,
Nagpur
Maharashtra - 440 018
Tel: (0712) 727363

VISHNOI SANGOSHTI
H.S. Bishnoi, President
C-158 A Dayanand Marg
Tilak Nagar
Jaipur
Rajasthan - 302 004
Tel: (0141) 63699

● WILDLIFE CONSERVATION SOCIETY
Navaneet   Bhatt, Vice President
'Bhav-vilas', Near Gaurishanker Lake
P.O. Bhavnagar
Bhavnagar District, Gujarat - 364 003
Tel: (0278) 5125

● WILDLIFE CONSERVATION SOCIETY OF
INDIA
S.P. Bhatnagar, Chairman
Vishwa Vihar
K/68 Krishna Gangh, Anasagar Link Road
Ajmer
Rajasthan - 305 001
Tel: (0145) 30516

WORLD WIDE FUND FOR NATURE-INDIA
Divisional Director
Baroda Divisional Office
5, Impala House, Vishwas Colony
Alkapuri,
Baroda, Gujarat - 390 005
Tel: (0265) 322438

WORLD WIDE FUND FOR NATURE-INDIA
Udaipur Divisional Office
The Palace
Udaipur, Rajasthan - 313 001

WORLD WIDE FUND FOR NATURE-INDIA
Ahmedabad Divisional Office
'SUNDARVAN' Jodhpur Tekra
Ahmedabad
Gujarat 380 015
Tel: (079) 409838

WORLD WIDE FUND FOR NATURE-INDIA
Rajkot Divisional Office, C/o. Vidyut
Electronics
Near Fire Brigade Station, Opp. Taluka
School, Sadar
Rajkot, Gujarat - 360 001
Tel: (0281) 46211

WORLD WIDE FUND FOR NATURE-INDIA
Valsad Divisional Office
Behind Post Office
Atul, Gujarat - 396 020
Tel: (02362) 596

● WORLD WIDE FUND FOR NATURE-INDIA
Jodhpur Divisional Office
Umaid Bhavan
Jodhpur
Rajasthan

WORLD WIDE FUND FOR NATURE-INDIA
Rajasthan State Office
Anokhi Premises,
Tilak Marg
Jaipur, Rajasthan - 302 005
Tel: (0141) 380539, 48817, 46129

CENTRAL REGIONS
Orissa, Madhya Pradesh

● ANTYODAYA RESEARCH AND ACTION
GROUP
Rabi Mohanty, Secretary
Gamhapur
P.O. Redhua,
Via Nalibar
Jagatsinghpur District
Orissa - 754 225

BANA BHARATI
Nimai Bhai, Secretary
At/P.O. Koraput,
Koraput District
Orissa - 764 020

FOREST PROTECTION COMMITTEE,
PATAUR
Hashim Tyabji,
Village Pataur
P.O. Tala,
Shadhdol District
Madhya Pradesh - 484 661

INSTITUTE FOR RESOURCES
CONSERVATION
H.K. Jain, Director
E/7/56 Area (SBI) Colony
Bhopal
Madhya Pradesh - 462 016
Tel: (0755) 63163

NATURE AND WILDLIFE
CONSERVATION SOCIETY OF ORISSA
S.K. Patnaik, Hon. Secretary
Mayur Bhavan
Janpath,
Saheed Nagar
Bhubaneswar
Orissa - 751 007
Tel: (0674) 53840

NATURE CLUB
Anurag Shukla
Mans Associates
Magarpara Road
Bilaspur
Madhya Pradesh
Tel: (07752) 22181

● ORISSA ENVIRONMENTAL SOCIETY
Sundara Narayan Patro, Secretary
N-6/530 Nayapalli
P.O. I.R.C. Village
Bhubaneswar
Orissa - 751 015

SARVODAYA PRESS SERVICE
Mahendra Kumar, Editor
29 Samvad Nagar
Navlakha
Indore
Madhya Pradesh - 452 001
Tel: (0731) 401083, 465863 (PP)

SOCIAL CULTURAL EDUCATION AND
ECONOMIC DEVELOPMENT
ORGANISATION
Rabinarayan Mishra, Secretary
P.O. Kathasirshi
Via Kuliana
Mayurbhanj District
Orissa - 757 030

SOCIETY FOR ACTION RESEARCH ON
APPROPRIATE TECHNOLOGY &
INNOVATION
K.N. Ramachandran, Director
44/1 Kota
P.O. University
Raipur
Madhya Pradesh - 492 010
Tel: (0771) 530323

SOCIETY FOR ENVIRONMENTAL
CONSERVATION
Vipin Vyas, Secretary
E-4/177 Area Colony
Bhopal
Madhya Pradesh - 462 016
Tel: (0755) 563062

VANYA
Pradip Krishen
Village Bariam
Pachmarhi
Hoshangabad District
Madhya Pradesh - 461 881

SOUTHERN REGIONS
Andhra Pradesh, Karnataka, Tamil Nadu,
Kerala

● ANNAMALAI REFORESTATION SOCIETY
S. Nawazuddin, Secretary
MIG 95, Tamarai Nagar
T.N.B.H. Colony
Tiruvannamalai
Tamil Nadu - 606 601

BHAGWATI ENVIRONMENT AND
DEVELOPMENT INSTITUTE
J. Paul Bhaskar, Chairman
Police Housing Colony
Trichy Road
Dindigul
Tamil Nadu - 624 009
Tel: (0451) 32021

BIRDWATCHERS FIELD CLUB OF INDIA
S. Sridhar, Publisher
2205, Oakwood Apartments
8th Main, Jakkasandral Layout, III Block
Koramangala
Bangalore, Karnataka - 560 034
Tel: (080) 5533684

C.P.R. ENVIRONMENTAL EDUCATION
CENTRE
Nanditha Krishna, Director
1A Eldams Road
Alwarpet
Madras
Tamil Nadu - 600 018
Tel: (044) 4341778, 4346526   Fax: 450656

CENTRE FOR ACTION, RESEARCH AND
TECHNOLOGY FOR MAN, ANIMAL &
NATURE
N.S. Ramaswamy, President & Director
870, 17E Main, VI Block
Koramangala
Bangalore
Karnataka - 560 095
Tel: (080) 5530121, 5530304

CENTRE FOR ECOLOGY & RESEARCH
V. Palaniappan, Secretary
538 Rani Vaikal Street
North Main Street
Thanjavur
Tamil Nadu - 613 009
Tel: (04362) 21410   Fax: 20355

CENTRE FOR INDUSTRIAL SAFETY &
ENVIRONMENTAL CONCERNS
V.T. Padmanabhan, Director
Kottamukku
Kollam
Kerala - 691013
Tel: (0474) 72765   Fax: (0474) 740945

COMPREHENSIVE RURAL OPERATIONS
SERVICE SOCIETY
M. Kurian, Executive Director
1-69, Snehapuri
Nancharam
Hyderabad
Andhra Pradesh - 501 507

CONSERVATION OF NATURE TRUST
R.S. Lal Mohan, Scientist
B/24 Gandhi Nagar
West Hill
Calicut
Kerala - 673 005
Tel: (0495) 52769   Fax: (0495) 51042

DEVELOPMENT ACTION FOR RURAL
ENVIRONMENT
K.Sridhar, Executive Director
1-1-770/5 Gandhi Nagar
Hyderabad
Andhra Pradesh - 500 380

DHARWAD ENVIRONMENTAL
ASSOCIATION
V.K. Deshpande, Secretary
Hembli Galli
Hosyellapur
Dharwad
Karnataka - 580 001
Tel: (0836) 43820

ENVIRONMENTAL CONSERVATION GROUP
S. Damodaran, Executive Director
31-A/29 Nesavalar Colony
Salai Road, Woriur
Tiruchirapalli, Tamil Nadu - 620 003
Tel: (0431) 23263

ENVIRONMENTAL SOCIETY-ERODE
V. Jeevananthan
Siddhartha Matriculation School
Tirunagar Colony
Erode, Tamil Nadu - 638 003
Tel: (0424) 74993, 72773

FRIENDS OF PERIYAR
Joseph Karoor, President
Periyar Wildlife Reserve
P.O.Thekkady
Idukki, Kerala - 685 536
Tel: (04869) 22169

● GANDHI MARG
K. Chiranjeevi, Executive Secretary
Jangareddygudem
West Godavari District
Andhra Pradesh - 534 447
Tel: (088212) 5555

● GOOD SHEPHERD RURAL
DEVELOPMENT TRUST
K.M. Chellasamy, Chairman
B-142, NGO B Colony
Tirunelveli, Tamil Nadu
Tel: (0462) 71497

GUTTUR RURAL EDUCATION AND
DEVELOPMENT SOCIETY
M. Hepzibath Margrate, President
Ammavarupalli
Guttur Post, Penukonda Mandal
Anantapur District
Andhra Pradesh - 515 164
Tel: (085572) 2326, 8134, 2235

HAREKALA LANDLESS POOR AND MARGINAL
FARMERS DEVELOPMENT SOCIETY
K.P. Manai, Secretary
Kisan Nagar, P.O. Harekala
Mangalore Taluk
Dakshina Kannada District
Karnataka - 574 181
Tel: (0824) 742393

● HIGH RANGE WILDLIFE
PRESERVATION ASSOCIATION
Chairman
Vagavurria Estate
P.O. Tallai, Kerala - 685 614

● INBA SEVA SANGAM
Lea Provo, President
P.O. Sevapur
Via Tharagampatty
Tiruchirapally District
Tamil Nadu - 621 311
Tel: (048556) 27, 28, 29

INDIAN SOCIETY OF SOIL BIOLOGY AND
ECOLOGY
G.K. Veeresh, Senior Professor
Department of Entomology
University of Agricultural Sciences
Bangalore
Karnataka - 560 065
Tel: (080) 330153 Ext. 213

JAGRITI
G. Gopalakrishnan Murthy, Secretary
Lucky Board Centre
Balaji Nagar Extension
Nellor
Andhra Pradesh - 524 002
Tel: (0861) 28171

JANAVIKASA SOCIETY
P. Subbarayudu, President
Christian Colony
Pathuru P.O
Khajipet District
Andhra Pradesh - 516 203

KARNATAKA RAJYA VIJNAN PARISHAD
S.K. Sreekanteshwaraswamy, Executive
Secretary
Indian Institute of Science
Campus
Bangalore
Karnataka - 560 012
Tel: (080) 3340509

KERALA NATURAL HISTORY SOCIETY
L. Namassivayan, Secretary
13/369, Kammath Lane
Kozhikode
Kerala - 673 002
Tel: (0495) 77076

LIFE ENVIRONMENT AWARENESS
FOUNDATION
K.R. Anand, Hon. Secretary
26-27, 9th Main
Raj Mahal Vilas
Bangalore
Karnataka - 560 080
Tel: (080) 343323

● MADRAS CROCODILE BANK
TRUST
Romulus Whitaker, Director
Post Bag 4
Mamallapuram
Tamil Nadu - 603 104
Tel: (044) 419196

MADRAS NATURALISTS SOCIETY
V.J. Rajan, Hon. Secretary
36 Fourth Main Road
Raja Annamalaipuram
Madras
Tamil Nadu - 600 028
Tel: (044) 450813

MADRAS SNAKE PARK TRUST
B. Vijayaraghavan, Chairman
Guindy
Madras
Tamil Nadu - 600 022
Tel: (044) 2350821

MERLIN NATURE CLUB
J.N. Prasad, Adviser
13 8th Cross 30th Main
Sarakki ITI Layout,
J. P. Nagar, Phase I
Bangalore
Karnataka - 560 078
Tel: (080) 644682

● METTUPALAYAM WILDLIFE
PRESERVATION SOCIETY
S. Mohamed Ali, President
250 Main Road
Mettupalayam
Tamil Nadu - 641 301
Tel: (04254) 2873

MINIVET NATURE CLUB
V.N. Sarasan, Secretary
Elenthikara
Ernakulam District
Kerala - 683 512

● M.S. SWAMINATHAN RESEARCH
FOUNDATION
Dr M.S. Swaminathan, Director
3rd Cross Street
Taramani Institutional Area
Madras
Tamil Nadu - 600 113
Tel: (044) 235 1698

● NAGARHOLE WILDLIFE CONSERVATION
EDUCATION PROJECT (NAWICOED)
K.M. Chinnappa
P.O. Kakur, Via Srimangala
South Kodagu
Karnataka - 571 217

● NALLAMALAI FOUNDATION
Pranay Waghray
130 Road 10, Jubilee Hills
Hyderabad
Andhra Pradesh - 500 034
Tel: (040) 638810

NATURE
R.J. Pradad, President
2-438/5-1 Teachers Colony
Waddepally
Hanamkonda
Andhra Pradesh - 506 370
Tel: (08712) 73176

NATURE ACTION GROUP
Shajan Thomas, Secretary
P.O. Kunnackal
Muvatotupuzha
Ernakulam District
Kerala - 682 316

NATURE CONSERVATION AND
EDUCATION COUNCIL
P. Gnanaselvan, President
Nature Home, 47A Main Road
P.O. Pudukudi
Thanjavur District
Tamil Nadu - 613 402

● NIYAMAVEDI (Progressive Lawyers Forum)
K. Nandini
Calvathy
Fort Kochi
Kerala

● NILGIRI WILDLIFE & ENVIRONMENT
ASSOCIATION
R. Radcliffe, Vice-president
C/o District Forest Office
Nilgiris North Division
Mount Stuart Hill
Ootacamund
Tamil Nadu - 643 001

PALNI HILLS CONSERVATION COUNCIL,
KODAIKANAL
M.S. Viraraghavan, President
Nutshell
Convent Road
Kodaikanal
Tamil Nadu - 624 101

PEERMADE WILDLIFE PRESERVATION
SOCIETY
Mathew Thomas, Hon. Secretary
Stagbrook Estate
Peermade
Idukki District
Kerala - 685 531
Tel: (04863) 32082, 32282

PRAKRITHI SAMRAKSHNA SAMITI
B. Sugathakumari, Secretary
Varada Nandavanam
Thiruvananthapuram
Kerala - 695 001
Tel: (0471) 60883

QUILON ENVIRONMENTAL GROUP
S.A. Saif, Joint Secretary
Jasmin Niwas
P.O. Ambalathum Bhagom
Kollam District
Kerala - 690 520
Tel: (0474) 61

● RISHI VALLEY EDUCATION CENTRE
Geeta Iyer
P.O. Rishi Valley
Chittoor District
Andhra Pradesh - 517 352
Tel: (08571) 22037
Fax: (08571) 22818

RURAL ENVIRONMENT SERVICE
SOCIETY
G. Sampath Rao
H.No.2-12-5 Vidyaranyapuri
Hanamkonda
Warangal District
Andhra Pradesh - 506 009
Tel: (08712) 78873

SCIENTIFIC SOCIETY FOR ECOSPHERE
AWARENESS
S. Hyma Singh, Secretary
Aripaka Village
Sabbavaram Mandal
Visakhapatnam District
Andhra Pradesh - 531 035
Tel: (08924) 85255

SOCIETY FOR ENVIRONMENTAL
EDUCATION IN KERALA
P. Janardhan, President
SEEK Bhavan
P.O. Edat, Payyanur
Cannanore District
Kerala - 670 327

SOCIETY FOR HUMAN DEVELOPMENT &
RURAL PROSPERITY
Sitaram Singh, President
B-2 Industrial Estate
Renigunta Road, Tirupati
Chittoor District
Andhra Pradesh - 517 506
Tel: (08574) 5204

SOCIETY FOR PRESERVATION OF
ENVIRONMENT AND QUALITY OF LIFE
S.R. Vijayakar, President
3-6-369/A/20 First Floor
Street No.1, Himayat Nagar
Hyderabad
Andhra Pradesh - 500 029
Tel: (040) 631883

SOCIETY FOR THE PROTECTION OF
ENVIRONMENT-KERALA
Unnikrishnan Nambeesan, General Secretary
Binoy Vista
Chevayoor
Calicut
Kerala - 673 017
Tel: (0495) 356000

● THE KARNATAKA ASSOCIATION FOR
THE ADVANCEMENT OF SCIENCE
T. Ananda Rao,
Scientist-in-charge
52/79, Surveyor Street
P.O. Basavangudi
Bangalore
Karnataka - 560 004
Tel: (080) 6609735

THEKKADY WILDLIFE SOCIETY
P.A. Joseph, President
Post Box 9, P.O. Kumily
Idukki District
Kerala - 685 509
Tel: (04863) 2133

● TIRUNELVELI WILDLIFE ASSOCIATION
K.S. Raman, Secretary
Abcoy Gardens
Sankarnagar
Tirunelveli District
Tamil Nadu - 627 357
Tel: (04644) 275, 299

VEMBANAD NATURE CLUB
K.V. Dayal, Adviser
Sreekovil
P.O. Muhamma, Alapuzha District
Kerala
Tel: (047886) 2489

● VISHVANEEDAM INTERNATIONAL
SARVODAYA CENTRE
S.A.R. Acharya, Director
13th km, Magadi Road
P.O. Vishvaneedam
Bangalore
Karnataka - 560 091
Tel: (080) 3351589, 3359603

● VISWADARSANAM
Umesh Babu, Director
Feny Land, Nariyapuram
Pathanamthitta District
Kerala - 689 513

VIVEKANANDA KENDRA
G. Paran, Secretary
Vivekanandapuram
Kanyakumari
Tamil Nadu - 629 702
Tel: (04653) 71232,71296

WILDLIFE AND ENVIRONMENT
CONSERVATION SOCIETY
V.S. Velayudan, Joint Secretary
Hotel Sangam Complex
Collectors Office Road
Tiruchirapalli
Tamil Nadu - 620 001
Tel: (0431) 44700 Fax: (0431) 41779

● WILDLIFE ASSOCIATION OF SOUTH INDIA
E.A. Naidu, Chief Executive
17/1, Victoria Road
Bangalore
Karnataka 560 047
Tel: (080) 578379, 563158

WILDLIFE AWARE NATURE CLUB
T.N.V. Murthy, Adviser
Nisarga
Nisarga Layout, Near Hotel Vaishali
Tumkur, Karnataka - 572 102
Tel: (0816) 78129, 75430

WILDLIFE CONSERVATION SOCIETY
Honorary Secretary
6-1-471/C-30 Behind Library
Khairatabad, Andhra Pradesh - 500 004

● WILDLIFE FIRST !
V. Krishna Prasad
248 - 4th Main Road, Chamrajpet
Bangalore, Karnataka - 560 018
Tel: (080) 6621544 Fax: (080) 6612936

WORLD WIDE FUND FOR NATURE-INDIA
A-22, A-Block, 6-2-1, View Towers
Lakdikapul
Hyderabad
Andhra Pradesh - 500 004
Tel: (040) 248194

WORLD WIDE FUND FOR NATURE-INDIA
Kamla Mansion
143 Infantry Road
Bangalore
Karnataka - 560 001
Tel: (080) 574685

● WORLD WIDE FUND FOR ATURE-INDIA
13, 1st Floor, 11th Street
Nandanam Extension
Madras
Tamil Nadu - 600 035
Tel: (044) 456414, 452267

● ZOOLOGICAL CLUB
T.P. Sreedharan, President
Payyanur College
P.O. Edat
Cannanore District
Kerala - 670 327
Tel: (04989) 2121

References and Further Reading

General

Ali, Salim & Ripley, S. Dillon. *Compact Handbook of the Birds of India and Pakistan.* 2nd ed., New Delhi, 1987.

Brander, A.A.D. *Wild Animals in Central India.* Natraj, Dehra Dun, 1982.

Centre for Science & Environment. *The State of India's Environment 1992-93.* New Delhi, 1992.

Champion, Sir H.G. & Seth, S.K. *A Revised Survey of the Forest Types of India.* GOI Press, 1968.

Corbet, G.B & Hill, J.E. *The Mammals of the Indomalayan Region: a Systematic Review.* British Museum (Natural History), Oxford University Press, 1992.

Corbett, J. *The Man-eaters of Kumaon.* Oxford University Press, London, 1944.

Daniel, J.C. *The Book of Indian Reptiles.* Bombay Natural History Society, 1983.

------------ *A Century of Natural History.* Bombay Natural History Society, 1983.

Ellerman, J.R. & Morrison-Scott, T.C.S. *Checklist of Palaearctic and Indian Mammals 1958 to 1964.* 2nd ed., Trustees of the British Museum (Natural History), London, 1966.

Forsyth, J. *The Highlands of Central India.* Chapman & Hall, London, 1971.

Gadgil, Madhav & Guha, R. *This Fissured Land.* New Delhi, 1992.

Gee, E.P. *The Wildlife of India.* Indus, Harper Collins, 1992.

Israel, Samuel & Sinclair, T. (ed.). *Indian Wildlife.* Apa Publications (HK) Ltd, 1993.

Krishnan, M. *India's Wildlife in 1959-70.* Bombay Natural History Society, 1975.

Krishnan, M. *Nights and days.* Vikas, New Delhi, 1985.

Lall, J.S. (ed.). *The Himalaya : Aspects of Change. A Selection.* Oxford University Press, New Delhi, 1995.

Panwar, H.S. *Kanha National Park : a Handbook.* Centre for Environment Education, Ahmedabad, 1991.

Prater, S.H. *The Book of Indian Animals.* Bombay Natural History Society, 1971.

Roonwal, M.L., Mohnot, S.M. & Rathore, N.S. (ed.). *Current Primate Researches.* Dept of Zoology, Jodhpur University, 1984

Seidensticker, J. & Lumpkin, S. (ed). *Great Cats: Majestic Creatures of the Wild.* Rodale Press, Emmaus, Pa., 1991.

Schaller, G.B. *Stones of Silence.* University of Chicago Press, 1975.

Schaller, G.B. *Mountain Monarchs. Wild Sheep and Goats of the Himalaya.* Chicago, The University of Chicago Press, 1977.

Schaller, G. B. *The Deer and the Tiger.* Chicago, 1967.

Singh, Samar. *Conserving India's Natural Heritage.* Natraj, Dehra Dun, 1986.

The Handbook of Wetland Management. Compiled by B. Gopal, New Delhi, WWF-India, 1995.

The Wildlife (Protection) Act, 1972. 2nd ed. (as amended up to 1991), Natraj, Dehra Dun, 1992.

Snow Leopard

Chundawat, R.S., Rodgers, W.A. & Panwar, H.S. Status report on snow leopard in India. In : *Proceedings of the fifth international symposium,* ed. by H. Freeman. International Snow Leopard Trust and Wildlife Institute of India, 1991.

Chundawat, R.S. *Ecological Studies of Snow Leopard and its Associated Prey Species in Hemis National Park, Ladakh.* Ph.D. Thesis, Jaipur, University of Rajasthan, 1992.

Chundawat, R.S. Land of the Snow Leopard. *Sanctuary,* XII:5, 1992.

Fox, J.L. *A Review of the Status and Ecology of the Snow Leopard Panthera Uncia.* International Snow Leopard Trust, Bellevue, Washington, 1989.

Jackson, R.M. & Hillard, D. Tracking the Elusive Snow Leopard, *National Geographic.* 169, 792-809, 1986.

Ibex

Fox, J.L., Sinha, S.P. & Chundawat, R.S. Activity Patterns and Habitat use of Ibex in the Himalaya Mountains of India. *Journal of Mammology.* 73:3, 527-534, 1992.

Heptner, V.G., Nasimovic, A.A. & Bannikov, A.G. *Die Säugetiere der Sowjetunion.* VEB G. Fisher, Jena, 1966.

Nievergelt, B. *Ibexes in an African Environment.* Berlin, 1981.

Walther, F.R. Das Verhalten der Horntrager. In *Handbuch der Zoologie,* 8, 10:30. Berlin, New York, 1979.

Cheetah

Ali, Salim, The Mughal Emperors of India as Naturalists and Sportsmen, Part I, II & III. *Journal of the Bombay Natural History Society,* XXXI:4, XXXII:1-2, Bombay, 1927-1928.

Alvi, M.A. & Rahman, A, *Jahangir — the Naturalist.* Delhi, National Institute of Sciences of India, 1968.

Beveridge, H. (transl.). *The Akbar Nama of Abu-l-Fazl.* Vol. II., New Delhi, 1979.

Divyabhanusinh. *The End of a Trail: The Cheetah in India.* Banyan Books, New Delhi, 1995.

Fenton, Lt.Col. The Hunting Leopard (*Cynaelurus jubatus*) in Kathiawar. *Journal of the Bombay Natural History Society,* XXVII, Bombay, 1920.

O'Brien, S.J., Wildt, D.E. & Bush, M. The Cheetah in Genetic Peril. *Scientific American.* 254:5, New York, 1986.

Rice, William. *Tiger-Shooting in India: Being an account of hunting experiences on foot in Rajpootana during the hot seasons from 1850-1854.* London, Smith Elder & Co., 1957.

Van Ingen & Van Ingen, Interesting shikar trophies : hunting Cheetah *Acivonyx jubatus (Schreber). Journal of the Bombay Natural History Society,* 47, 1948.

Blackbuck

Abul Fazal 'Allami, *The Ain-i-Akbari.* Vol. I. Trans. H. Blockmann, Asiatic Society of Bengal, Calcutta, 1983.

Babur, *The Babur-Nama in English (Memories of Babur).* Vol. II. Trans. A.S. Beveridge, New York, 1922.

Daniel, J.C. Point Calimere Sanctuary. *Journal of the Bombay Natural History Society,* 64:3, 1967.

Dharmakumarsinhji, R.S., The Changing Wildlife of Kathiawar. *Journal of the Bombay Natural History Society,* 75:3, 1978.

Ranjitsinh, M.K. *The Indian Blackbuck.* Nataraj, Dehra Dun, 1989.

Dhole

Burton, R.W., The Indian Wild Dog. *Journal of the Bombay Natural History Society,* 41, 1941.

Davidar, E.R.C., Ecology and Behaviour of the Dhole or Indian Wild dog (*Cuon alpinus Pallas*). In Fox, M.W. (Ed.). *The Wild Canids,* New York, 1975.

Johnsingh, A.J.T. *Ecology and Behaviour of the Dhole or Indian Wild Dog (Cuon alpinus Pallas 1811).* Ph.D. thesis, Madurai Kamaraj University, Madurai, 1980.

Johnsingh, A.J.T. Reproductive and social behaviour of the dhole, *Cuon alpinus (Canidae). Journal of Zoology, London,* 198, 1982.

Johnsingh, A.J.T. Large mammalian prey-predators in Bandipur. *Journal of the Bombay Natural History Society,* 80, 1983.

Venkataraman, A.B., Arumugam, R. and Sukumar, R. (in press), The foraging ecology of the dhole (*Cuon alpinus*) in Mudumalai Sanctuary. *South India Journal Zoology,* London.

Elephants

Douglas-Hamilton, I. & Douglas-Hamilton, O. *Among the Elephants.* London, 1975.

Eltringham, S.K. (ed.). *The Illustrated Encyclopaedia of Elephants,* London, 1991.

Hanks, J. *A Struggle for Survival : the Elephants Problem.* Feltham, 1979.

Lahiri-Choudhury, D.K. The Indian elephants in a changing world. In *Contemporary India : Essays on the Uses of Tradition,* ed. C.M. Borden, Oxford University Press, New Delhi, 1989.

Laws, R.M., Parker, I.S.C. & Johnstone, R.C.B. *Elephants and Their Habitats.* Oxford, 1975.

Sukumar, R. *The Asian Elephant : Ecology and Management.* Cambridge, 1989.

Sukumar, R. *Elephant Days and Nights : Ten Years with the Indian Elephant,* Delhi, 1994.

Great Indian Bustard

Dharmakumarsinhji, K.S., Ecological Study of the Great Indian Bustard *Ardeotis nigriceps (Vigors) (Aves: Otididae)* in Kathiawar Peninsula, Western India. *Journal of Zoological Society Ind.* **9**, 1957.

Goriup, P.D. & Vardhan, H. (ed.). *Bustards in Decline.* Tourism and Wildlife Society of India, Jaipur, 1980.

Johnsgard, P.A. *Bustards, Hemipodes, and Sandgrouse : birds of dry places.* New York, 1991.

Rahmani, A.R. *The Great Indian Bustard : final report.* Bombay Natural History Society, Bombay, 1989.

Rahmani, A.R. & Manakadan, R. Movement and flock composition of the great Indian bustard *Ardeotis nigriceps (Vigors)* at Nanaj, Solapur district, Maharashtra. *Journal of the Bombay Natural History Society,* **83**, 1986.

Rahmani, A.R. & Manakadan, R. *Bustard Sanctuaries of India.* Bombay Natural History Society, 1988.

Rahmani, A.R. & Manakadan, R. The past and present distribution of the great Indian bustard *Ardeotis nigriceps (Vigors)* in India. *Journal of the Bombay Natural History Society,* **87:2**, 1990.

Asiatic Lions

Berwick, S.H. *The Community of Wild Ruminants in the Gir Forest Ecosystem, India.* Yale University, 1974.

Berwick, S.H. The Gir forest : an endangered ecosystem. *American Scientist,* **64**, 1976.

Chellam, Ravi. *Ecology of the Asiatic lion Panthera leo persica.* Ph.D. Thesis, Saurashtra University, Rajkot, 1993.

Chellam, Ravi & Johnsingh, A.J.T. Management of Asiatic lions in the Gir forest, India. *Symposia of the Zoological Society of London,* **65**, 1993.

Dharmakumarsinhji, S.K. & Wynter-Blyth, M.A. The Gir forest and its lions. *Journal of the Bombay Natural History Society,* **49**, 1951

Joslin, P. *The Asiatic Lion: a study of ecology and behaviour.* Ph.D. Thesis, University of Edinburgh, 1973

Joslin, P. The environmental limitations and the future of the Asiatic lion. In : *Journal of the Bombay Natural History Society,* **81:3**, 1984

Saberwal, V.K., Gibbs, J. P., Chellam, Ravi , et al., Lion-human conflict in the Gir forest India. *Conservation Biology* **8:2**, 1994.

Lion-tailed Macaque

Green, S. M. & Minkowski, K. The lion-tailed macaque and its South Indian rain forest habitat. In : *Primate Conservation,* ed. by H.S.H. Rainier, III and G. H. Bourne, New York, 1977.

Karanth, K.U. Ecological status of the lion-tailed macaque and its rainforest habitats in Karnataka, India. In : *IUCN/SSC Primate Specialist Group Newsletter,* July 1985.

Kumar, A. *The Ecology and Population Dynamics of the Lion- tailed Macaque (Macaca silenus) in South India.* Ph.D. Dissertation, Cambridge University, 1987.

Kurup, G. U. Distribution, habitat and status survey of the lion-tailed macaque, *Macaca silenus. Journal of the Bombay Natural History Society,* **75**, 1978

Pascal, J.P. *Forest Map of South India.* French Institute, Pondicherry, 1986.

———— *The Wet Evergreen Forests of the Western Ghats of India.* French Institute, Pondicherry, 1988.

Sea turtle

Banerjee L.K. & Rao, T.A. *Mangroves of Orissa Coast and their Ecology.* Dehradun, 1990.

Bustard H.R. World's largest sea turtle rookery. *Tiger Paper,* **3:3**, 1976.

Dash, M.C. & Kar, C.S. *The Turtle Paradise — Gahirmatha.* Interprint, New Delhi, 1990.

Kar, C.S. & Bhaskar, S. The status of sea turtles in the Eastern Indian Ocean. In *The biology and Conservation of Sea Turtles,* ed. by K. Bjorndal, Smithsonian Institution Press, Washington, D.C., 1982.

Tiger

Karanth, K.U. Estimating prey densities from camera trap data using capture-recapture models. *Biological Conservation,* **71**, 1995.

McDougal, C. *The Face of the Tiger.* London, 1977.

Mills, J. A. & Jackson, P. *Killed for a Cure: a review of the worldwide trade in tiger parts.* Traffic International, Cambridge, 1994.

Sankhala, K. *Tiger.* Glasgow, 1978.

Seidensticker, J. & McDougal, C. Tiger predatory behaviour, ecology and conservation.. *Symposia of the Zoological Society of London,* **65**, 1993.

Smith, J.L.D. The role of dispersal in structuring the Chitwan tiger population. *Behaviour,* **124**: 3-4, 1993.

Sunquist, M. E. The social organisation of tigers (*Panthera tigris*) in Royal Chitwan National Park, Nepal. *Smithsonian Contributions to Zoology,* **336**, 1981.

Sunquist, F. C. & Sunquist, M.E. *Tiger Moon.* University of Chicago Press, Chicago, 1988.

Tilson, R. L. & Seal, U.S. (ed). *Tigers of the World: the biology, bio politics, management and conservation of an endangered species.* Noyes Publications, New Jersey, 1987.

Thapar, V. *Tigers: the secret life.* London, 1989.

------- *The Tiger's Destiny.* London, 1992

Man and Animal

Boal, Barbara M. *The Konds.* Warminster, 1982.

Dyson, K. K. *A Various Universe.* New Delhi, 1978.

Gadgil, M. & Subash Chandra, M.D. Sacred Groves. In : *Indigenous Vision.* G. Sen ed. New Delhi, 1992.

Hastings, Marquess of. *The Private Journal of the Marquess of Hastings.* 1858.

Kipling, J. L. *Beast and man in India.* London, 1891.

Kumar, S.V. Koondakulam. *Sanctuary,* **XIV: 6**, 1994.

Pereira, W. The sustainable lifestyle of the Warlis. In : *Indigenous Vision,* G. Sen ed., New Delhi, 1992.

Rangarajan, M. *Fencing the Forest.* New Delhi, 1996.

Rangaswami, S. & Sridhar, S. *Birds of Rishi Valley.* Rishi Valley Education Centre. 1993.

Savyasaachi, The Tiger and the Honey-bee. *Seminar,* **423**, 1994.

Sherwood, M. *The Life and Times of Mrs Sherwood (1775-1851) from the dairies of Captain and Mrs Sherwood.* F.J. Harvey Darton ed., London, 1910.

Sleeman. *Rambles and Recollections.* V.A. Smith ed., 1915.

Vigorelli, L. *Naga : Forme disciplinate del Bello.* Bergamo, 1992.

Whitaker, R. *Common Indian Snakes.* Macmillan, 1978.